√ 3760(i)

Laboratory On-line Computing

Laboratory On-line Computing

An introduction for engineers and physicists

JOHN E. BRIGNELL

GODFREY M. RHODES

Intertext Books

Published by
International Textbook Company Limited
Kingswood House, Heath & Reach, Leighton Buzzard, Beds LU7 0AZ
and 450 Edgware, Rd., London W2 1EG

First published 1975

ISBN 0 7002 0258 7

Printed in Great Britain by Galliard (Printers) Ltd,
Queen Anne's Road, Great Yarmouth, Norfolk.

Contents

Preface

In a book concerned with one of the most rapidly developing fields of knowledge in human history, the preface, as the most up-to-date part, assumes an importance greater than usual. Perhaps the best way to make use of it is to put the hypothetical question: 'How would we change our approach were we to start the whole lengthy process of producing a book on this subject now?'

Above all, it is important to state that none of the many recent developments has produced any change in the fundamental principles which the following pages are intended to convey. The main changes of emphasis have been in hardware. For example, ROMs are more important, as is the whole of the larger scale of integration. Even more significant is the heralded emergence of the first microprocessors with a speed and word-length capability to put them in the signal processing league, and as such they become suitable vehicles for the implementation of many of the techniques of on-line computing described here. Certainly, the early examples of such devices were far too slow and cumbersome to merit serious consideration for the majority of laboratory applications.

Many of what we have identified as minor adverse trends have continued. For example, literal mnemonics are becoming more dominant, yet all our experience with numerate students points to the superiority of the algebraic kind.

It is necessary to qualify the subtitle, as its brevity ignores the existence of some engineering courses with a negligible electronics content, and to say that the text is meant to be an introduction to the relatively new subject of Computer Aided Measurement for anyone who has completed two years of a modern honours degree course with electronics and mathematics. Primarily this means any physicist or electrical engineer—final year, post-graduate or practising, though it will include others who have been trained under one of the newer and more variable course patterns. The philosophy of the book is basically that anyone with such knowledge is thereby less constrained in his

ix

use of the on-line computer, and can make more profitable use of it, than can scientists in other specialities.

It is now possible, with relatively little effort, to design and build digital subsystems of hitherto undreamed of scope, owing to the advances of integrated circuitry. Many people, including influential politicians and businessmen, have failed to see that the small versatile computer is a far more significant innovation than the large glamorous number-crunching machine, but laboratory workers have been quick to appreciate this fact. These two aspects, the computer and the special-purpose digital subsystem which connects it directly to an external device, form a tool of immense capability in the laboratory.

To use this book properly, the reader must be continually aware of one important fact—*it is not a compendium*. It is not intended to be used in isolation, but rather as a guide to the widely varying sources of useful technique. Examples have sometimes been included for their illustrative value rather than for their currency of use, and the purpose throughout is to establish the principles of a subject whose practice is diverse, though well documented. The foundations on which we propose to build are the knowledge of mathematics and basic electronics that should already be available to the reader and the ordinary techniques of scientific programming that he will have acquired formally or informally during his training.

Nevertheless, there are peculiarities of the subject of laboratory on-line computing which make it difficult to present in the circumscribed way that is usually expected of text-books; yet these difficulties need to be emphasized as they are a manifestation of the fundamental nature of the subject, and understanding them is necessary to the avoidance of the blinkered approach which characterized some of its beginnings.

This book differs from conventional text-books in many ways, and one of them is the emphasis placed on team-work. So important is this in laboratory on-line computing that we dedicate this book to the group of workers who at various times formed part of our own team: Tony Beddow, Colin Buffam, Alan Buttle, Adrian Dickens, John Evison, Brian Green, Terry Hewish, Brian Mears, Klaus Metzmacher, Kerry Pocknell, Andy Reichert, David Spreadbury and David Swan; all of whom have contributed to the ideas expressed in these pages. There are also many people from outside our own department who have provided stimulating comment and discussion, especially Colin Binnie and David Lloyd of Bart's Hospital, whose work is given a briefer discussion than it merits in Chapter IX. Finally, within a busy schedule of teaching, contracted research and laboratory organizing, our managing to produce a final manuscript was largely due to the initial encouragement of Ann Drybrough-Smith, the help of Gillian Baker and her colleagues in the preparation, and the patience of Lynn Bevan at the editorial stage.

Chapter I

Introduction

This is a short book about a long subject, which can be just about as safe an enterprise as a long walk on a short pier. Moreover the subject itself is fraught with dangers and difficulties for the would-be author. Not only is it one of the most rapidly changing subjects imaginable, but it is also one whose practice is unusually dependent upon the choice of vehicle; so the same on-line measurement task tackled with different computers might be approached in entirely different ways. This aspect of 'machine-dependence' poses a basic dilemma in the writing of a text book—whether to quote specific detailed examples which may only have relevance to a few readers, or to concentrate on the broad picture with the danger of being so general that the resulting text is of no use to anyone.

Fortunately there is an extensive body of literature produced by the various manufacturers of on-line computing equipment, and it is the existence of this more specific source of information which prompts us to attempt the more difficult task of presenting a wider view. This also has the advantage of avoiding some of the more controversial views of the subject (since workers in the field, once committed to a particular system, tend to become passionately devoted to it, warts and all, to the exclusion of considering any alternative), though no doubt our own prejudices will emerge quite clearly from the treatment of the material in this text.

At the outset we did begin to collect literature from the various manufacturers of minicomputers, and we are very obliged to some of them for their helpful attitude. It soon became obvious, however, that this book could have become a catalogue of catalogues, so we decided to eschew description of particular systems, and while this gives parts of the book an air of vague generalization, it does avoid the inclusion of details which would be confusing and irrelevant to the majority of readers. Every manufacturer has made a different set of compromises of price and facilities, and each computer has

1

its own field of pre-eminence, so while we have tried to give some guidance about the choice of machines for our particular area of application—the laboratory—we have not attempted to pre-empt the choice itself, which will be conditioned by local factors (financial, technical and historical). Nevertheless we do exclude by implication some machines, even ones of considerable laboratory importance, such as the specially hard-wired variety, since it is our object to encourage the reader to tackle a variety of experimental tasks. Thus *versatility* is an important prerequisite for our purpose.

Hence we have chosen to face the dangers of generalization and its possible consequence of superficiality. There are, however, several broad principles of laboratory on-line computing which need to be understood; though because the subject comprises a number of disparate elements, it is not always easy to put these in concise form. Strangely enough, one of the greatest problems is the ease of use of the computer—the fact that a few glib lines of program written on a semi-intuitive basis can set in train a complicated and far-reaching sequence of actions. This is bad enough in conventional off-line computing, but in on-line computing where the machine interacts directly with its external environment it can be serious indeed.

Consider the simple example of smoothing a data sequence by taking a running mean:

$$y_i = \frac{1}{n} \sum_{k=0}^{n-1} x_{i-k}$$

This is a method we have often found in use, frequently having been developed spontaneously by the user, but very few users seem to understand precisely what it does (for example if the sequence were disturbed by the presence of two different sinuosoidal components, how would the running mean separately affect them?). We discuss this particular method further in Chapter 6.

Because of the dangers that accompany this easy power, it is necessary to emphasize the two different aspects of the laboratory measurement which require a full understanding—the test-object and the test-method. The test-object can be anything from a jar of oil to a human brain (which happen to be two examples which we shall discuss more fully later on), but whatever it is, one cannot, as the uninitiated might suppose, treat it as a 'black box' which can be made to reveal all instantly by connection to a computer. There are substantial constraints upon the ways that the computer can be used, which are conditioned by the nature of the test-object itself. An obvious simple example of such a constraint is the importance of the highest significant frequency in the signal from the test-object, which by dint of the sampling theorem determines the sampling rate, and hence circumscribes the possibilities for real-time processing. The test-methods available are just as various as the test-objects; after all the chief reason for using a computer is to get access to the variety of processes offered by software; but this need to understand their implications will (or should) act as a curb on any temptation to get carried away by the ease with which processes can be realized through programming.

This argument applies to all computing, of course, so why do we give it so much emphasis in an introduction to laboratory on-line computing? Two of the chief reasons are that in on-line computing the raw data are not necessarily accessible and available for reprocessing and that there is often interaction with the external world, which at worst can cause physical danger (we shall later discuss briefly the example of the computer-controlled high-voltage power supply). Digital signal processing can bring us into closer contact with the physical realities (for example, by providing accurate estimates of quantities which are only calculable indirectly, such as the internal temperature of a device), but if it is not used properly it can do just the opposite and act as a muffle, degrading the quality of information rather than enhancing it. The means at our disposal to avoid this hazard of ill-judgement of the effects of a process are chiefly the techniques of analysis provided by signal theory, and particularly discrete signal theory.

This is an appropriate point at which to emphasize that this book is not intended to be used in 'stand alone' mode. The very broadness of the subject makes that impossible. Rather it is intended to be a guide to the range of subjects which need to be covered by anyone who intends to make proper use of the techniques. Most readers will find parts of what follows too obvious to be worth putting down and other parts unfamiliar, but the division between these parts will vary with the background of the reader. We have subtitled this text 'an introduction for engineers and physicists' because this is the identifiable group of workers who should have sufficient knowledge of electronics to enable them to do more than simply accept what the market offers in the way of digital instrumentation. The standard required to appreciate the material in this book is roughly the completion of two years of an honours degree course which includes mathematics and electronics. It should be useful to final year undergraduate students who are involved with project work on on-line computing, to post-graduate students and to practising engineers and scientists who need to exploit the techniques of on-line computing. Much of the material is informal in nature, and has in fact been built up through the informal teaching of both undergraduate and post-graduate students, though some reference has been made in Chapter 6 to part of the more formal material which is included in an up to date degree course.

Because this is not an independent text, the references are very important, and they have been deliberately pared down to an absolute minimum number of books which should be consulted (though of course there are many equivalents which may be substituted according to the preference of the reader). Also a mnemonic method of citing these references has been used, so that they may be identified (e.g. SigProBeau, which happens to be a very useful source of further references, and the compendious DiSiRaRa). Furthermore, in addition to the texts cited in the brief list of references, the literature produced by the manufacturers of computers and components is essential reading for an up to date appreciation of the state of the art—no text-book can possibly be less than one year out of date, and in a field as rapidly changing as this one a year is a long time, which is a further argument in favour of treating general principles rather than technical details. Manufacturers' literature includes computer handbooks, component data sheets, application reports, programming manuals, etc., and is a useful guide to the state of the jargon as well as of the art.

It will be apparent that there is a significant 'do it yourself' content in the philosophy of this book, and in many fields this might smack of amateurism. Quite the reverse is true in laboratory computing, for the simple reason that every problem is unique and so requires an individual approach to its solution. Admittedly, if the computing demands of the problem are low, then a number of liberties can be taken with both hardware and software, so that a more general purpose approach is possible, and such an approach has an important place in the laboratory; so that general purpose input/output channels represent an important facility that ought to be present. It must be realized, however, that the difficult (and on the whole more relevant) measurement problems will tend to strain the capabilities of the computer (unless it is grossly overpowered for the tasks in hand).

Some aspects of computing will get very little mention in the following chapters, not because they are considered unimportant, just less important than some of the points which need to be made in a restricted space. An example is the question of operating systems, a subject of great importance in a wider context, but one of relatively minor concern in the laboratory, where other than in subsidiary activities, such as program preparation, they represent unnecessary overheads. This is perhaps not quite so true as the computer system grows to the point where it carries substantial backing store (and this idea of the growing system is basic to our philosophy) but the important gains in the laboratory are made with the introduction of the small computer and these are the gains we are mainly concerned with; once they are understood the benefits of larger systems become self-evident.

What do we mean by these gains? Let us mention just two examples which will be dealt with later. Perhaps the simplest and most obvious example is the freedom to deal with non-linearities. It is fairly typical that the sensing devices of high sensitivity are non-linear (e.g. the thermistor) and they tend not to be used in conventional continuous electronic systems, other than for null setting instruments, because of the difficulties of coping with this non-linearity. In the computer, however, the non-linearity is easily compensated for by means of a stored calibration table (or in more complex cases some more elaborate form of model), so it is no longer a significant problem. As a second example, digital electronics has produced recently, among other things, an instrument designed to find electronic needles in haystacks. This instrument, the transient recorder, being of digital construction is ideal for connection to a computer, and the two in combination make a whole which is greater than the sum of its parts. With such gains both the range of experimental problems that can be tackled and the efficiency with which this can be done are greatly extended.

Now, as we have implied, these gains, as always, are only achieved at the expense of a certain amount of effort, principally in the design and construction of interface equipment to enable laboratory instruments to work to the computer, but also in associated software development. It is convenient to speak of the designer and the user as separate people, when they are often one and the same, but there are reasons for doing this. The design task is moderately complex (though in these days of integrated circuits not nearly as complex as it used to be) and it would be a feat of memory beyond most of us to retain a working knowledge of the design for any length of time after its completion. Therefore, whether the user is a separate person or not, we need to employ the normal link between designer and user—*documentation*. This is a most important aspect of laboratory computing, and one which is easily overlooked at great cost. Together with team-work in general it is one of the features of the subject which we shall be at pains to emphasize in the following pages.

This book is divided into two parts. The first part deals with the tools of the trade—software, hardware and mathematics—while the second part covers certain more practical aspects of their application in the laboratory. As explained earlier the marked machine dependence of the subject does not lend itself to very specific examples which would be of general use, but in the penultimate chapter we shall make reference to the way the principles apply to actual laboratory programs.

There has been an unfortunate tendency for computer applications specialists to split into two quite separate camps—hardware and software. As a result many optimum paths have been missed. The disadvantages will become more important as developments proceed and the concept of a computer *per se* becomes more diffuse. The authors' department has responded to this situation by developing a new degree course in Computer Engineering which combines digital electronics with programming and advanced mathematics. The present text, however, is directed mainly towards conventionally trained engineers and scientists who may wish to apply their electronics and programming knowledge to a more efficient use of available computing resources.

We do not claim that such knowledge and methods are essential to the performance of experiments on line, but without them the experimenter may have to accept a number of unnecessary limitations, e.g.

1 Waiting for the delivery of comparatively trivial items of equipment.
2 Accepting a performance which is degraded by the fact that the equipment is necessarily designed for general use rather than the particular purpose to which it is to be applied.
3 Accepting, for similar reasons, a degree of redundancy of hardware and software, which means that the budget will not stretch as far as it might have done.
4 At worst, having to abandon an idea because the techniques are not available commercially at the time. In competitive areas of research and development this is particularly sad.

We have little to say to those fortunates who have the backing of large teams of experts or virtually limitless budgets, but the majority of working scientists and engineers do not fall into this category.

Even in the narrower world of the on-line variety of computing one tends to find two quite distinct species of user—the head-in-air mathematical type and the down-to-earth practical type. Two instances might illustrate this. The first concerns a brilliant, mathematically biased research student who, to confirm a theory, found that he needed to build a timing monostable. After staring blankly at a tray of components for some minutes he cried despairingly 'Well, I know that I need a pole in the right hand half-plane'. The second concerns an industrial programmer who was given the task of writing a piece of program to keep an actuator in a complex defence system in a central position. Easy enough, he thought, and simply provided a restoring force proportional to the displacement!

Now it is beyond most of us to be master of both mathematics and practical engineering, but in a field such as on-line computing it is essential to have at least part of a foot in each camp, or at a very minimum be aware of the constraints (and freedoms) imposed by each approach.

Part 1: The Tools of the Trade

Chapter II

Why Use a Computer On-Line?

All innovations meet resistance, and the scientific world is just as full of entrenched conservatism as any other. The entry of the computer into the laboratory has not been immune to opposition, largely on the grounds that it is a frivolous and unnecessary complication. However, even if it were not for the fact that many of today's measurement problems are insoluble without a computer, there is still one overriding advantage it possesses—its objectivity. Would it be too facetious to suggest that this is a reason for it being resented in some quarters?

The fact that the reader has got as far as Chapter 2 of this book suggests that we would be preaching to the converted if we were to extol the virtues of the computer, and the scientific worker who does not use one in his everyday activities must by now be a very rare beast. Also it is not necessary for us to go into the details of conventional computing techniques as these have become familiar, and there is a number of useful texts dealing thoroughly with them (e.g. NuMeHam, CoMeLaFa). Nevertheless, we shall start with a brief description of off-line computing as it helps to give a framework for the description of the subject in hand.

2.2 OFF-LINE WORKING AND DATA LOGGING

In contrast to on-line computing, the off-line variety has certain clear characteristics, which are:

1 All the data are presented in a restricted format before execution and the results obtained afterwards.

2 The exact nature of the output is predetermined by the program and data, and, if these remain unchanged, will not vary from run to run.

3 A restricted range of peripherals is available (typically card reader, tape reader, line printer, digital plotter, disc, drum, magnetic tape deck).

4 There is no possibility of intervention in the running of the program.

5 And in any case there are no intermediate results on which to base it.

6 Speed of execution is immaterial (the processor could be anything from an ultra-fast machine with optical logic to a thousand Buddhist monks slaving over their abaci).

7 The details of how the program (whatever the source language) is interpreted are immaterial.

These characteristics, and the way they have been framed, give some clues to the need for an alternative approach, and we shall discuss some more positive reasons in the next section. Nevertheless, most of the principles on which on-line computing are based are inherent in the off-line techniques which preceded them, and the hardware has much in common.

Laboratory on-line computing has another important forbear—data logging. This was a technique developed to meet the growing need for the collection, digitization and recording of data from a number of diverse points in space and time, and it introduced the concepts of analogue to digital conversion and multiplexing.

These then are the two major ingredients of laboratory on-line computing. Stir them together with a bit of digital electronics, add a soupçon of control and signal theory, and you have a valuable whole which is considerably greater than the sum of its parts.

2.3 ADVANTAGES OF ON-LINE COMPUTING

The first five characteristics in the above list are fairly obviously disadvantageous to the experimentalist, and point to some of the reasons for the move to on-line techniques. The last two, however, are advantageous and they give a clue to some of the complications likely to be met when we go on-line.

At this stage we should establish the meaning of 'on-line computing'; for it is obviously a very different activity when practised by, say, a booking clerk at an air terminal. A computer may be said to be on-line when it interacts with its physical environment in some way. The environment we take to include any human beings involved in the activity, but we exclude accidental interactions such as a deleterious effect of elevated atmospheric temperature. The result of such an interaction is that some or all of the characteristics enumerated above are lost.

It is also important to define a major subset of *on-line* computing, namely *real-time* computing (these terms are not interchangeable although they are sometimes carelessly treated as such). Real-time computing takes place when the response time of the on-line computer is critical, either because of the rate of external data generation or because the response is one of the parameters of a closed-loop system. The critical test for real-time is to imagine that the clock generator driving the computer logic is gradually slowed down; if at some stage this would cause an *essential* breakdown in the process being considered the computer is working in real-time. It is also useful to distinguish an important subset of real-time, which we might call *strict-time*, where the computation actually includes a reference, directly or indirectly, to the value of time or time interval occurring in the external world as labelled in man-made units (e.g. sidereal seconds). Thus we have the following structure of classes of computing:

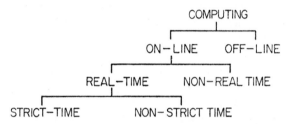

Simple examples of the three classes of on-line computing are *non-real time*—calculation of the roots of a quadratic equation from coefficients typed in any time after the previous answer is received. *Real-time (non-strict)*—pulse height analysis of signals from a nuclear radiation detector. *Strict-time*—digital filtering of speech signals from a microphone. In the last case, the timing is strict because the characteristics of the required filter are expressed in units of hertz, which are directly derived from the second. Typically, this strict timing is imposed not by the computer clock generator but by the clock generator controlling the sampling frequency, and should this vary, the characteristic frequencies of the filter will vary in due proportion.

Let us now examine some of the reasons for adopting these different classes of computing. We can enumerate several reasons for on-line computing as a whole

1 The human brain in activities such as pattern recognition is supreme, so it is highly advantageous to allow it to work in the closest possible co-operation with the computer.

2 Transporting data in an intermediate form (e.g. punched paper tape) is very cumbersome and uneconomic, especially when they start and finish in the form of electrical signals.

3 Human intervention during calculations, in response to the nature of intermediate results, greatly enlarges the possibilities of computation.
4 In particular, the ability to abort the run if anything goes wrong and make corrections removes the extensive delays associated with turn-round time in off-line computing.
5 Virtually any scientific instrument can be adapted to play the rôle of peripheral.
6 It becomes possible to operate in a *closed-loop* mode with enormous gains of efficiency.

Now, in the laboratory, we find ourselves more often than not involved in real-time computing. There are two major basic reasons for this. Firstly, quantities and rates of data from most experiments are too large to allow them to accumulate for processing at the computer's leisure; and secondly the time allowed for a calculation in closed-loop operation is out of the control of the computer and is subject to the nature of the external system to which it is connected.

There are also two chief circumstances in which real-time operation becomes restricted to the narrower strict-time form: firstly when time-referred operations are included in the on-line process (e.g. differentiation and integration with respect to time, digital filtering, etc.); and secondly when the incoming and outgoing data are inherently time-referenced in such a way that the computer has to take cognisance of the time values (e.g. the measurement of the impulse response of a noisy system by averaging the responses to repeated stimuli). The strict-time element may derive from control of the sampling rate or from a real-time clock connected directly to the computer.

Time is so important in most laboratory experiments that strict-time is usually the rule, and this tends to determine the nature of laboratory computing. Thus one of the major differences between a laboratory computer and a number-crunching one is that the hardware for handling input and output forms a much greater proportion of the former and will typically be equal in size to the central processor, and often much larger. Consideration of time also pervades the whole of the activity of the laboratory computer user, both in programming and the development of hardware connections to the experimental apparatus. As we shall observe later, one of the marks of a good laboratory computer is the degree to which it can shield the user from some of the more irritating aspects of timing. Nevertheless, the chief characteristic of this form of computation will always tend to be a preoccupation with timing, and data are often regarded as though they form a sort of fluid whose treatment depends on how quickly it can be pushed through various bottlenecks which are actually created by the exigencies of time.

2.4 MAN–COMPUTER INTERACTION

The relationship between man and the computer is a subject that is frequently aired, and the objective of much on-line work is to optimize it, so that the computer becomes a sort of mental prosthesis extending the capabilities of the brain. This idea can be useful in the laboratory, but it must be handled with a little more circumspection than in some other fields, as there are certain quirks of the human brain that can be detrimental to the objectivity which is supposed to be the goal of the experimental scientist. With this proviso we can say that successful man–computer interaction can greatly enhance the usefulness of the laboratory computer.

Let us see what the human body has to offer in this context of interaction with a machine. It has five input transducers, the senses; but we can disregard two of them as slow and unreliable. This leaves three; sight, hearing and touch, of which the first two in particular are very effective indeed. Of the output transducers we can disregard one, the voice, not because it is inefficient, but because we cannot yet make effective use of it. The other, musculature, especially of the fingers, is again highly effective. It is used in closed-loop co-operation with the sense of touch as a mechanical actuator. Thus the main entry of information to computer from man is via switch arrays or keyboards (and to a lesser extent light pens).

Output from the computer to man is almost exclusively visual, apart from alarms such as the bell on a teletype machine, although vocal output is well within the range of current technology. This means that teletype, visual display unit, plotter and line printer are the main channels of communication.

How do the central processors of the two compare? The human brain has great strengths but also great weaknesses. Its strengths are versatility, ability to relate disconnected entities (the very essence of intelligence), ability to deal with non-numerical values, inspiration (inexplicable but powerful sub-conscious reasoning), inventiveness and freedom of action. Its weaknesses are unreliability of memory, unpredictability, variation of speed of operation, fatigue (especially with repetitive tasks) and worst of all subjection to covert subconscious motivation.

In contrast, the computer has the strengths of reliability of memory and programmed action; untiring, constant, high-speed operation; obedience and accuracy. Its weaknesses are restriction to numerical values (including binary logic); restriction to preprogrammed activity and absolute unintelligence.

Setting out their characteristics in this way demonstrates the fact that computer and brain are ideal candidates for partnership; but such a partnership can only be successful if it is organized in such a way as to emphasize the strengths and suppress the weaknesses of each partner. This is the fundamental principle in programming for human intervention.

The other important consideration is the asymmetrical nature of the channel of communication between man and computer; information travels very much faster one way than the other. This means that care must be taken to optimize the system of message input to the computer; which applies to the selection of points at which intervention may occur, to the balance between condensation and clarity in the message repertoire and to the hierarchical structure of the program.

We must not, however, exaggerate the significance of human interaction in laboratory programs, which is much less marked than in some adjacent fields. At best it is a great convenience and its absence can be extremely irritating once one has become accustomed to its availability. The human channel is several orders of magnitude slower than other quite ordinary laboratory peripherals, so there is usually no question of man interfering in the data acquisition process. Also there are sound philosophical grounds for severely limiting his power to impose a change of mind, as one of the benefits of programmed experiments is the fact that one is obliged to lay one's cards on the table at the outset, which is particularly important when questions of statistical significance are involved.

In some of the subsidiary activities, such as program preparation, well organized man–computer interaction can be of great benefit. For example, a good on-line text-editing facility can save many hours of trivial activity. During the actual runs of experiments it will tend to be restricted to fairly gross changes of direction between bursts of activity in which the fundamental rate of operation is beyond the capacity of man. Nevertheless, the five-fingered variety of typing is a skill well worth learning since it reduces the constraints imposed by sheer tedium. It is not always remembered that the computer is the best fitted partner to perform straightforward operations such as coding and decoding, so the form of message encoding employed can be based mainly on human convenience. Surprisingly often one finds laboratory computer users employing the most inscrutable message vocabularies, presumably because of some programming convenience, but also possibly because of failure to avoid the temptation to establish an esoteric cult—an inexcusable but widespread fault which has bedevilled computing and hampered its wider acceptance.

2.5   The ideal laboratory on-line computer

Some of the aims and constraints of laboratory computing may be clarified by the exercise of imagining the ideal computer for this purpose. If any of the terms used here are unfamiliar their meaning should become apparent in later chapters. At this stage, therefore, the three important components of the computer need to be considered—the central processor, the input–output organizer and the software.

The most fundamental characteristic of any computer is its word length, which should be as large as is economically possible. The basic reason for requiring a long word is that this is the unit of information in the computer and the amount which can be conveniently shifted about and operated on in one go. This quantity of information prescribes both the accuracy of data and the range of actions definable in a single machine order (it is, of course, quite possible to pack either data or instructions into more than one word, but unless genuine hardware multiple-length operation is provided for, this only produces a sacrifice of speed for whatever benefits accrue). Several immediate advantages arise from the long word. For example, single-length floating point numbers can be used without the need to shift mantissa and exponent around separately (and in the ideal computer such numbers will be handled by a hardware rather than a software routine). Furthermore, a comprehensive order code becomes possible since there is room in the word for a large repertoire of basic instructions together with the addresses of the operands.

Why should we require the complication of a wide repertoire of instructions? For these reasons—ease of programming, economy of storage and speed of execution. As we shall observe in Chapter 3, any programmed action can be achieved with a remarkably small repertoire of instructions, but only at the expense of lengthy and convoluted sequences of orders. The most fundamental restriction in this respect is the amount of space available in the word for specifying the addresses of operands. For example, the simple action of adding two numbers to form a third can require many instructions or only one depending on how many addresses over what range can be specified in a single order. Both speed and storage are markedly affected by this feature. There are also many fundamental actions frequently required in on-line work (e.g. shifts, jumps, masks, strobes, operations on single bits, etc.) which, if not specifiable in basic instructions, can greatly multiply the length and run time of a program.

Some of the more complicated actions which occur with great frequency (multiplication, division, floating point operations, shifts, etc.) can slow down operation considerably if they have to be decimated in the computer to form sequences of simpler instructions, so in our ideal machine they will be performed directly by special hardware features.

As far as software is concerned, it must be able to provide easy and efficient use of the hardware facilities. The first requirement is a compiler for an easily understood mnemonic assembler language which preserves the one-to-one correspondence between written orders and machine orders. This allows us to maintain that greater degree of control over detail which characterizes on-line computing, yet tempers the intellectual demands of machine-code programming. Higher level languages especially designed for real-time use can also be of great assistance, but they must have provision for inserting pieces of program conceived at a lower level, since the specialized interactions with the external laboratory world are inherently concerned with the lowest level of programming. The final software requirement is a large and relevant library of standard subroutines and utility programs, all fully specified and to the highest standards of integrity and efficiency.

We are left with the final aspect of the computer which is of unique and dominating importance in laboratory work—the organization of input/output operations. This must provide speed, flexibility, reliability and ease of use. The best form of channel to and from the external world is a standard fast, parallel handshake interface; the standard part on the user's side being provided on a circuit board with space for his own additions of logic elements to connect with his external hardware. These channels should be controlled and organized by internal hardware to provide a comprehensive interrupt system with fast priority assessment, yet permitting the external peripherals to operate with the highest possible degree of autonomy. For the very fastest peripherals, direct access to the main store of the computer, by-passing the central processor, should be available.

Last, but by no means least, the whole concept of the computer, both hardware and software, should be modular, so that the potential user can select the options which best suit him. This ideal computer does not exist, and some of the characteristics mentioned are mutually antagonistic, so that each manufacturer will make his own individual trade-off decisions thereby imparting the individuality to his particular product, and we have not mentioned the most important factor—cost—which is involved in the major trade-off decision made by the potential user when he chooses his system. One cannot expect a cheap mass produced item to yield the highest standards of performance in a particular application, but one must cut one's coat according to one's cloth. Yet the most economic way of tackling a task is not always the obvious one, and the choice and purchase of a laboratory computer require very careful consideration, perhaps involving several months of patient analysis of the task and the potential tools available for tackling it.

2.6 CORRUPTED DATA

With a few trivial exceptions, all data received by the laboratory computer are in one or more senses corrupted. We may consider this in an abstract way by referring to the acquisition of data as a mapping of some aspect of the real world into numbers in the computer store. The very fact that this normally involves mapping a continuum into a finite set implies a sacrifice of definition. This is a form of corruption which is fundamental to computer processing, and we deal with it under the headings of quantization and sampling noise.

There are also forms of corruption which occur in all engineering systems. No real system is absolutely linear. No real system has a response which is ideal (in time or frequency). These facts imply that there are always corruptions in the form of non-linearity and convolution distortion. The extent to which these can be dealt with depends largely on our prior knowledge of their nature, and digital processing can be uniquely successful in overcoming their effects.

Then there is the fact that the real world itself is quantized and in a state of continuous thermal agitation, so uncertainties are inherent in physical variables, and the resulting random noise imposed on received signals is nearly always a significant ingredient of the measurement problems of today. Again, depending on the existence of prior knowledge of the signal, such effects can often be greatly reduced by dint of the calculating capabilities of a digital computer.

Consciousness of the sources and degrees of corruption of received data is one of the marks of a succesful on-line computer user, and he must also be aware of the effect of the various numerical procedures on the corrupt part of the data; for in many cases this can be amplified, even to the point of producing an autonomous instability. Hence many processes which are originally conceived in idealized form become ineffective in a practical digital realization, particularly as the economics of cost and time tend to exert pressure towards acceptance of the maximum tolerable levels of corruption. Fortunately, most simple numerical procedures lend themselves to a signal processing form of treatment in terms of spectral theory, which gives a good appreciation of the effect they have on data and noise. We have mentioned, for example, that the commonly used method of smoothing sequences of data by taking a running mean has a precise interpretation in the frequency domain, and, as one would expect, it turns out to represent a crude form of low-pass filter. This example is analysed more completely in Chapter 6.

Appreciation of this aspect leads us to take the reverse approach, and start from the idealized signal processing characteristic to produce a numerical procedure, thereby arriving at the powerful concept of digital filtering. We predict with confidence that this will soon be the dominant form of signal processing in low and medium frequency applications, e.g. telephony. Meanwhile it is also a powerful weapon in the laboratory armoury.

Sampling is the dominant source of corruption in on-line computing, and the sampling theorem is of utmost importance. All non-trivial on-line measurements involve time-varying quantities, and it is the sampling theorem which circumscribes their digital realization.

Nevertheless, while corruption is inherent in the computer approach to data handling, and would therefore seem to constitute a disadvantage, it is in that context a quantifiable and to some extent disposable aspect, which is why consideration of the inevitable corruption of laboratory signals leads to a positive answer to the question posed in the title of this chapter.

2.7   COMPUTING TO GAIN INSIGHT

One of the texts recommended for use in conjunction with this one [NuMeHam] is suggested not least for its motto: *The purpose of computing is insight not numbers:* which, while not quite as directly applicable to laboratory computing as to mathematical work, is well worth remembering. The capacity of the computer to egest vast columns of figures tends to bemuse many people into uncritical acceptance of such results without due thought being given to the limitations of the process by which they are produced.

The danger is slightly lessened in on-line work where the results may be in the form of curves or modes of behaviour of a system, but it is still ever present. The naive adoption of a given technique (e.g. Newton's zero finding iteration), under the illusion that it appears in text-books and therefore must always work, is bound to lead to errors. In the worst case, such errors go undetected, and in a complex on-line calculation their effect can be very subtle indeed.

An essential part of the preparatory work for the implementation of a new, complex technique of measurement or control is a stage of investigatory computing. This might be an open-loop test on a closed-loop system, or taking samples of a proposed criterion function in an optimization problem to see whether it is sufficiently well behaved.

Each subroutine must be separately tested with prepared input data to check that it behaves in the expected manner, and associated subroutines should be tested in their natural groupings. This, of course, applies in all forms of computing, but it is even more important in the branch we are considering here. It is always better to anticipate trouble than have to face up to it in the last complicated stage when the program is assembled and run. For, unlike a straightforward off-line mathematical routine, an on-line program with several peripherals in interrupt mode operation is likely to be doing several things at once when the fault occurs, and failure is likely to be heralded by the illumination of an array of transfer-fail lights (or other indications, however provided).

Thus we are obliged to pay for the greater power of on-line methods by having to exercise more patience and vigilance in the preparatory stages (which is not to say that off-line computation should not be carefully prepared!). Certainly, faults are far more serious and difficult to locate in on-line work, and at worst one may have to dismantle the whole operation to test the component parts. Since hardware and software are more closely inter-dependent, it is not always immediately clear which of them initiates a particular failure. The best weapons in the armoury are insight and anticipation.

As far as the motto quoted above is concerned, it could be applied to the whole of experimentation, not just computing. The object of laboratory experiments is not (or at least ought not to be) the mere acquisition of numerical data, and the purpose of laboratory instrumentation as a whole is to extend our comprehension into areas which would otherwise be inaccessible. The on-line computer does just this only more so. It provides us with senses geared to the speed and physical quantities associated with the system under test, to enable us to appreciate the precise nature of that system. It allows us to prod the test-object to see how it responds, and the prod can be of one microsecond duration or several hours: also the prod can be mechanical, electrical, optical, chemical, etc. Nevertheless, there is only a difference of degree of complication between this activity and the first proddings of primitive man as he strove to gain insight into his environment. Often the on-line computer can free us from the tyranny of numbers by providing more assimilable graphical output. So the motto is well worth bearing in mind, though we must also not forget that one of the main objectives of science is to quantify.

In this brief chapter we have rather cursorily examined the reasons for adding the on-line computer to our armoury of laboratory instruments, and later we shall justify it even further, but meanwhile it is necessary to make a mention of some of the tools of the trade, and this will preoccupy us for the rest of Part I.

Chapter III

Mainly Hardware

3.1 INTRODUCTION

This chapter is concerned with the basic electronic building blocks of on-line digital computer systems. It is *not* a comprehensive treatment, as such a treatment would require several books rather than one chapter. However, our aim is to underline those aspects of practical electronics which have particular relevance to the practice of the art of on-line computing. In order to adopt the philosophy promoted in this book it is essential to have some capability of developing small digital subsystems. The chapter is divided into two parts; the first being concerned with the fundamental building blocks, and the second with their use in the on-line computing system.

3.2 BUILDING BLOCKS

3.2.1 ELECTRONIC LOGIC

In electronic logic the fundamental operations of Boolean arithmetic are realized by the basic gates which constitute the building blocks for large systems of complex logical function. The three most fundamental units are conveniently labelled by means of their nearest verbal equivalents, namely AND, OR and NOT, but it should be particularly noted that OR corresponds more closely to the verbal combination 'either-or', since it performs a signal mixing function. The symbols for these elements are shown in Figure 3.1 together with the *truth tables* which conveniently summarize their input–output relations.

It so happens that the NOT, or inversion, operation occurs in the common emitter transistor amplifier, which, for a reason discussed below, is now

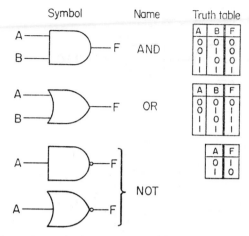

Figure 3.1   The basic logic symbols and truth tables

incorporated in logic gates. Its use reduces the number of basic operations to two, namely NAND (i.e. NOT-AND) and NOR (i.e. NOT-OR), since NOT is then realized as a one input NOR gate. The symbolic representations of these elements are shown in Figure 3.2.

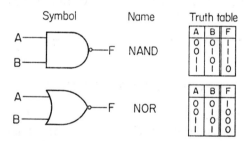

Figure 3.2   Symbols and truth tables for NAND and NOR functions

3.2.2   COMBINATIONAL LOGIC

Assemblies of logic which operate on functions of the present inputs to the circuit *without dependence on previous states* of the circuit are called combinational or non-sequential logic. Two simple examples are the implementation of a three-input OR function, Figure 3.3(a), and the *exclusive-OR* function, Figure 3.3(b), each using four NAND gates.

As an example of a slightly more complicated combinational problem let

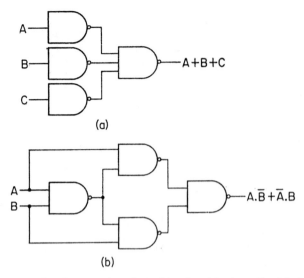

(a)

(b)

Figure 3.3   Two simple examples of combinational logic realized in NAND gates
(a) 3-input OR (b) exclusive-OR function

us consider the *full adder*. This circuit is the subsystem which adds corresponding bits of two binary words X and Y with the carry bit C from the lower bits to produce a sum S and a new carry bit C′ to the higher bits.

Algebraically this is:

$$S = \overline{X} . \overline{Y} . C + \overline{X} . Y . \overline{C} + X . \overline{Y} . \overline{C} + X . Y . C$$

and

$$C' = X . B + X . C + Y . C$$

as shown in Figure 3.4.

Any reader who is completely unfamiliar with the art and science of logic design is advised to make at least a cursory study of the basic principles. A suitable text [LogGirl, LogLew] should be pursued at least to the point where one is aware of such ideas as minimization of the number of gates under constraints such as *fan-in* and *fan-out* restrictions. Nevertheless, knowledge of logic circuitry to a great depth is not absolutely necessary for our present purposes, i.e. the development of links between systems and the modification of instrumentation to form small digital subsystems, al hough one needs enough insight to avoid gross redundancy of design and system unreliability.

We are not in the business of the mass production of large logic systems, and so can tolerate a certain degree of redundancy for the sake of perspicuity. Large assemblies of combinational logic are rarely needed for our purpose,

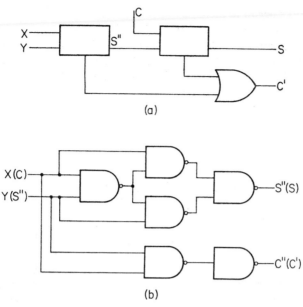

Figure 3.4   Combinational logic for full adder (a) in block form (b) internal logic of one block (the half-adder)

and many of the commonly required medium-scale ones are available in integrated form. The design of a quite complicated piece of interface logic can emerge naturally from a step by step consideration of the requirements of the two systems to be linked, so that it is built up from relatively simple subgroups of logic elements. On the other hand it is not unknown for a novice to produce a system, half of which makes no contribution to the resulting operation whatsoever (other than reducing its reliability).

Much more important, however, is a knowledge of the various practical constraints, disregard of which can lead to malfunction; in its most pernicious form—the intermittent fault. Therefore, though we are obliged by the exigencies of space to omit a discussion of the finer points of logic design, we shall refer in the following sections to some of the possible pitfalls.

3.2.3   IMPORTANT LOGIC TYPES

In the absence of modern integrated circuit techniques, early realizations of the basic gates were based on discrete components. It was possible, for example, to obtain the basic AND and OR operations by means of simple combinations of diodes and resistors, but since such passive elements dissipate signal power the need to include an amplifying stage soon became apparent as logic networks began to increase in complexity. So as soon as circuit integration became possible, the dominating forms became NAND and NOR gates with integral common emitter amplifiers to provide power gain and isolation during the transition between states. As circuit technology advanced, a complicated family of devices emerged, as can be seen in the simplified family tree in Figure 3.5.

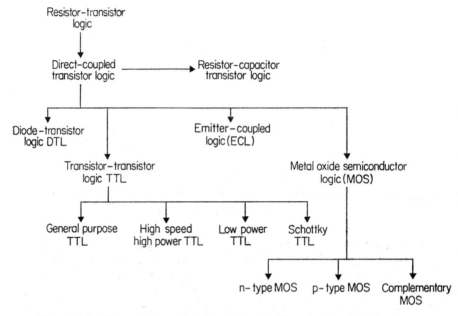

Figure 3.5   The evolution of logic device families—a simplified family tree

Space does not allow a comprehensive description of the ramifications of this tree, but some discussion is necessary since the choice of which class of technology to adopt is a central design decision in the development of special hardware. For detailed information on present trends and new device types the reader is urged to study the latest application reports produced by the major manufacturers of integrated circuits, since the progress of this technology rapidly outpaces any attempt to review it.

Diode–transistor logic (*DTL*) DTL circuits follow fairly closely the original discrete component concepts of a logic element (Figure 3.6). The diodes work in a current steering mode by diverting the bias current which would flow through resistor R_B to turn the transistor on. Thus, connecting either diode input to the lower rail results in a change of the output from the lower to the

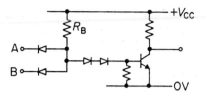

Figure 3.6   The basic DTL gate

upper rail potential. The principal disadvantage of DTL arises from the saturated condition of the transistor when it is switched on, so that, during the switch-off transient, time is required to remove the stored charge carriers. Hence an upper frequency limit is imposed on the operation of the gates. A typical propagation delay is of the order of 35 ns, although some manufacturers have improved this figure to a level comparable with TTL.

Transistor–transistor logic (*TTL*) One of the configurations which is easily fabricated by integrated techniques is a transistor which has several separate emitter–base junctions, but only one base–collector junction. This special type of transistor replaces the input diodes used in DTL circuits and has the advantage of lower capacitance, since it is fabricated on a smaller area than the diode form. Consequently the switching speed of the gate is improved, the propagation delay for general purpose TTL logic being about 15 ns. The output stage shown in Figure 3.7 is a typical push-pull, or totem-pole,

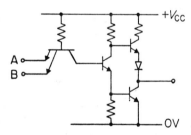

Figure 3.7   The basic TTL gate

configuration which also helps to improve the switching time of the overall device, particularly when a capacitive load is being fed, since the output impedance is considerably lower (typically below 100 Ω). It is quite likely, however, that a current spike will be generated during the transition from one logic level to the other using this type of output, since the transistors both conduct momentarily.

Variations on the basic TTL configuration have been introduced to improve certain aspects of the performance, usually at the expense of performance in some other respect. For example, an increase in speed might be traded off for a higher power dissipation.

One development which, at the time of writing, can provide nearly the shortest propagation delay (about 3 ns) is Schottky clamped TTL. This branch of the TTL family uses a configuration which prevents the transistors from becoming saturated. All the transistors have a Schottky barrier diode connected between base and collector, as shown diagrammatically in Figure 3.8.

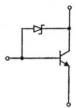

Figure 3.8   Schottky-clamped transistor

The forward voltage of this type of diode is less than that of a normal silicon diode and hence it can divert a proportion of the base current into the collector as the transistor approaches saturation. The fast turn-on time of the diode ensures that the transistor cannot become saturated, since diversion of current flow occurs first, and hence the fast switching performance is achieved.

Emitter-coupled logic (*ECL*) It is obvious from our brief considerations of DTL and TTL logic that any increase in gate switching speed can only occur if the transistors can be prevented from entering the saturated state. This has been achieved in the family known as emitter-coupled logic (ECL). The basic circuit is little more than a variation on the long-tailed pair used in differential amplifiers, as can be seen in Figure 3.9. The propagation delay can be reduced to typically 2 ns in an ECL gate, since the voltage swing is smaller and there is no saturation. The simple device can provide two outputs, as seen for example in the OR/NOR gate shown in Figure 3.9. Typical operating voltages are indicated in the figure, and power dissipation per gate is constant at about 25 mW.

The ECL approach can easily be extended to produce more complex large-scale devices on a single chip with the advantage of increased operating speed. Compatibility with other types of logic is achieved by using special interfacing gates, thereby allowing large mixed-logic circuits to be designed. ECL is one of the more recent logic families, but it is already proving very popular and is becoming a serious competitor to TTL as far as high-speed usage is concerned.

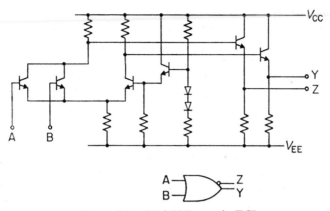

Figure 3.9   OR/NOR gate in ECL

Metal oxide semiconductor (MOS) devices Another important development in digital integrated circuits is MOS technology, based on the field effect transistor, which introduces the advantages of high input impedance ($\simeq 10^{14}\Omega$), low power consumption, simplified fabrication and low space requirements. Consequently it is very suitable for large-scale integration (LSI) whereby very complex logic networks can be constructed on a single chip, for example shift registers, memory units and even entire central processors. All such devices can be made easily compatible with other logic types, although power supply voltages may be higher. At the time of writing MOS logic has a slight speed disadvantage which tends to limit the range of application.

Complementary MOS It is relatively easy to produce the two complementary types of field effect transistor (*p*-enhanced and *n*-enhanced) on a single chip, which permits a number of variations of the complementary circuit type. In particular, a complementary output stage consisting of the two devices connected in series has an extremely small quiescent power requirement as the on/off resistance ratio is extremely large, so significant power consumption is restricted to the actual switching period.

The collector diffusion isolation (CDI) process We have just noted that the simplified fabrication inherent in MOS technology makes it very suitable for application in large-scale integration (LSI), where increased packing density and a greater circuit complexity are required.

Conventional bipolar circuits are, on the other hand, more complicated to fabricate and require a larger chip area, hence they are limited to use in medium-scale integration. However, a new bipolar fabrication technique—collector diffusion isolation (CDI)—has been developed, which is comparable with MOS for ease of construction and saving in chip area.

The reader is referred to the manufacturer's literature for more details on the process: we would simply point out here that CDI technology circuits are compatible with the other logic families and are said to be highly reliable. A further advantage of the CDI approach is the ability to combine both digital and linear continuous circuits in a single package, a feature which will no doubt be widely developed in the future.

3.2.4 POSITIVE AND NEGATIVE LOGIC

By definition, binary logic systems operate between two stable states, logical '0' and logical '1'. Thus they can be represented by any electric circuit where the signal is either entirely present or absent, but never exists stably at an intermediate level. This is, of course, inherently non-linear behaviour and early examples were based on the characteristics of relays and valves, followed by magnetic materials and transistors. When a logic network is translated into electrical terms a specific voltage level must be assigned to each logical state. It is conventional to describe as *positive logic* those systems in which the logical '1' state is represented by a more positive voltage than the logical '0' state. In *negative logic* the relationship is reversed. It is therefore very important to distinguish between the electrical and logical interpretations of a signal, *particularly when referring to logical '0' and 0 volts*, which may not be the same thing.

In the system design stage only the logic symbolism is required, and it is not until the later stages of hardware development that the electrical convention need be stated. Obviously any existing system can be interpreted by the positive- or the negative-logic convention, and it is evident from de Morgan's theorem that, to change from one to the other, one simply treats all NAND gates as NOR types, and vice versa.

3.2.5 LEVEL CHANGING

Most logic devices are now designed to work at levels of 0 volts and 5 volts, and both positive and negative logic conventions are found in the literature produced by different manufacturers. So a NOR gate from one manufacturer may be identical to a NAND gate from another. It is, of course, necessary in practice to allocate tolerance bands, and normally the lower level is defined as 0 to 0.5 volts, while the upper one is $+2$ to $+5$ volts. Nevertheless, one still finds an appreciable amount of digital equipment designed to operate at different logic levels (e.g. 0 and -12 volts), often in peripheral equipment.

In such cases it is necessary to include a simple level changing circuit in each data or control line between the two systems at a point which becomes the interface, in the strictest sense of the word. In the simplest case—voltage reduction without inversion—a resistor divider or zener-diode circuit can be used; though as these do not provide the buffering effect of a transistor amplifier they are seldom preferred. Thus we find ourselves in one of the few areas of computer utilization which still requires some discrete component design; albeit at a very simple level. Provided that reasonably accurate equivalent circuits are known for the signal source and the load, the problem is well defined, and the only other major design parameter is speed of operation, which may complicate matters by dictating non-saturating operation. It is assumed that the reader is familiar with various general design considerations—the dangers of using an emitter follower to drive a capacitive load, for example, otherwise a text-book should be consulted. We will confine ourselves to showing in Figure 3.10 a typical circuit for level changing with inversion. Remember that such simple parts of the system as this must not be allowed to malfunction, and, at a minimum, worst-case analysis of the equivalent circuit in its two extreme states must be applied.

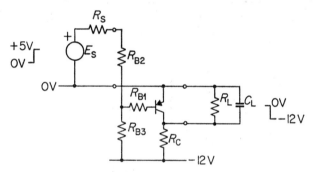

Figure 3.10   An inverting level changer with simple source and load equivalent circuits

3.2.6   LOADING

The design of logic circuits can be largely carried out as a mathematical exercise based on the methods of Boolean algebra backed up by the various graphical and other simplification procedures which have been developed over recent years. There is always a point, however, at which the nature of the hardware realization has to be taken into account. Thus, for example, a theoretical minimization of a logic network is pointless if it does not take account of practical limitations such as the maximum number of inputs (fan-in) or outputs (fan-out) permitted for the logic elements to be used. Output requirements also have to be considered when the circuit is required to drive external elements such as transmission lines, relays, indicator lamps, etc. The most usual output circuit is the common emitter amplifier, and the load current has to be provided by either the collector resistor or the output transistor, depending upon the rail to which the load is effectively connected. Power gates are available for situations where a high current is required, and one can, of course, always resort to a discrete power transistor when the requirement is abnormal. The reader will be aware of the extra caution necessary for inductive loads, but all unconventional loading situations should be analysed with care.

A further degree of freedom is offered by the availability of gates without an internal collector load. Obviously there will be for each device a maximum total conductance permitted to act as the external load, and this must be effectively connected to the collector rail. Reactive loads will tend to prolong the switching transient during which power dissipation is high, thereby exercising a further constraint on the total load.

One way in which an unloaded gate can be used to effect economies is in the wired-output configuration shown in Figure 3.11. Here two gates are made to share a common load. A common application is in the provision of a signal inhibit facility. Note that the logic function actually represented depends upon the polarity ascribed to the logic levels.

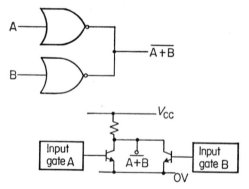

Figure 3.11   The wired-output configuration for NOR

3.2.7   TRI-STATE LOGIC

Common connection of the outputs of several gates, as in the wired-output configuration just discussed or in data highways having a number of trans-mitters and receivers in common, is not permissible with standard TTL logic. This is because the active totem-pole output stage, which is used to increase operating speed and improve loading, presents a low output impedance at both logic levels. Thus if we were to connect the outputs of two standard TTL gates together, when they were in opposite states, a low impedance path would be produced between the supply voltage and earth resulting in high current flow and castastrophic failure of the gates. One solution to this problem is to use open-collectored TTL gates, but this, of course, sacrifices the speed advantages of using the totem-pole output. A better solution has now been provided for this problem with the introduction of tri-state logic. This type of logic is essentially TTL but, in addition to the usual low impedance high and low states, the output can assume a third high impedance state which is produced by a control signal as shown in Figure 3.12.

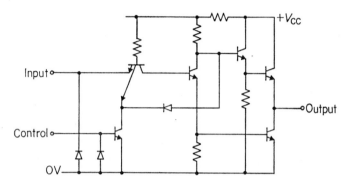

Figure 3.12   A single-input tri-state TTL circuit

3.2.8   LINE DRIVING AND BUFFERING

When digital signals are transmitted along a line of appreciable length, the shunt capacitance can cause the edges of the waveform to be degraded sufficiently to prevent correct logic switching. Furthermore, electromagnetic fields associated with external sources and adjacent lines induce the spurious signals collectively known as 'pick-up'.

When the line is being driven in the simplest way, by raising and lowering the source potential, these effects are minimized by ensuring that the source and load impedances are low and similar to the characteristic impedance of the line. This (voltage drive) method is subject to a degree of signal degradation which depends upon the speed of operation, the cable length and the deficiencies of the environment, and with so many individual factors it is difficult to specify a maximum operating length.

A better method relies on the allocation of a twisted pair of cables to each signal, and these are driven differentially so that their mean potential is always zero and the signals advancing along the cables are in the form of equal and opposite currents. This form of balanced current driving greatly improves the performance of the lines both as sources and acceptors of interference, and is invariably used in difficult situations. It is, however, costly and wherever possible the cheaper method is preferred. We shall return to the subject of line driving with reference to control and data highways (see Figure 3.29).

3.2.9   INTEGRATED CIRCUITS

The philosophy of this book, which is largely based on the computer-user's ability to adapt virtually any piece of scientific equipment for connection to the machine, is only viable through the existence of a wide range of integrated circuits. Parallel binary representation of numbers in a digital system implies that a large number of manipulations are needed to perform even a simple operation to a reasonable precision. Thus the hardware will contain a large number of similar basic building blocks (or gates). The physical size of a system has up to now depended mainly upon the amount of space occupied by an individual gate, while the cost has depended largely on the labour required to perform the necessary interconnections.

The first computers to be built on a commercial scale utilized the valve technology which was then current, resulting in machines of enormous physical size and power consumption. The first machine used by the authors for on-line work (a Ferranti Pegasus) occupied a sizeable room, and the electrical machines to supply the power were housed in a separate room. An equivalent machine could now be housed in a matchbox and be supplied by a battery. The physical nature of the machine was not however a limiting factor in its on-line use. Much more important was the fact that any interface work had to be accomplished by connecting together a large number of discrete components which involved a great deal of time and labour in construction and commissioning. The advent of the transistor improved the situation greatly and produced a generation of smaller, more powerful and faster machines, besides making the user's task easier.

A much greater advance, however, was made with integrated circuits. Each integrated circuit package contains a number of gates of various types and interconnections, the one major restriction being the number of external contact pins available. The packages are produced in standard sizes (e.g. 14 or 16 pin dual-in-line or flat pack, or sometimes in transistor-type cases, e.g. TO-5).

Integrated circuit technology has caused a stupendous reduction in the size and cost of general purpose digital equipment, and it is largely for this reason that the minicomputer has made such a dramatic entrance into research and teaching laboratories, in addition to its use in the automation of industrial processes. With equal suddenness the cost and difficulty of connecting equipment to the computer have been reduced to easily manageable proportions. The trend is likely to continue, but, unless there is a great deal more standardization, the rate of reduction in size and cost of purpose built equipment is likely to fall because of the need for interconnections between the elements. For, although it is comparatively easy to make connections inside the package, they are then no longer at the disposal of the user, so there is a sort of equilibrium between the capability and the versatility of circuit elements. There is, however, a wide range of integration complexity. Let us examine a couple of the smaller and therefore more generally useful integrated elements.

3.2.10 FLIP-FLOPS OR STATICIZERS

Memory is one of the most powerful elements in the make-up of a computer. The basic unit for storing one bit of information electronically is the flip-flop or staticizer. It is essentially a d.c. amplifier with sufficient positive feedback to make it unable to adopt stably any output condition other than one of the two extremes. The various forms of flip-flop arise mainly from the addition of extra gating to provide different methods of triggering the circuit to make a transition from one binary state to the other. The simplest realization in logic terms is a pair of cross-coupled gates or inverters (i.e. each input connected to the other output). Reference to the truth tables for these elements shows that they are obeyed as long as one of the outputs is 1 and the other 0, so there are two stable states. The only way of triggering to the opposite stable state is to force one of the inputs to reverse. Thus we form a simple asynchronous memory unit.

Let us for the sake of brevity discuss the action of two of the useful clocked staticizers without going into their electronic realization. The J-K flip-flop is a very commonly used form, which is shown in a block diagram in Figure 3.13; it has a clock terminal, two synchronous inputs, two asynchronous inputs and two outputs. The synchronous inputs act in conjunction with the clock pulse, so we have to use a modified form of truth table, shown in the same figure, such that the input conditions are as established before the

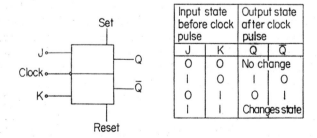

Figure 3.13   Block diagram and truth table for the J-K flip-flop

clock pulse, while the output states refer to the conditions after the clock pulse. The set and reset terminals S and R have to be used with care as they force the output independently of the gating effect of the clock (this is the basis of the S-R flip-flop which may be considered as a separate type). It will be seen that the various input combinations allow the device to be used in a great variety of ways.

Often, however, we only require a flip-flop to record the state of one input at the time of the clock pulse. For this purpose we can use the D-type which is shown as a derivative of the J-K in Figure 3.14, together with its truth table.

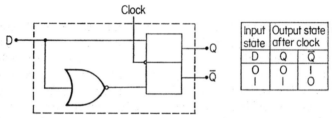

Input state	Output state after clock	
D	Q	$\bar{Q}$
O	O	I
I	I	O

Figure 3.14   Block diagram and truth table for the D-type flip-flop

It is, of course, quite feasible to construct complete binary word units, each consisting of a set of flip-flops, to make up a complete memory unit, though such a scheme would be rather impracticable and costly using small-scale integrated units (i.e. normally two flip-flops to a package). The basic hardware registers of the computer are, however, normally formed from arrays of flip-flops, while individual ones may be found throughout the central processor and other parts of the machine exercising the various control functions which require the element of memory.

Flip-flops are also of great importance in interface equipment; either to freeze data temporarily for later use, or simply to record the fact that certain events in the sequence of operation have taken place. In the latter application it is usually obvious when the setting of the staticizer should occur, but sometimes a little more thought is needed to decide when to clear it for the next cycle of events. An elementary mistake that can be made is to neglect to ensure that the clearing operation does ultimately take place for all possible combinations of events. Apart from this, staticizers are easy to use, even at high clocking rates, though in this case one may have to take precautions in the circuit board layout in respect of the clock signal distribution, otherwise degradation in the waveform can result in faulty triggering.

Large-scale integration (LSI) techniques make possible the more widespread use of staticizers as general purpose storage units, though unlike memories dependent upon hysteresis in materials they are inherently dependent upon continuity of the power supply, which can be a disadvantage. One immediate application is in the provision of dedicated buffer stores for various types of peripheral, particularly very slow or erratic devices, so that computer time is not wasted in organizing data which are arriving intermittently.

A final point to note is that two different types of clocking action may be found among staticizers. In the first type, the input information is gated through to the flip-flop for the duration of the clock pulse, which may be greater than 20 ns, and the input information must therefore be present for at least a period slightly exceeding this, so there is a basic speed limitation. The second is the edge-triggered type, in which the gating period is determined by the rising edge of the pulse, and as this is much shorter the operating speed may be much greater, though the information must still be present for a certain period and the clock waveform is much more critical.

3.2.11 MONOSTABLES

A monostable circuit is one in which a trigger pulse will produce a temporary change from a stable '0' state to a quasistable '1' state. The duration of the consequent pulse can be chosen by selecting values of an external resistor and capacitor. Various input terminals may be available, so that besides a simple trigger there may be a trigger-inhibit facility, while for use with ill-defined waveforms, a Schmidt trigger input may also be provided.

A monostable often appears to provide an obvious simple solution to many digital circuit problems, but in our experience they should be used with some degree of caution. This is because they are fundamentally asynchronous and tend to form the weak link in any chain of operations. They are more subject to spurious triggering than devices working under the discipline of clocked operation, and their period is dependent upon component values which may drift slightly. A certain road to disaster is to develop a system whose successful operation depends on the timing accuracy and triggering of a large number of monostables, so alternative circuits using a clocking system should be developed where possible (and this means almost always). This is not to say that they are not useful devices in non-critical applications. A typical one is in deciding whether a transfer failure has occurred, by using a monostable to generate an interval in which the delay between request and response must lie for the transfer to be deemed successful. As this interval is made much longer than a normal transfer would require, it only comes into operation in the pathological case and its exact value is non-critical.

3.2.12 PROPAGATION DELAYS, HAZARDS AND RACES

We have seen that there is a characteristic switching delay associated with each type of logic gate arising from effects such as charge storage. These delays impose an upper limit on operating frequency, depending upon the complexity of a circuit, and they place a further practical constraint upon the straightforward algebraic design of logic networks.

Hazards are defined as sources of malfunction due to unequal delays in different parts of a combinational circuit. They can occur when two signals nominally change state simultaneously, if there is an appreciable additional response time in either case. Consider a simple subnetwork, such as that shown in Figure 3.15. If gate 2 is slower in response than gate 1 a spurious pulse can occur at point F, when inputs B and C change as shown in the diagram.

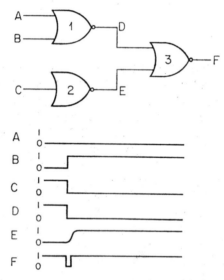

Figure 3.15   A simple hazard: sluggish gate 2 produces a spurious output at point F

In sequential circuits, unequal delays cause *races* between different inputs which can be either non-critical or *critical*. This means that in the former case the correct output is ultimately achieved, whereas in the latter case different outputs will occur depending upon which sequence won the race. It is often difficult to guard against these problems, and if an asynchronous device such as a monostable is included in a circuit, then the whole operation may be critical. This point underlines the possible dangers of asynchronous systems, and suggests that it is advantageous to arrange for a circuit to be synchronous with the appropriate delays included to avoid any races. It is, of course, possible to employ a propagation delay quite deliberately to produce a short pulse from a step, though a synchronous version is more reliable (Figure 3.16).

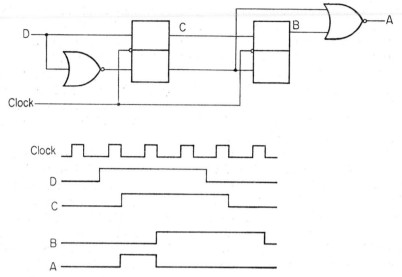

Figure 3.16 Diagram and waveforms of a 'pulse-from-step' generator

3.2.13 DATA STORAGE COMPONENTS

We have seen that staticizers provide one means of storing data, although till now their application in the computer has been restricted to the temporary memory registers and calculating areas. The main storage function has been largely allocated to magnetic devices, on the grounds of cheapness and inherent non-volatility. Incidentally, magnetic and dielectric storage are closely analogous to the electronic kind since they also operate by dint of positive feedback, but produced in these cases by the interaction of dipoles through the internal field of the material.

It seems that the traditional type of static magnetic storage may never be really cheap because of the topological problem inherent in its manufacture, whereas LSI is continuously producing larger memories at decreasing cost, and even the volatility problem is diminished in some devices with very long charge decay times. The main magnetic storage devices, listed in order of increasing access speed and increasing cost per bit, are

1 Magnetic tape
2 Magnetic disc
3 Magnetic drum
4 Ferrite core.

Of these only the last has sufficient speed and flexibility to form the basis of the fast random-access store required by a modern computer. The others are very important in providing the backing store necessary to all but the simplest system, for handling less urgent data and program information.

The magnetic core store of a computer is conventionally arranged in blocks of 1024 words, and this number, written 1 K, is taken as the basic quantity. Note that 1 K of 24 bit words is equal to 2 K of 12 bit words in both size and capability. Magnetization of each core in one direction is taken to represent logical 1 and the reverse direction logical 0. Detection of the stored state is more complicated than in the semiconductor store where it is more accessible and compatible with the logic system.

We need to have some understanding of the basic storage cycle as it influences the mode and timing of a computation, so we shall discuss it very briefly. Imagine for simplicity an arrangement of horizontal and vertical wires with a magnetic core threaded at each intersection so that each core is specified in Cartesian coordinates by two wires (Figure 3.17). Then if a current I is passed through one horizontal and one vertical wire, one (and only one) core will experience a magnetizing force of $2I$ ampere turns. The rest will experience I or zero. An extra wire (the sense wire) threaded through all the

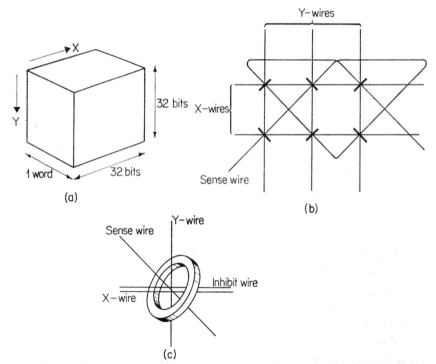

Figure 3.17.   (a) A 1k block of core store (b) part of a plane showing address and sense wiring (c) the wiring of a single core

cores will carry an e.m.f. should any core experience a flux reversal, so if I is set to be slightly more than half the switching force, an e.m.f. will signify that the one specified core has reversed its state. Now, by making the direction of I such that it tends to cause a transition from 1 to 0, we make the presence of the e.m.f. a test of whether a 1 was stored in the specified core. Note that this test is destructive, since every tested core will be set to zero. This *destructive read-out* complicates the read cycle, as the bit read has to be stored in a *temporary memory register* and rewritten in the core as the second phase of the cycle, unless it is to be replaced by new information anyway. Writing a 1 is accomplished by applying the currents I in the reverse direction along the horizontal and vertical wires. A zero is written most conveniently by means of a fourth wire (inhibit) which carries a current I in the appropriate direction to reduce the effect of the total magnetizing current, so that it is insufficient to change the state of the core.

It follows from this simplified discussion that the memory access cycle time always includes the time for one read and one write cycle. Furthermore we have ignored, at present, the complications inherent in the random accessing of one word in a large block of store, which are also time consuming. For these reasons we tend to write our programs in such a way that random access memory references are minimized, and if the computer designer provides us with a number of fast registers, forming a small *scratch pad*, we always use these in preference to the core store whenever practicable.

The actual waveforms emerging from a core store tend to be rather nasty, with ringing and breakthrough occurring, so that the output circuits need to perform a rather delicate decision operation. Consequently this tends to be one of the problem areas of computer production and reliability.

3.2.14 SEQUENTIAL CIRCUITS

Our rather compressed survey of the hardware tools of the trade has so far taken us through two important stages of development. Starting from individual electronic components we developed the basic gates which are capable of realizing logic functions in the form of combinational assemblies. Then, from these gates, we developed the slightly larger units which are capable of retaining logical information. The third important step is to build these units into *sequential circuits*. A sequential circuit is such that its present state depends on its immediately previous state and on its most recent input. These states and inputs are preferably defined with respect to successive clock pulses.

Flip-flops themselves are, of course, sequential circuits by this definition, but they also tend to be the fundamental building blocks for more elaborate forms.

3.2.15 SHIFT REGISTERS

The simplest form of sequential circuit is a linear array of flip-flops connected as shown in Figure 3.18, and this arrangement is termed a shift register, since a single clock pulse causes the state of each unit to be transferred to the next one to the right of it. The S-R inputs, which are not shown, can be used to set up the contents of the whole register initially, or they could be shifted in bit by bit from the left.

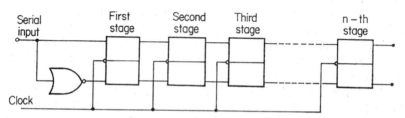

Figure 3.18   The basic shift register formed by J-K flip-flops

In computation, shifting is a fundamental operation, since in any number system it represents multiplication or division by the number base (which is itself an element of multiplication or division by any number). It is also a very useful operation in the manipulation of packets of logical information, whether they actually represent numbers or not. It can, for example, form the basis of one of the simpler methods of conversion between serial and parallel forms of words.

As we shall see later, this form of conversion is frequently required for such applications as data transmission. Figure 3.19 shows in skeleton form a serial

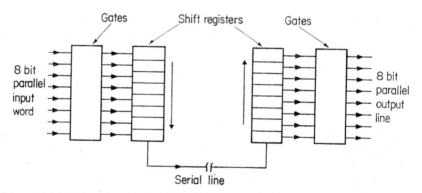

Figure 3.19   The use of shift registers for parallel/serial and serial/parallel conversion of information in signal tranmission

data transmission system with conversion to and from an 8 bit parallel form at either end. The parallel word at the source is gated into the register via the S-R inputs. Eight clock pulses are then applied which cause the word to be transmitted in serial form to the receiving shift register, where, after the final pulse, it is available for gating out as a parallel word.

It will be realized that Figure 3.19 is incomplete as the system cannot operate without the transmission of synchronization information, but at this stage we are only concerned with the contribution of the shift registers. Also, it should be pointed out that this is not the only way of tackling the conversion problem. There are, for example, integrated circuit conversion units for this purpose which rely on the gating being controlled by read-only memories accessed by synchronous counters.

A more elaborate form of sequential operation can be obtained from a shift register by applying the feedback concept to it. In its simplest form, this means connecting the output of a register to the input so that it forms a circulating store. This application is very useful in equipment such as visual display units (VDUs), where information is inherently staticized but has to be continuously represented in a cyclic fashion. For this use, gating must be provided in the feedback line so that the stored information can be inhibited in favour of new incoming information when necessary. Here again there are obvious synchronization problems which are readily solved and do not concern us at the moment. Also, we have in this case an obvious need for registers with very large numbers of stages, and we shall discuss the fulfilment of this need a little later.

The application of feedback to sequential circuits suggests the possibility of autonomous operation, and the feedback shift register is an important example which, as we shall see, has applications in some powerful on-line methods. A register with n stages can represent 2^n different binary numbers, as this defines the maximum number of possible states. For any given feedback function, at least one of these will be a null state, which perpetuates itself, so a sequence of $2^n - 1$ is said to be of *maximal length*. Furthermore it is possible to provide feedback functions, based on exclusive-OR combinations of the states of some of the stages, that produce the property of apparent randomness over the sequence length. Thus we are able simply to generate an important class of signals the maximal length *pseudorandom binary sequences* (PRBS).

3.2.16 COMPARATORS

A very useful adjunct to sequential circuits is the comparator which gives us a signal when the contents of two separate registers become identical. It is particularly useful in conjunction with circuits which are to some extent autonomous, either through a feedback mechanism or through interaction with an external system.

Consider two registers as in Figure 3.20(a). The corresponding stages are individually compared through exclusive-OR gates, which give 0 output only when their inputs are the same. Thus by combining all these in a NOR gate we obtain a 1 output only when the entire contents of the registers are identical.

The full comparator circuit is not necessary if we only require indication of the arrival at one particular state. Say for example we need an output pulse when an 8 bit shift register passes through the state where the outputs $Q_1, Q_2, Q_3, Q_4, Q_5, Q_6, Q_7, Q_8$ are 11010100. Then, if the complementary outputs are available, this state corresponds to the combination $(\overline{Q}_1 + \overline{Q}_2 + Q_3 + \overline{Q}_4 + Q_5 + \overline{Q}_6 + Q_7 + Q_8)$ being zero, giving the arrangement shown in Figure 3.20(b). If the complementary outputs are not available, then we are obliged to treat the ones and zeros separately, e.g. perform the operation $\overline{(Q_1 \cdot Q_2 \cdot Q_4 \cdot Q_6)} + (Q_3 + Q_5 + Q_7 + Q_8)$, Figure 3.20(c).

Comparators can also be used to test whether the contents of one register exceed those of another.

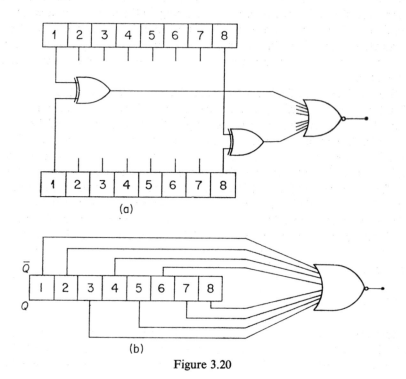

(a)

(b)

Figure 3.20

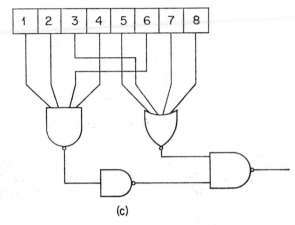

(c)

Figure 3.20 Useful in autonomous subsystems (a) full comparator circuit using exclusive-OR gates (b) detection of a given state using the complementary outputs of a register (c) detection of a given state without complementary outputs

3.2.17 COUNTERS

Another important class of sequential circuits is that of counters or scales. The basic counter consists of a register, the stages of which are coupled in such a way that the binary number represented by their contents is incremented by one on receipt of each clock pulse. At its simplest this can be realized by a chain of cascaded flip-flops where the output of each stage is used to clock the next, as shown in Figure 3.21. In this case the flip-flops are simple divide-by-two circuits (for our purposes we may regard them as J-Ks with J and K held at 1).

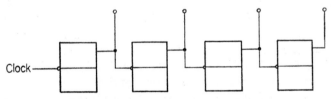

Figure 3.21   Ripple through counter (up)

This asynchronous form of circuit is of limited application as it is not immune to spurious triggering, and this *ripple-through* form of carry leads to speed limitations or ambiguities. Figure 3.22 shows how it can be converted to a synchronous form with fast carry by the addition of some AND gates.

Counters appear in various forms, an important variation being the

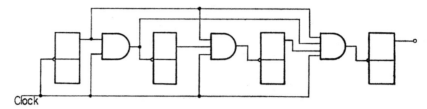

Figure 3.22   Synchronous binary counter (up)

reversible (or up-down) counter, and one should not be so prejudiced by their numerical origins as to be blinded to their usefulness as devices of a certain sequential behaviour which can be exploited in many ways.

3.2.18   LARGE-SCALE INTEGRATION (LSI)

We have already touched upon the possibilities of LSI in our introduction to staticizers, but as, at the time of writing, this is the most rapidly developing and portentous branch of technology, we must conclude our survey of the building blocks with at least a fleeting glance at its impact upon logic design. We have already noted that MOS technology and the CDI process offer advantages of ease of fabrication, high packing densities, low power require- ments and low volatility of information in the form of stored charge, so it is not surprising that these are the primary areas of expansion of LSI.

Like any other mass market phenomenon, LSI provides enormous ad- vantages as long as one's requirements are standard. Perhaps in the not too distant future it will be possible for a computer to design and manufacture a one-off assembly from a complete operational specification. Meanwhile, manufacturers will continue to produce items for which there is a significant demand. This is not too restrictive, however, since all designers face similar problems, but one should not look to LSI to provide a complete panacea. On the other hand it does allow us to look at our problems in a completely new way, and some novel and elegant solutions thereby become possible. The great limiting factor in LSI is the one we have already hinted at, namely the physical number of terminals available on a package.

Let us examine a few devices to see how these freedoms and restrictions emerge.

3.2.19   THE LSI SHIFT REGISTER

It is a simple matter to produce a shift register which will hold 1024 bits, or more, of data in a single package, but, as a package with a thousand terminals would be rather cumbersome, we would not expect to have access to all the stages of the device. Thus the growth area for LSI registers is chiefly in applications where data are fed in at one end and extracted at the other, principally for long delays or recirculating stores. For the latter purpose, the package might also contain additional logic for gating in new information and suppressing any recirculating information which is to be overwritten.

A typical application of the recirculating store is found in alphanumeric displays. A 6 bit number contains sufficient information to define a character, so six recirculating stores can represent characters continuously in parallel for each scan of a CRT face. These 6 bit characters have to be presented through another LSI circuit, however, to decode them into a visible dot pattern.

We cannot discuss the detailed internal operation of the registers, but must note in passing that there are two basic types of MOS shift register—static and dynamic. In the static type information can be held in store for the whole time that a power supply is applied, whereas the dynamic type stores data as a charge on a capacitor during a clock pulse, after which the capacitor is effectively gated off from the supply to reduce power dissipation. As the stored charge will tend to leak away with time, a minimum clocking frequency must be imposed so that the data can be periodically refreshed. Typical operating ranges are 0 to 2.5 MHz for static registers and 10 kHz to 4 MHz for dynamic ones. The advantages of dynamic registers arise from the higher operating speeds, greater packing densities and lower power consumption that can be achieved.

3.2.20 READ-ONLY MEMORIES (ROMS)

The ROM is one of the most potent devices given to us by MOS technology. It is basically a storage unit which is either preprogrammed in manufacture or by the user, so that any given combination of inputs on its address lines produces a prescribed set of outputs. Thus, in mathematical terms, it performs a one-to-one mapping from one set of binary numbers to another, a function which though theoretically possible in terms of combinational logic is hardly practicable in those terms.

Let us take as an example of the use of a ROM the application already considered above, the alphanumeric display. There are altogether 36 numbers and letters as well as a number of other symbols, so a 6 bit binary number is sufficient to define each uniquely. However, the minimum size of dot matrix to give a visual impression of each character is about 7×5, or 35 bits of information, some data being 'on' and others 'off' to represent the pattern. The standard ROM for this purpose therefore has nine address lines (six representing the input word and the other three allowing each column to be decoded in turn), the output being seven parallel bits to form the rows in sequence.

Having provided the storage and decoding facilities described above, the only remaining question is how to utilize the information to produce a visible character on the screen. The most obvious answer is to provide a pair of incremental x and y digital to analogue converters which are driven by counters to scan the character area, while the ROM, which is interrogated by the same counters, provides a beam unblanking signal whenever a bright dot is required. A more elegant, though perhaps less versatile method is to build up lines of characters row by row on a television raster. Thus the first line scan would produce only the top dot rows of a whole line of characters in succession, the remaining rows being built up on the screen in successive line scans. The great advantage of the latter technique is that the characters are being produced by a method which depends only on the timing, so that no digital to analogue conversion is involved.

The important lessons from this example are that the same character generating ROM can be used to produce characters on any suitable display device (e.g. an array of light-emitting diodes, a chart recorder, etc.) and that it replaces a software routine which is wasteful of computer time and storage. Also the ROM allows a comparatively small amount of information to specify a large amount. Thus, properly used, ROMs can perform their specified function in a variety of applications, thereby relieving the central processor of repetitive work. Note, however, that they do not always exhibit the versatility of software solutions to problems, and the choice between the two approaches is a matter which will occupy us a great deal in the course of the text.

There is a wide and growing variety of ROMs available. A 24 pin package can contain typically 4096 bits of data, which are grouped into words whose length is determined by the application. Each ROM comprises three main sections—an address decoder, the memory matrix and an output buffer—but the user only needs to be aware of its input–output specification, being relieved of the need to consider the internal operation.

Again there is a choice between static and dynamic devices, as in the basic shift registers. When a static ROM is addressed, the output appears after a delay equal to the memory access time and remains until the address is changed. The dynamic ROM, however, produces clocked information which is valid only for a short period. The latter is therefore suited to the preferred synchronous mode of operation.

3.2.21   RANDOM ACCESS MEMORIES (RAMS)

The RAM is an LSI device which promises to put an end to that unloved and unlovely feature of computers—the magnetic core store. For, compared with the latter, it offers the following advantages:

1 Read out is non-destructive
2 Operation is inherently faster
3 It is more rugged
4 It is already cheaper, and becoming more so.

The main disadvantage is that the stored data are essentially volatile, if only to the extent that they are lost in the event of a power supply failure. However, the decay time for stored charge is continually being increased as manufacturing techniques improve, and static RAMs can already cope with supply interruptions of short duration.

The concept of a RAM, of course, adds enormously to the potential versatility of small logical assemblies, such as peripheral controllers, and it becomes possible to achieve very high speed data acquisition and buffering at a terminal remote from the computer, with subsequent block data transfers to the main computer store.

3.2.22 OPERATIONAL AMPLIFIERS

Although we have not attempted to provide a complete list of the electronic building blocks, it is important not to forget, through a preoccupation with digital methods, one of the most valuable in laboratory measurements—the operational amplifier. This is an integrated circuit giving linear continuous amplification with high gain, high input impedance, low output impedance and a good frequency response. It is almost always used in such a way that its behaviour is defined by a few discrete components connected to its terminals (the two basic forms for simple resistive combinations are shown in Figure 3.23). There is a great variety of circuits with applications such as level-changing, signal integration, amplification, line-driving and receiving, summation of signals, active filtering, impedance matching, electrometers, etc., in fact a large proportion of the electronics that needs to be developed for on-line measurement.

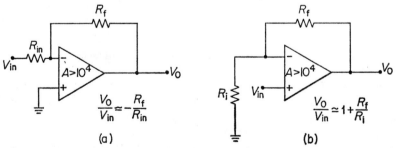

Figure 3.23 The basic resistive operational amplifier circuits (a) inverting (b) non-inverting

One mistake to be avoided is getting used to the assumption that the operational amplifier *is* ideal. It has defects such as output voltage drift due to thermal changes and limitation of response (slew rate) which are important in the case of very small or very fast signals. The reader is no doubt familiar with the elementary feedback theory upon which the circuits are based, and that this is further simplified by consideration of the establishment of a 'virtual earth' at the input terminal. The simplest and most important circuit for measurement applications is the current-voltage transducer, which merely has a single resistor connected between input and output, and is the basis of the form of electrometer most frequently used in the laboratory.

3.3 THE ON-LINE COMPUTER SYSTEM

3.3.1 THE ON-LINE COMPUTER

The variation in architecture of on-line computers is wide, and is made wider in appearance by the differences in the ways that the various manufacturers describe their systems. At a very simple block diagram level, however, most will correspond to Figure 3.24. There are three important blocks—the central

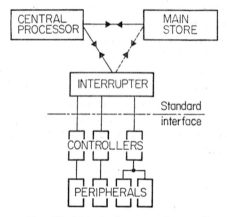

Figure 3.24 Simplified block diagram of an on-line computer

processor, the main store and the input/output transfer organizer for which we shall use the shorter name interrupter. The interrupter provides the connection with the external world through units which link it to the peripherals—these we shall call controllers. Each of these separate connections constitutes an input-output *channel*, and as we shall see later these channels may be combined in various ways for laboratory purposes.

The boundary between the interrupter and the controller is a very important one, and it is realized in a special stylized way to form the *standard interface*. The standard interface comprises two separate interlocking electronic packages, one in the interrupter and one in the controller. They are the same for all channels, and it is only beyond the interface electronics that each channel develops its own individuality.

Figure 3.24 is, of course, greatly simplified; within the central processor we have included *the function unit, the control unit* and *the temporary storage registers*. The function unit is the part of the computer which carries out the manipulations of data in the various arithmetical and logical ways that constitute the repertoire of the machine. This is the feature of the machine which imparts its character as far as the programmer is concerned. The control unit counts the steps of the program, causes the fetching of instructions from the store and their subsequent execution via the function unit and the temporary storage registers. The mechanisms of decoding and executing instructions are very interesting, but it is not actually necessary to study them for our present purpose, and further details can be found in the literature [e.g. CoOrgFlo, CompLew].

The store is rather more important because its mode of operation does affect the operation of the computer in the context of its links with the external world. Earlier in this chapter we discussed some data storage components, and particularly the magnetic core, which has enjoyed a brief reign as the supreme method of main data storage. One of the complications is the destructive nature of read out from magnetic cores, which means that each read cycle must be accompanied by a write cycle, and this all has to be done via temporary storage registers. Another complication is the fact that the electromagnetic circuits of the individual core have a topology which is difficult from the manufacturing point of view (interlocking rings) which means that storage has been expensive and has required careful husbandry.

The feature of the main store that exerts most influence on the ways things are done in on-line computing is the method of accessing stored information. The user is not aware of the destructive nature of the basic read mechanism, apart from the fact that time is required for the additional rewrite, and the normal read facility is non-destructive in effect. Information is accessed by setting up an address, which uniquely specifies one unit of information (a word), and this address is put into the *store address register*. The words can be thought of as being set out in a square array, so that the address can be broken up into two parts which are used as the Cartesian co-ordinates specifying the stored word. This is done simply by gating the read pulse onto two wires which intersect at the appropriate point, though this has to be repeated in parallel for all the bits of the word, so that the block of store is actually a solid prism of depth equal to the word length. The resulting signals in the sensing wires are conveyed in parallel to a temporary memory register where they are available to the processor.

The use of the main store is one of the features of on-line computing that makes it different from the off-line variety (at least in respect of the awareness of the user). When the computer is in operation the store is divided up into a number of separate areas by the software, and some of these areas are in a dynamic relationship with the external hardware. There are various ways of organizing the operation of these areas. For example some may operate on a 'first-in, first-out' basis and others on a 'first-in, last-out' basis (these we shall discuss later under the titles *cyclic buffer* and *push down store*). The idea of a buffer is very important in the handling of input/output operations, and together with the associated setting up problems it is something which we must discuss more fully in a later chapter. The reason for mentioning it here is the need to emphasize the dominating influence exerted by the store, both in its speed and the repertoire of instructions associated with its use.

The random accessing of information from the store is quite a lengthy business when one takes into account the necessity to set up the address in the first place in an index register (which often needs a store reference of its own), and it is fortunately possible in most on-line applications to reduce true random access to a minimum by making use of special *index* and *modify* instructions which allow one to alter an existing address rather than set up a new one. As data are usually set out in some systematic way in the store, they may be accessed cyclically by the use of such instructions. The whole idea of addressing is very fundamental to on-line computing, and we shall have more to say about it in a software context.

The most characteristic part of the computer for on-line use is what for brevity we have called the *interrupter*, though this appears under various names and forms in the different varieties of machine, and sometimes it is not easy to identify as a separate physical unit. The function of the interrupter is to handle input/output operations, and to do it in such a way that there is minimum interference with the processor in the execution of its program tasks. It is the interrupter which allows the computer user to organize each activity separately and not have to bother about possible interactions during the running of the program. One of the chief sources of difficulty for the newcomer to on-line computing is this question of input/output mechanisms. He may be used to off-line high-level programming in which one simply makes a WRITE or PLOT statement and it all happens, or he may have worked with one of the older small-scale machines in which assigning a quantity to a certain register causes the program to be halted while the contents of the register are communicated to the external world.

The clue to the interaction of software and hardware necessary for efficient transfer of data to and from the computer is the existence of *staticizers*, which can be *set* or *tested* by program. These staticizers form part of the system of sequential logic that constitutes the interface, and they condition, or are conditioned by, its behaviour. For standard or established peripherals, there is no need for the programmer to be aware of these staticizers, but, in the development of new peripherals, direct use must be made of them. These staticizers act as *flags* which trigger off appropriate sequences of input/output operations *provided that certain essential information concerning the quantity, location or destination and nature of data has been previously set up* (see Section 4.11). The power of such a method of operation lies in the fact that the computer hardware can take action on any number of such flags in appropriate order without needing to halt its programmed action. Furthermore complex simultaneous multiperipheral operation can take place, yet the programmer will only have needed to consider each one separately. Thus the flip-flop or staticizer is one of the key elements in the mechanisms of on-line computing, being the essential link between the separate and apparently disconnected elements of hardware and software.

The computer is an assemblage of the sort of elements discussed in the first part of this chapter—gates, staticizers, registers, counters, etc. As users we are not concerned with the details of its internal arrangement, but only with its appearance from two different directions. The first direction is the point of view of the programmer which we will discuss in the following chapter, but the second direction is looking in at the standard interface, which is more peculiar and important to on-line computing, and will require discussion in this chapter. There are, however, one or two characteristics of the computer layout which affect its nature from both points of view. The most important of these is the length of the computer word.

A glance through an information journal for on-line computer users reveals that there is a very wide variation in word length, the usual sizes being 12, 16, 24 and 32 bits. What are the design constraints that produce such a range of different compromises? There is one dominating consideration which exerts pressure towards a smaller word—the economic one. Modern machines are almost invariably parallel (i.e. the bits of the word are transported and operated on simultaneously rather than consecutively), though one should mention that some microprocessors are repeating the history of their larger predecessors by going through a serial phase. Thus almost every part of the internal logic of the computer has to be duplicated for each bit of the word.

The converse pressure for a long word arises from the fact that this is the unit of information which is conveyed in a single package throughout the computer system, and the longer this fundamental unit, the more efficient the handling of information. This consideration applies equally to the two quite distinct guises of the computer word—as a datum or as an instruction.

To see how word length affects the operation of the machine, let us examine briefly the process whereby the programmed instructions are obeyed in a short-word machine. If the computer has just completed all the actions required by the previous instruction, its first task is to acquire a new instruction. The contents of the *program counter register* are incremented by one, and then used as an address supplied to the *store address register* so that a read/write cycle may be initiated to *fetch* the next instruction into the *instruction register*. Here it is decoded by the logic of the processor and will specify a unique *operation* on a unique *operand*. Thus the instruction word must contain the information to identify these two entities, and its length will prescribe the number of different possible combinations (an n bit word will specify 2^n different combinations of operation and operand).

Usually, the specified operation will require that the operand be obtained by a further store reference, and the part of the instruction word allocated to this contains the information as to how it is to be obtained. This process can be indirect in that a store reference is first required to obtain the address of the required operand. However, the important fact is that the number of possible operations and operands can be severely curtailed when the instruction word is short. Typically a 12 bit machine allocates 3 bits to the specification of the instructions. One of the resulting eight combinations is reserved to specify operations which do not require an operand, therefore making use of the rest of the instruction word, and another is used for input/output operations on a similar basis. This leaves only six possible different operations involving a separately specified operand, which may not seem much but is quite sufficient for the realization of any required programmed action, though possibly in a rather circumlocutory way. Only 9 bits remain to specify the operand, and as this is obviously inadequate the machine designers have to resort to further clever and devious tricks to extend the capability; but consideration of them is beyond our present scope, other than to say that it obviously implies overheads upon the amount of computing required for a given task [CoOrgFlo].

As the length of word is increased, so it becomes possible to specify more operations and operands, and even to specify more than one operand per instruction. Some simple orders of great power enter into the repertoire (e.g. indexing and modification, which we have already mentioned in the context of addressing the store), but the logic for decoding and executing naturally becomes more complex and expensive.

Now we can see why there is such a wide range of word lengths and machine facilities. At one extreme there is the short-word machine with minimum hardware which is so incredibly cheap that it is quite feasible to think in terms of dedicating if to a particular task. At the other extreme there is the long-word machine with a wide repertoire of instructions, a wide addressing range and great versatility, which is expensive, and for laboratory use would not be dedicated to a particular task. Nevertheless, the economic and technical considerations are not simple, and as we shall see there are sound reasons for inclining towards the latter alternative.

We shall not burden the reader with any greater detail of the organization of the computer as the information is readily available in the literature [e.g. CoOrgFlo and commercial booklets] and we have more pressing matters to deal with.

3.3.2 THE STANDARD PERIPHERALS

The most important aspect of the on-line computer is its communication with the external world. Much of this communication is standardized and stylized because it takes place through peripherals which are common to most installations. This is therefore an aspect which is well documented and which we can deal with summarily.

The most essential are the *paper tape reader* and *punch*. These are the favoured means of preparing and presenting programs for laboratory use. There are alternatives to paper tape such as cards and magnetic tape cassettes, but these have not yet offered a serious challenge. Paper tape is cheap, simple, reliable and scrutable. The normal standard is eight hole tape, since 7 bits are sufficient to span the whole of a set of alphanumeric and control characters, and the eighth serves as a parity check. The chief characteristic of the reader and punch in the on-line context is that in electronic terms they are extremely slow. This means that they must not be allowed to interfere with the operation of faster devices, and that they will not suffer unduly if they are made to attend on the servicing of such devices. In other words they are peripherals of the lowest priority in an interface sense, if not in a sense of utility. The next peripheral in order of usefulness is the teletype (or its visual display equivalent), which has been the chief avenue of direct communication between man and machine. It is closely allied to the paper tape peripherals in its format of 8 bit words, and the same machine can often be used for preparing tape and communicating with the computer. Again it is an extremely slow device and imposes a negligible demand at interface level, yet it is extremely important as a central feature of on-line programming methods and tends to dominate the organization of software.

The *incremental plotter* is of much greater importance in the laboratory than it is in many general computer facilities, because what is being dealt with is not essentially a set of numbers but rather the variation of physical quantities which can usually best be presented in graphical terms. The plotter accepts orders consisting of a few bits which direct it to move incrementally in the x or y direction and to raise and lower its pen. The plotter may be even slower than the aforementioned devices and it is often necessary to make provision for the output to the plotter to be set aside for later issue, so that the experiment is not held up.

The need to store large quantities of data within the hardware system brings us to the next peripheral—*the backing store*. It is by no means essential, but once available it can introduce great benefits. Almost invariably it is based on ferromagnetism in the form of magnetic tape, disc or drum. Tape is suitable for recording and transporting large quantities of data which only require serial access of relatively low speeds. The disc can be exchangeable or fixed and offers a higher access speed. The drum is a fixed store which can be used for high access speed, particularly in adverse conditions such as on board ship. Note that in comparison with the computer main store we are talking about much greater quantities of data (megawords instead of kilowords) but very much longer access time (milliseconds instead of microseconds). Disc and drum require to be treated as fast peripherals, because the high packing density of data on the magnetic surface compensates for the inherent mechanical nature of the system, and produces relatively high rates of serial data. Apart from this consideration the use of the backing store is largely a software matter, which we will mention later but not in too much detail as it represents a refinement rather than an essential element of laboratory computing technique.

Finally we come to the *visual display unit* (VDU), a title which covers a multitude of different facilities. At its simplest the VDU is an equivalent to the teletype, the paper being replaced by a cathode-ray tube screen. At its most complicated it is virtually a small computer in its own right, with multicoloured graphical display, internal cassette tape recording, etc. The VDU is without doubt the dominant peripheral for man–computer communication, and depending on how important this is in the given situation it can be of tremendous value. It is very good value for money and the promise of cheap, reliable subsidiary hard-copy units promises the early demise of the electromechanical teletype.

These, then, are the six peripherals whose presence we will tend to take for granted, though the last two may be considered as optional, and we shall only mention them in so far as they are important to specific aspects of laboratory on-line computing. A computer with just these peripherals would make a very useful scientific tool and would enhance the facilities of any laboratory, but these benefits are almost negligible in comparison with those which accrue once the experimental equipment of the laboratory itself becomes part of the computer system, and this is the aspect which concerns us more deeply.

3.3.3 THE INTERFACE

The term *interface* is used throughout computing, unfortunately with a number of different meanings. In a software context it is used to describe a piece of program designed to link together two other programs which would otherwise be incompatible. In a hardware context it is sometimes taken to mean the whole body of electronics linking the computer to an external device. Properly speaking, however, an interface is something without depth and we shall use it to represent the dividing line between the electronics which are general to the computer and the electronics which are particular to the operation of an external device.

The basic problem occurring at the interface is that we have two autonomous systems which require to exchange information, and to do so they need a set of rules. An analogous situation occurs in radiotelephony where a common code of procedure ensures that two interlocuters do not clash with each other in their attempts to communicate information. Even in an ordinary conversation there are rules which have been developed by society over the years, but they are based on clues and signals of extreme subtlety which take all the power of a superb processor, the brain, to unravel. In contrast the signals used by the electronic interface must be very simple and foolproof.

The first obvious requirement is for each side to be able to initiate communication, and this requires a unique signal and a unique reply, but one must also be able to specify the required direction of travel of the information and perhaps something about the nature of it (e.g. whether it represents data or control instructions). Thus we find that, in addition to the lines required to transmit the actual data, there is a need for further lines to facilitate its error-free transfer.

The critical moment in the operation of the interface sequence is when the exchange of a datum actually takes place, and this is where the principal design choices will have been made. Firstly, the transmission may be serial or parallel (i.e. there is only one data line or as many data lines as bits in the computer word), and the main difference is that parallel is fast and serial is cheap. Secondly, the exchange may be on a 'strobe' or 'handshake' basis, (i.e. synchronous or asynchronous). Being synchronous, the strobe system suffers from a basic disadvantage in that the timing is critical. (This is not a sudden conversion from the creed of the first part of this chapter, that synchronous logic is superior. The connection of independent autonomous devices is a completely different problem from the development of an integral piece of logic.) In the strobe system, one side of the interface (the computer side) is dominant, because it issues the pulses which determine when the data are read, whatever the direction of transfer, and all the peripherals must conform to the imposed synchrony.

The handshake system on the other hand treats both sides with much greater equality, though possibly in a way that recognizes the fact that the computer's time is more valuable than the peripheral's. The essence of the handshake system lies in two special control lines, to enable each side of the interface to say 'I am ready for the transfer'. When the potentials of both these lines are at logic 1, the data are also on the data lines and the handshake is taking place, i.e. there is an asynchronous transfer of data. Obviously, one of the lines must have taken the initiative by being the first to go to logic 1, and the other must have responded to it. Furthermore other signals must have passed previously to establish the nature and validity of the handshake before it occurs. We shall not go into the detail of how these other signals play their part, but merely mention the sort of information they might convey, e.g.

> This transfer is in the direction to (from) the computer.
> There is an error in the last datum transferred.
> The next word is an address.
> The next word is a control word.
> The next character is the last in the data block.
> Parity is being used in the next transfer.
> The peripheral will be required in the current program.

To illustrate the principle of handshake transfers we shall assume that certain of the above lines are present and functioning appropriately and consider the waveforms on only four further particularly important lines, which for convenience we shall call Computer Command, Peripheral Request, Computer Handshake, Peripheral Handshake. Add to these a composite Data line, for which logic 1 represents data on the line. Now even with this restricted format there is room for variation, so in Figure 3.25 we show one

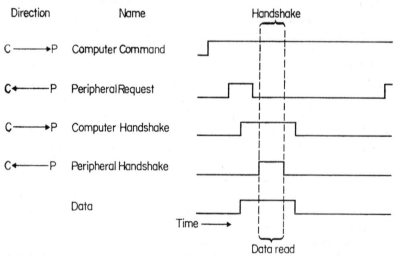

Figure 3.25   A possible handshake sequence for transfer of data from the computer to the peripheral

possible way that a handshake might occur for output of data from the computer to the peripheral. Firstly the computer issues a command which informs the peripheral that it has data to send. No further action occurs, however, until the peripheral issues a request for the transfer thereby guaranteeing that it is completely ready and will not waste the computer's valuable time by prolonging the handshake. Once it has received this signal the computer can initiate the handshake by placing data on the lines and issuing its handshake signal. The peripheral responds by raising its own handshake line potential while it reads the data and lowering it as soon as reading is completed. The computer then acknowledges by lowering its own handshake potential and the transfer is completed. Note that there are no rigorous timing requirements (though it is sensible to set a maximum time for the handshake to ensure that the whole system does not get locked up by one faulty peripheral controller). What happens next really depends on the contribution of the lines we have omitted, There may, for example, be further transfers as a result of the same command.

The British Standard Interface is an example of a handshake system. It is designed to link two computers, i.e. devices of equal status, and therefore has completely separate circuits for each direction of travel of data, and each consists of eight control lines and eight data lines. The data are thus transmitted in the form of 8 bit bytes [SigProBeau].

The different relationship between the computer and its peripherals means that it is not necessary to provide separate go and return lines. Indeed, it is only necessary to provide one set of data lines for all peripheral controllers (the highway or bus) since only one can be engaged in a handshake with the computer at any time. Figure 3.26 shows a possible arrangement where each

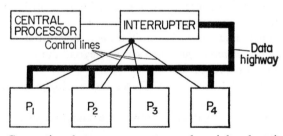

Figure 3.26 Connection between computer and peripherals using a common (bussed) data highway and star-connected control lines

controller has its own control lines but shares the data highway with all the others. This represents an important saving in a parallel machine with a long word, in addition to its conceptual importance. The computer has an internal clock-signal generator, but with handshake interfaces this has no external significance, and mainly serves as a basis of the synchronous nature of the internal sequential logic. The peripheral thereby gains a great deal of *autonomy*, which is an important idea worth returning to later.

3.3.4 PERIPHERAL CONTROL

In the simplified diagram of a computer (Figure 3.24), the standard interface has been presented as a boundary between what we have designated the interrupter and the controllers. Now, it may be that some (or all) of the controllers are actually housed in the computer cabinet, so it is important to establish the implications of placing them outside this conceptual boundary. The *interrupter* is an essential part of the on-line computer itself, and, though it offers a number of channels to external peripherals via standard interface outlets, these channels are indistinguishable from each other (with the possible exception of the existence of a priority ranking). On the other side of the boundary the *controllers* are each unique to a peripheral, yet they could be plugged into any standard interface channel; they are not essential parts of the computer; they are not in synchrony with it, and their failure would not (or at least, should not!) interfere with its internal operation.

The controller's relationship to the computer is restricted to exchanging information with it (i.e. words representing data, control instructions or addresses). With the peripheral it has a very intimate relationship, and its whole design is subordinated to the needs of the peripheral. Some of the functions of the controller are:

Check the validity of incoming data (e.g. by parity).

Decode control words and realize them in terms of actuating control signals.

When controlling more than one peripheral, distribute and gather information appropriately.

Pack/unpack data words for rapid exchange with the computer.

Initiate *program interrupts* when service beyond the simple exchange of information is required.

Perform digital to analogue (D–A) and analogue to digital (A–D) conversion.

Assemble and send words informing the computer of the status of the peripherals.

Perform minor preprocessing of data, if this can be done simply and will relieve the central processor of a mundane task.

Check for fault conditions and generate appropriate alarm signals.

Decode any incoming trigger signals from other parts of the experimental apparatus.

Produce any relevant synchronizing signals required by other equipment.

The main functional blocks for carrying out these procedures are shown in Figure 3.27, though several of them may be absent for a simple laboratory peripheral.

There is little point in giving an example of the design of a controller, as it would depend so much on the specification of the interface and the requirements of the peripheral that it would have no didactic value. The design problem is not generally difficult, though it may be complicated in some cases. The reader is recommended to examine in detail the design of a controller within a computer system with which he is familiar and to see how it contrives to provide a match between digital words passing across the standard interface and the more various signals exchanged with the peripheral. Note also how the design is integrated with the software, so that both software and hardware offer their respective advantages.

The main ingredient of controller design is the manipulation of electronic logic, but on the peripheral side there are likely to be other more traditional engineering problems, such as matching, loading, signal transmission, inductive transients, noise, etc. The design of the device which is to act as a peripheral has a great bearing on the ease of the controller design task, and in the case of some modern instruments digital operation and provision for connection to a computer are built in, so the task is a simple one (the transient recorder which we shall discuss later is a good example). Other more traditional instruments do not conform quite so easily, though with modern aids, such as single package D–A converters, there is rarely any great difficulty. Perhaps the most awkward circumstance occurs when one or more of the variables is non-electrical, in which case the necessity to find a suitable transducer arises, but again transducers of almost every kind are available, and it is comparatively rarely that one needs to go to the length of constructing one specially.

The reader will have gathered at this stage that every instrument or device in the laboratory that can provide signals or be controlled is regarded as a potential peripheral, and usually its needs are fairly simple. There are of course controller design problems of great complexity (the controller for a disc store can be as large as a central processor) and it is not suggested that the laboratory experimenter should attempt them. Nevertheless, there is frequently a choice between tackling this often straightforward piece of circuit design and doing without the benefits of on-line computing.

Typically, a controller will consist of two circuit boards, one will be provided by the manufacturer and will carry the electronics associated with the 'outside' half of the standard interface. The other, designed and built by the user, contains gating and decoding logic and circuits to provide output signals in suitable format for the peripheral. Sometimes, however, the controller may be physically divided into two parts separated by a signal

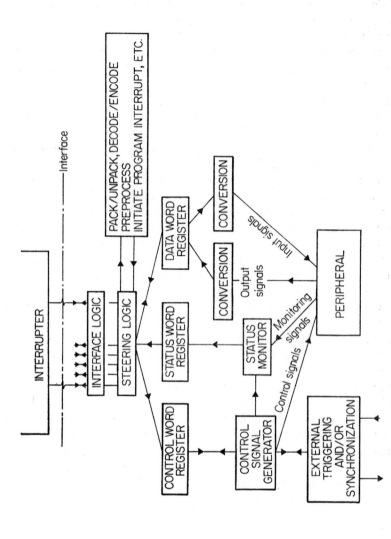

Figure 3.27   The functional parts of a peripheral controller. Many of these features may be absent in a particular case

transmission system, one part being close to the computer and the other close to the peripheral. This would normally occur as a result of a special problem, such as high processing demand, a poor electromagnetic environment or a very remote peripheral. Before leaving the subject of peripheral control it is therefore necessary to say a few words about the problem of signal conversion and transmission.

Had this book been written five years earlier, it would have been necessary to include a lengthy description of the processes of D–A and A–D conversion and the methods of realizing them. Now that converters come as standard packages it is important to make use of this fact and not get involved in unnecessary design exercises. In a typical D–A converter the flip-flops that make up the digital registers each control, via steering circuits, the entry of a current to the summing junction of an operational amplifier. The contribution of each of these currents is weighted according to its rank in the binary number, either by differences in the magnitudes of the currents themselves, or by means of a ladder network of resistors. The most important practical effect of this summation is the fact that the precision of the whole device is determined by the precision of the contribution of the most significant bit. Thus if the largest current (or the resistor associated with the most significant bit) offers a precision of, say, one part in a thousand, 10 bits would represent the maximum sensible size of the converter word, as this would make the variations due to the presence or absence of the least significant bit of the same order as the errors in the most significant bit.

A measure of goodness of a D–A converter is the speed-accuracy product, and as we shall see later the same applies throughout the on-line system. Thus with a given technology it tends to be possible to convert a few bits quickly or a lot of bits slowly. This idea applies even more rigorously to A–D conversion, which is a more complicated process (basically because it represents a many-to-one mapping rather than one-to-one, as in D–A conversion). In almost every practical case the A–D converter is based upon the use of a comparator to match the input voltage with sums of appropriately weighted fractions of an internal reference voltage. It is in the formation of the weighted sum that the various methods are distinguished. In essence a D–A converter is being used to provide the voltage to match the incoming voltage. One way is to use it as a feedback element, relying on the band-limited nature of the incoming signal to ensure that successive corrections are small. Perhaps the best method is the one based on successive approximation. Each bit is tested in turn, starting from the most significant, and if the result of adding the contribution of that bit is that the incoming signal is exceeded, then the bit is set to zero, otherwise it is set to one. By the time the last bit has been tested and set in this way the best approximation has been reached. Figure 3.28 shows an idealized version of this process for a 5 bit conversion of a signal

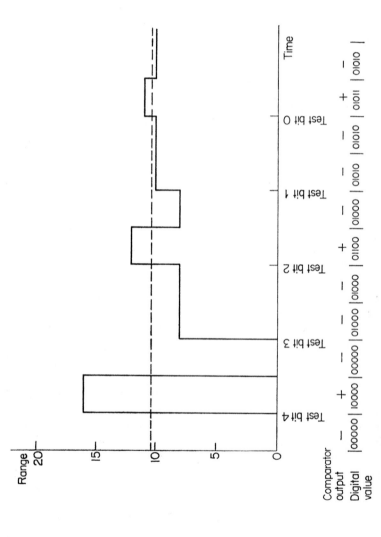

Figure 3.28   The response of a 5 bit A–D converter of the successive-approximation type to a held voltage of 10.4 volts

of about 10 volts which has been sampled and held. This illustrates some of the features of A–D conversion; firstly there is a characteristic settling time which increases with the number of bits of precision, and secondly, the characteristic error is of the order of the voltage increment corresponding to the least significant bit (though, again, in a converter which has the maximum number of bits, the accuracy is determined by the error contribution of the most significant bit).

For fast A–D conversion it is necessary to stretch the technology to the limit. For this reason the fast converter is an important piece of laboratory equipment, and we therefore elevate it to the status of a peripheral in its own right, with a controller designed to optimize its interaction with the computer.

A–D and D–A converters for slower rates, however, can now be regarded as just further single packages to add into a subsystem such as a controller, and the only thing to bother about is the specification. The availability of integrated packages is, of course the basic reason for our ability to tackle a job like the design of a controller, which in the days of discrete components would have been too onerous for the laboratory worker, whereas now it is quite feasible for a single package (a microprocessor) to be the major part of a very complicated controller.

One of the aspects of conversion which one needs to be aware of is that there is an essential operation of sample and hold within the process. For output this can be represented by a linear operator, but for input it is essentially a *non-linear* operation (again because of the many-to-one nature of the mapping) and it will be necessary to examine the implications later (in Chapter 6).

Signal transmission is a basic problem in on-line computing, though in many cases where the demands of speed and distance are low it is a comparatively minor one. An example we shall discuss in Chapter 9 is the use of the computer for EEG monitoring, in which the signal transmission problem is greatly simplified by the low frequency nature of the signals themselves. In such a case the obvious method of transmission is in analogue form over coaxial lines with linear drivers and receivers at each end (these would be simple circuits employing integrated operational amplifiers). Duplication of equipment is avoided by having a multichannel A–D converter at the computer end.

At the other end of the scale, some laboratory applications demand the fastest possible handling of the digital signals, and in such cases certain basic transmission problems become apparent. These are

1 The degradation of the signal due to imperfections in the transmission characteristics of the line.

2 Degradation due to mismatching at either end.

3 The induction of noise due to the presence of fluctuating magnetic fields along the transmission path.

4 The existence of a delay between the sending of a stimulus and the receipt of a response, a delay which is at best twice as long as the transmission time along the cable.

As often happens when technology is being pushed to the limit, the solutions to these problems tend to be mutually antagonistic. This applies particularly to 1 and 3 above since the first implies a requirement for a large bandwidth, which only serves to aggravate the effects of the other. The question of transmission time is much more basic than the other three, since it is largely independent of the technology employed. Indeed, it is bound up with the fundamental physical ideas of relativity and the impossibility of ensuring the simultaneity of events displaced in space. The language of relativity can be quite useful when one is discussing the measurement of phenomena in the nanosecond region of time, since displacements in both time and space contribute to the interval between events and without care the 'time-like' and 'space-like' intervals can easily be confused, especially when events at several points in space are being considered.

Undoubtedly the best solution to the transmission problem, when the difficulties of speed or environment are pronounced, is the current-driven parallel transmission line in the form of a twisted pair. The basic schematic diagram is shown in Figure 3.29. Points to note are the separate matching, the symmetry about earth and the high impedance drive and receive circuits.

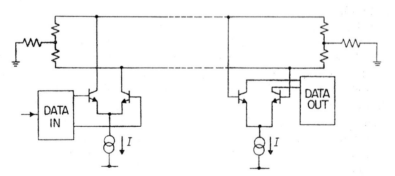

Figure 3.29   Basic scheme of current-driven highway

Digital signals travel along the line as equal and opposite fronts, so that their magnetic and electric fields tend to cancel. Similarly the receiver is designed for such antiphase signals and is relatively insensitive to spurious signals induced in both lines by stray fields. The features of good matching and high common-mode rejection greatly extend the permissible length of the transmission path beyond what is possible with simple voltage-driven lines.

Another point to note is that there is no reason at all why there should not be several drivers and receivers on one line, provided that they are gated by some control system which prevents spurious interaction. This thought leads to the idea of the common data bus or highway.

There are, in fact, two basic ways of distributing signals from one central point to several other points. Either separate lines may radiate from the central points, or one line may pass through each point in turn. These are respectively known as star and bus distribution. An earlier example (Figure 3.26) showed a combination of the two—starred control and bussed data, which is a particularly effective compromise, less expensive than all-star and less wasteful in address-decoding time than all-bus.

Before leaving the subject of hardware in general and peripheral control in particular, we must make some reference to the operation of the on-line computer when, as normally would be the case, several peripherals are active. It will be understood at this stage that the computer works in fits and starts, and that these are conditioned by *interrupts* from the external devices. The concept of peripheral autonomy is very important in this activity, as it contributes greatly to the efficiency and versatility of the system. A number of hardware features can contribute to this; one is the handshake interface which allows the peripheral to initiate transfers asynchronously. At this level hardware is always preferable to software as the medium for realizing low-level functions, and a good example of where it can make a telling contribution is in the assessment of *priority*.

The range of speeds of peripherals varies greatly, as does the urgency with which their data needs to be treated, and it is particularly important in the laboratory that high-speed, signal-processing peripherals should not be held up by slow devices such as keyboards, which means that priority is particularly important. This is a complicated subject, and we shall make further reference to it in a software context, but for now we just give a simple example of how priority can be realized by hardware. The earlier discussion of handshake systems showed that each peripheral can request a transfer by sending a signal on a particular line, and that there will be one such line for each peripheral. This leads to an obvious first step in the introduction of a priority system— the insertion of a gate which does not permit the request to go through while higher priority requests are pending. A simple realization of such a system is shown in Figure 3.30 as a block with its Boolean expression and in terms of gates. In fact, though it serves to illustrate the point, this method would barely be adequate (consider, for example, the effect of propagation delays down the enable signal chain). Nevertheless, in comparison with a software routine it would be orders faster, which matters at this most critical part of the operation.

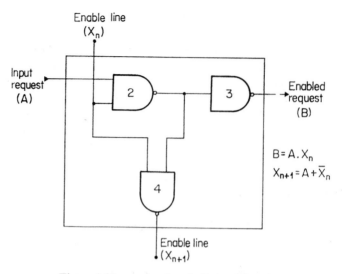

Figure 3.30   A simple priority-enable gate

There is no getting away from the fact that the crucial area of on-line computing is around the standard interface when the hardware and software come into close interaction. It is this very interaction which poses the greatest problems to the newcomer to the field, in that it seems to combine two unrelated fields of study. We have already mentioned one important element of such interaction—the staticizer—but another of great importance is the state of preparedness of the software on the arrival of the data through the interface, and to discuss this it is first necessary to examine in general terms the fundamentals of on-line programming.

Chapter IV

Mainly Software

4.1 INTRODUCTION

The approach to software brings out many of the major differences between laboratory on-line computing and mathematical computing. In mathematical computing we are concerned solely with the solution of a problem, be it by analysis or simulation. This is also an element of laboratory computing, but an equally important aspect is programming for a pattern of behaviour. Consider a commonly used process, low-pass filtering. This is not a mathematical process, though because its realization can be most conveniently achieved by means of a mapping into mathematical functions we tend to think of it as such. We can produce low-pass filtering action by a computer procedure, by using a combination of capacitors and inductors, or by stuffing cotton wool in our ears. Each of these is a physical process, and it is only in the sense of a model that mathematics has any relevance.

In a pure control function the production of a pattern of behaviour is all important, and mathematics has only a subordinate modelling rôle. In the analysis of results mathematics becomes more important and the activity is more similar to conventional computing. On the whole, however, in this field of computing our requirements are radically different, and we must examine our attitudes to language and the minutiae of programming.

In this chapter we assume familiarity with the principles of mathematical programming in an off-line mode, and attempt, by comparison and contrast, to extend this familiarity to the on-line field. The chapter is not, therefore, a self-contained exposition on on-line programming, but rather on the whole a collection of hints and sermons designed to preserve the reader from some of the pitfalls. In contrast, there are some normally trivial aspects of programming which assume much greater importance in the on-line mode, and, as far as space allows, we have approached these from simple fundamentals.

67

4.2 Levels of computer language

We usually categorize computer languages by speaking of them as if they were arranged in a vertical spectrum. We have seen in Chapter 3 that a computer operates by obeying a set of instructions which have been loaded into the store in binary format. This represents the lower bound of the continuum of languages, and it is characteristically the most dependent upon the variety of computer with which it is associated. The upper end of the spectrum may be considered to be the totality of language of human communication, the language of literature, science and mathematics.

It is typical of off-line computing that it is almost always conducted in the highest level of language available, i.e. the one nearest the thought processes of the programmer. FORTRAN and ALGOL are well established as languages for scientific and engineering use, although there are other higher variants for such purposes as algebraic manipulation, list-processing, simulation, etc. Other languages, such as COBOL are conceived for non-scientific users, and therefore do not concern us. As we stated in Chapter 2 it is of no interest to the off-line programmer how his program is actually executed—a steam driven machine or a row of clerks with quill-pens would serve—although he might then have complaints about turn-round time.

The on-line, real-time, programmer, on the other hand, is very intimately concerned with the manner of execution of this program. He is programming for a system of which the computer is only a part, though a vital one. It therefore follows that he is much more conscious of the nature of language and its interpretation. There are high-level languages, such as CORAL, which are specially conceived for real-time work, but in our flexible approach to on-line experimental work we must be prepared to cope with language at a considerably lower level. This would normally be one on the third rank of the hierarchy.

As we have stated, the elements of the lowest level of language are pure binary words. The second rank language, MACHINE CODE, consists of the same elements but they are grouped into *fields* which have an operational significance and are expressed in decimal or octal form. At its simplest such an element might contain two numbers, one representing a function or operation and the other an address of the relevant data or an operand. The third rank of language is represented by AUTOCODE or ASSEMBLER LANGUAGE. This still retains a one-to-one relationship with the binary pattern of orders, but it is written in mnemonic form so that the programmer can conceive orders directly.

There are two common forms of mnemonic—alphabetic and algebraic. The alphabetic form relies upon compressed versions of the English words representing the relevant operation. For example

ADA   add to A
SBA   subtract from A
LDA   load A
STA   store A

The progress of one of these triliteral groups might be as follows: from the mind of the programmer to three keys on a keyboard; thence to three rows of holes on a paper tape; thence via a tape reader to form a 24 bit pattern in the machine store; thence via a translating program to form a binary field, the function part of a machine order. One-to-one correspondences are preserved throughout the process, but the final form is the only irreducible one, free of the redundancy associated with human language. The alphabetic form of coding tends to be associated with machines with a shortish word which can only represent one function and one address.

A longer order word can support a larger combination of functions and addresses. For example it is possible in a 24 bit word to specify the following instruction: add the contents of store location one to the contents of store location two, increment the contents of the first index register by one and consign the sum to the store location whose address is given by the new contents of that register. This is obviously beyond the capabilities of the triliteral system, and the algebraic form of coding is much more apposite. The order might then be written

$$VN1 = V1 + V2, N1 + 1$$

Here we maintain one of the advantages of higher languages, the almost self-evident meaning in mathematical terms, with the vital one-to-one correspondence with the machine instructions.

Why are we so concerned about this correspondence? There are several basic reasons:

(1) Storage: we know that each order occupies one word of store, so we can precisely specify the utilization of storage and can locate any particular instruction.

(2) Timing: precise timing information is available from manufacturers for each basic type of instruction so we can estimate the time occupied by any segment of program. As we shall see later, we never operate in such a way that we have to rely on accurate timing, but we may be faced with the situation where there is an upper bound to the available time. An example of this is the case where it is essential to perform certain calculations between successive samples of a signal, yet maintain the highest possible sampling speed.

(3) Debugging: the reader will be familiar with the many ways that off-line programs can go wrong, and the possibilities for failure of on-line programs are even greater. Except when the machine is operating under an

advanced multiprogram operating system, it is possible to insert flag or stop instructions in the program. When the machine has stopped it is possible to examine the contents of all relevant store locations and know their significance. It is possible to change individual instructions by handswitch operations, etc.

(4) Input/output: when unusual or unique varieties of input/output channels are instituted, they can only be accessed at a basic level through the software instructions related to the standard interface.

(5) Compilers are always to some degree inefficient in their use of time and storage, an important factor in the use of small systems. Thus, in short, we avoid abdicating control over the realization of the computation to a compiler, as one would have to when using a high-level language. It is actually possible to have the best of both worlds if the manufacturer has organized his standard software suitably. That is to say, provided he has defined a suitable software interface and adhered to it, one has the possibility of combining segments from different source languages at will.

The problems of language and machine design are closely bound together. It is the need for high-level compilation which has produced machines which execute a few very basic orders quickly, giving rise to the short-word, single address machine which is irritating to program at low level. More elegant machines with multiple addressing and a wide repertoire of orders are more efficient in themselves but are much more difficult to write compilers for. The next generation of computers will actually work at a higher level of language. The development of fast multipliers and other facilities will allow the machine to incorporate variables of different types and lengths which it will be able to unravel without undue loss of speed.

In less than a generation man has created a new Babel of more than two hundred programming languages. Their history and philosophy makes a fascinating study [ProLaSe], but it is one which has only a background relevance to our present interests. It is often the economic or political power of its proponents that determines the success of a language, and FORTRAN is still the dominant language for engineering and scientific work, while ALGOL is well established and highly respected for its influence on the formalism of the definition of languages and later developments such as PL/1.

The features which normally commend a high-level language are the very ones which make it largely unsuitable for laboratory on-line work. The concept of *machine-independence* loses its value when the very essence of the method is the development of a unique hardware configuration. Reduction of programming time is worthless if the penalty for it is a crippling loss of speed at execution time. Simplicity of the written program is wasted if it results in inscrutability of the stored program.

One important property of the popular high-level languages must not be forgotten, their *transportability*. A compiler or simulator for a microprocessor, for example, might be written in FORTRAN which is unsuitable in every way except that it is realizable on virtually any machine.

4.3 WORD LENGTHS

We have seen in Chapter 3 that word length is an important parameter of machine performance. Economic considerations work against a long computer word, especially in the hand wired parts of a parallel digital system. As far as the software aspect is concerned, it is another of the factors that one is more conscious of in on-line working. This is not to say that one is entirely oblivious of it in off-line computing, where, for example, one is often given facilities such as COMPRESS INTEGER, which allows a sacrifice of accuracy and range to conserve storage. The most direct effect that word length has in any form of computing is on the accuracy of both fixed point and floating point number representations. It is rare for input/output devices to demand great accuracy, as the measurement tolerances are usually wider than the un-certainty of representation (a 12 bit word represents a precision of better than one part in 4000 of FSD, which would be considered satisfactory for most forms of instrumentation). There are, however, many ways in which word length does affect the speed and efficiency of calculation. Fundamentally, they all boil down to the fact that information is passed around much more quickly if it is held in large packets. A computer with short words will always achieve the result in the end, just as it is possible to consume a bowl of soup with a teaspoon, but one must treat with great care the apparent economies offered by the manufacturers' literature on such machines.

There are various hidden penalties that go with a short computer word which may not be obvious, but which degrade the overall speed of operation. Imagine that we have three machines: A with 8 bit words, B with 16 bit words, and C with 24 bit words, and the manufacturers each quote a time for the load order of say 1 μs. Then for repeated loading the bit rate for C is three times that of A and $1\frac{1}{2}$ times of B. Thus a section of data requiring 24 bits, say the word AND or the number TEN MILLION AND ONE, would be transferred in 1 μs by C, but correspondingly longer by A and B. We are, of course, oversimplifying. The load order cannot stand alone, there must be at least an accompanying index order. Also 8 bit characters within a 16 or 24 bit word require packing and unpacking instructions at some stage. The net result is that there is a gain of overall speed as the word length is increased but not in direct proportion.

A further point to note is that a 4 K store of 24 bit words holds 50% more information than a 4 K store of 16 bit words. Store utilization can be more efficient with a long word, especially with regard to stored program. Again it is difficult to make a direct comparison, as the philosophy of programming tends to vary with the machine system, but the same proportionality applies, i.e. the 24 bit machine instruction contains 50% more combinations of types of order and addresses than the 16 bit machine instruction. Indeed, the gain in speed and reduction of storage can be greater than the direct proportionality to word length because the need for some of the subsidiary orders (loading, indexing, etc.) tends to disappear as the word length increases to the point where it can support a multi-address order structure.

Thus we see that machines can only be compared in their ability to perform a given complex task when optimally programmed in their own way. Unfortunately, specious comparisons have often been made on the basis of isolated instruction times. These will always favour the short-word machine as it apparently exhibits a better speed/cost ratio; so remember that the word length controls the amount of information in both the data and the instruction words, and that the time taken to move this information around the machine depends on the size of the packets in which it is contained and the number of subsidiary instructions implied—two factors which degrade performance as the word length is reduced.

The next generation of machines will probably be based on infinitely variable word lengths, and this particular cause of controversy will presumably disappear.

4.3.1 FIELDS

Each n bit word in a computer can contain 2^n distinctive combinations of ones and zeros. The importance of the word as a unit is that it is the basic packet of information that can be shifted about the machine in single operations. The interpretation of the contents of these packets is however entirely flexible. Basically they each represent one of 2^n possible numbers, but the word, or any part of the word, may be used to represent any enumerable set of entities.

Consider the English word AND as an input to a 24 bit machine. In order to take cognisance of it and action upon it the computer must store it temporarily and compare it with other English words in its stored vocabulary. This involves a considerable amount of shifting of computer words between the store and the temporary memory registers. Now the alphanumeric characters are an enumerable set and they have been conventionally allocated a number code which, including parity, requires (together with certain control characters) 8 bits of information. Thus if the letters AND are stored in three consecutive locations, the contents might look like this:

$$000000000000000001000001$$
$$000000000000000001001110$$
$$000000000000000001000100$$

This is obviously most unsatisfactory. Not only are 3 × 16 bits of the store unused, but it takes three orders at least to summon up this triliteral combination. The obvious technique is to *pack* the characters into one word:

010000010100111001000100

Now this computer word has no significance unless one knows that for the purposes of interpretation it is divided into three 8 bit *fields:*

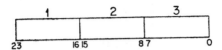

An even more fundamental example of division into fields occurs in the typical order, in which there is a field defining the function and one defining the address:

FUNCTION	ADDRESS

Obviously, the word can be divided into any combination of fields representing numbers, letters, orders, flags, etc. The motivation for doing this may be to save storage, but more significantly it is to associate entities which belong together so that they do not have to be called up from the store separately. Sometimes a binary number is divided into fields as an artifice; for example, to declare a particular binary pattern for program purposes it is often easier to divide it into 3 bit fields and write the pattern as an octal number.

While on the subject of fields we should mention the fact that the concept is available to the programmer, and is useful in the context of efficient use of storage. This is particularly true in on-line computing where long streams of data are entering the machine, and these are rarely defined with sufficient accuracy to warrant the use of a full word for each one. Characters occupy only 8 bits each. Thus there is much to be said for *packing* the data into defined fields in the words for storage, and *unpacking* them for later use. Such fields can be as small as one bit (for example, in pseudorandom binary sequence testing, the input signal can be stored in one bit and the response in the rest of the word). The technique of packing and unpacking is centred round the shift order, but in wide repertoire machines other orders, such as *mask*, greatly facilitate the process.

4.4 NUMBER REPRESENTATION

Conventionally, *fixed point* numbers, be they interpreted as fractions or integers, have their most significant bit as a sign bit, and negative numbers are written in two's complement form. Thus, for example in 5 bit integer form, we have the equivalents

$$6 = 00110$$
$$7 = 00111$$
$$13 = 01101$$
$$-7 = 11001$$

and with this form of representation subtractions become additions with overflow, i.e. $13 - 7 = 13 + (-7)$
or

$$01101$$
$$+ \; 11001$$
$$\overline{}$$
$$= 00110 = 6$$

A simple rule of thumb to negate a binary number is 'starting from the right hand end, write down each 0 and the first 1 you come to, and thereafter reverse every bit until you get to the left hand end'. This is equivalent to the more fundamental procedure 'Complement each bit (the number is then in one's complement negative form) then add to the result the number 1 (or in fractional interpretation, the smallest possible fraction)'.

The same 5 bit numbers could have been interpreted as fractions with the bits representing powers of $\frac{1}{2}$ rather than 2 as in the integer case, yielding different equivalents

$$00110 = 0.3750$$
$$00111 = 0.4375$$
$$01101 = 0.8125$$
$$11001 = -0.4375$$

Note that the result of the above summation is valid in either interpretation. This two's complement form for negative numbers can be a pitfall for the unwary in on-line computation, and we quote a particularly dangerous example in Chapter 7.

Unfortunately the interchange of interpretation between integer and fraction does not extend to multiplication, where truncation is necessary to restore the original length to the number.

For example, the number 00001 would represent unity or 0.0625 in our 5 bit system, its square would be a 9 bit (eight plus sign) number representing unity or 0.003906. Truncated to 5 bits, it would represent unity or zero, since opposite ends are removed in the truncation of fractions or integers. If this point is unclear, the reader is recommended to work through a few examples in binary format. This with the corresponding problem in division is the one inelegant feature of fixed point arithmetic.

The reason that fixed point representation plays an important part in on-line computing is that this is the natural form in which numbers arrive from the outside world through the standard interface, and in which they are returned. *Floating point* representation therefore tends to be reserved for intermediate calculations, where these are complicated. There are various forms of floating point format. The common feature is that a number is divided into an exponent y and a mantissa x, so that its numerical value is equal to $x * 2^y$. An interesting form is the short or single-word floating point where the exponent and mantissa, each having its own sign bit, are allocated to separate fields in the word. Thus

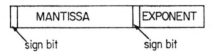

In order to obtain a *unique* representation, the mantissa is always reduced to a standard form, i.e. x is made to lie within the ranges

$$-\tfrac{1}{4} < x \le -\tfrac{1}{2} \quad \text{or} \quad \tfrac{1}{4} \le x < \tfrac{1}{2}$$

and y is adjusted accordingly.

Various forms of *double length* number are also found in computer repertoires. In these, a numerical value is distributed over two words in either fixed or floating point form. This is rather cumbersome unless the machine has special hardware features such as double length shifts and arithmetic.

The basic reason for resorting to floating point and double length arithmetic is the restricted range of the fixed point numbers. The range of our input numbers is usually well defined, and that of the output numbers can often be deduced indirectly, but the difficulties arise throughout the intermediate calculations. In, for example, a calculation involving matrix inversion, it is very difficult to predict the range of incidental results which produce the output value. Loss of most significant bits from the left hand end of the number is so serious that it nullifies the whole computation. Hence when an instruction produces a result which exceeds the capacity of the computer word, this is signalled to the operator as an *overflow* warning. The opposite process, loss of least significant bits, can be equally, if more subtly, disastrous, especially as it is unheralded. The processes of multiplication and division nearly always tend to cause loss of information, as their intermediate double length results have to be truncated. In simple calculations the worst effects can sometimes be obviated by the choice of order of operations. A digital system having, say, 10 bits available to its input and output channels will produce nonsense if some intermediate result, through an oversight, is restricted to 2 or 3 bits. Such effects can often be eliminated by scaling the input numbers, by way of a shift of several places to the left, and applying the reverse scaling before output. In general, however, multiplication and division in fixed point require careful thought, especially if integer and fraction interpretations are included in the same program.

Why, then, do we persist in the use of fixed point arithmetic? It is a question of speed. There are two ways in which the use of floating point arithmetic can seriously degrade the speed of calculation:

1 Every input number has to be passed through a *float* routine, and every output number through a *fix* routine. These routines would be standard macro- or micro-programs, and they take time to operate.
2 Very few small machines, as yet, have floating point arithmetic as a hardware option, and, as it is otherwise realized in the form of a sequence of fixed point instructions, it takes more time.

4.5 MODE OF ADDRESSING

Addressing is one of the most fundamental concepts of computer operation as it is the means by which data and instructions are accessed. There are two important ways of classifying modes of addressing, by directness and by multiplicity.

Direct addressing occurs in the simplest type of order, where, as we mentioned in our discussion of fields, there are two parts, a function and an address. The order simply says: do *this* to the number held in *that* address. In *indirect addressing* the implication of the order is slightly more complicated. It says: do *this* to the number whose address will be found at *that* address. Thus the second part of the order is not the location of the operand, but the location of the *address* of the operand. Indirect addressing has two major advantages:

1 The address of the operand, being allocated to a whole word rather than a restricted field as in the direct mode, covers a much wider range of locations, usually the whole core store.
2 This address can be a computed value (whereas the direct address is a pre-programmed quantity) thereby giving rise to the whole gamut of advanced computing techniques.

Indirect addressing is usually associated with the use of *index registers*. These are special hardware registers, with their own special instruction subsystem, which are provided specifically to provide these facilities and a few other related ones. A common programming error is the confusion of the address of a location with its contents, particularly if the addressing is *doubly* indirect.

The other important parameter of the addressing mode is its multiplicity, i.e. whether the machine is single-, two- or three-address in concept. The single-address machine is one in which the order structure provides only for a function and one address to be included, so by implication either the source of the data or the destination of the result must be the *accumulator*. The two-address machine permits two operands from different locations to be combined in one function and then assigned to the accumulator. The three-address machine allows the result of such a function to be assigned to a third specified location without the need for the accumulator to act as an intermediary.

A three-address machine can perform in one order a calculation such as $X = Y + Z$, where X, Y and Z are the contents of specific locations, whereas a single-address machine would require three orders involving the accumulator, A, which might be written

LDA Y	Load Y into the accumulator
ADA Z	Add Z to the contents of the accumulator
STA X	Store the contents of the accumulator in X

Obviously, the three-address mode is much more desirable from the point of view of speed and ease of programming, so why is the single address mode more common? The sort of reasons given are:

1 The specification of a three-address order requires a much longer word, which makes the machine more expensive.
2 As most computers are designed to work with high-level compilers, the philosophy of design of the machine should be to make it simple and quick. It is much easier to design a compiler to make efficient use of simple instructions than it is to choose between the alternatives offered by a complicated instruction set.
3 A simple machine organization reduces the chances of making some of the more subtle programming errors which can be so difficult to trace.

These reasons, however, are not entirely valid in experimental on-line computing, where multiple address coding can be beneficial, for instance:

1 At least part of the programming will have to be performed at low level, i.e. the part associated with the operation at the standard interface.
2 A three-address mode permits the use of an assembler language giving one-to-one correspondence with machine code, but having some of the mnemonic characteristics of a high-level language, the principal difference being that only one operation is permitted per line. There is thus little difficulty in doing most of the programming at this level.
3 Although the necessary word is longer, a three-address machine actually

uses less storage for a given program task than a single-address machine, as the number of orders is greatly reduced.

4 If a three-address machine and a single-address machine have the same quoted time for addition etc., the former will be considerably faster in the execution of a given task because it has to obey fewer orders.

In practice it is not necessary to have the whole store directly addressable in three-address mode, provided this facility is available over a sufficiently large working (or kernel) store, since true random access is seldom required, and main store accessing can usually be accomplished by cyclic operations based on the modification of the contents of index registers.

4.6   THE REPERTOIRE OF INSTRUCTIONS

The fact that there is a restricted field allocated to the function part of the instruction word means that the number of different functions is bounded. In fact an m bit function field provides for 2^m different functions. Of course, the manufacturer is not obliged to use all of these, but it would be rather absurd if much less than half were used. Let us take two specific examples from the range of machines.

(1) In a 16 bit machine, 5 bits are allocated to the function field, and the remaining eleven to the address. This gives 32 possible functions, and the basic function list contains, in fact, 30 different single-address functions. Twenty of these are taken up by add, subtract, load and store; because there is one of each associated with the program pointer, accumulator, auxiliary accumulator, index register and a special base address register. The remainder include multiply, divide, shift, jump, etc.

(2) A 24 bit machine allocates 9 bits to the function field giving 512 distinctive possible functions, of which 248 are used. These include three-address direct access to a restricted (23 word) kernel store, and various combinations of indirect addressing with self-contained load, index or modification instructions; various types of conditional jump with logical and arithmetic tests; various types of fixed point and floating point multiplication and division; masks, etc.

Obviously the philosophy of using these two machines is completely different. With the first, low-level programming is simple but rather tedious, though a comprehensive range of compilers is available. For real-time applications, however, assembler language is recommended, though it can be mixed with a compiled high-level program, e.g. FORTRAN.

With the second machine, programming, as such, can also be simple (after all the basic single-address functions are also a subset of its comprehensive function list), but efficient programming involves use of the whole repertoire. The assembler language is extremely elegant (being in an algebraic mnemonic form), versatile and easy to use in real-time situations. Possibly for this reason software back-up, such as high-level compilers, tends to be poor.

The important word in this context is *philosophy*: for one's whole system of thought in using a machine must spring from its basic principles of organization. It is, of course, quite possible to convert a program from one language to another by means of a translating program, known as an *interpreter*, and this is standard practice for the preservation of programs written for machines which have become redundant. It is, however, a practice whose utility is almost entirely restricted to off-line applications. It tends to fall down in on-line, real-time applications for two basic reasons:

1 Some of the program instructions are too close to the basic hardware realization of the interface, etc., to be interpretable in a general way.
2 The loss of efficiency is often too great to be tolerable, except for the least demanding tasks.

Let us quote a simple example of a way that efficiency can be lost. Imagine two machines: A has a very fast shift facility with relatively slow multiplication, while B has very fast multiplication hardware, but shifts in a cumbersome one-place-at-a-time shift system. Imagine also that we have a certain computing task which requires a large amount of scaling, in the form of multiplying and dividing by 2^8. A program written for machine A would achieve this by a simple order calling for a shift of eight places, while a program for machine B would simply multiply or divide by the number 256. If *either* program were interpreted for the other machine, the less desirable method would have been instituted and speed lost. Various other effects of greater or lesser subtlety would contribute to the loss of speed and an inefficient use of storage. Nevertheless, there may be cases where the use of some segments of program from such a doubtful source might be preferred to the onerous task of rewriting them. A similar problem occurs when a programmer switches from one type of machine to another; since it requires a great effort of will to abandon one's hard-won knack of choosing the right method, and start again to acquire another one. Let us not, however, exaggerate the difficulties of writing low-level programs. Anyone can do it, but it takes experience to produce efficient programs.

Let us examine further the construction of a repertoire of instructions by referring to an imaginary machine which has, say, a 12 bit instruction word, with the function field restricted to the first 3 bits. We then have a maximum repertoire of eight possible functions to allocate. If we restrict ourselves to direct addressing, these might be:

Decimal form	Binary form	Action
0	000	Clear accumulator
1	001	Add contents of location specified into accumulator
2	010	Subtract contents of location from accumulator
3	011	Transfer contents of accumulator to location
4	100	Transfer control to location specified (jump)
5	101	Jump to location if contents of accumulator are positive
6	110	Jump to location and store return address (subroutine entry)
7	111	Jump to return address (subroutine exit)

Note that instructions 6 and 7 imply the existence of a subsidiary index register. We have now constructed a very crude system but one which is capable of performing any mathematical calculation (though by a round-about method). Note that it is the existence of instruction 5 which makes the machine a computer rather than a calculator.

All more advanced functions have to be realized in terms of these basic orders. For example, we have as yet provided no means of stopping the machine. One way of doing this would be to ensure that the order 4 0 (i.e. the number 100000000000) was contained in location 0 (perhaps by hardwiring rather than loading that word into the core store). Then a *loop* stop could be obtained at any point in the program by writing the order 4 0. Thus 0 becomes the address of a special register.

How would we turn the machine into a simple on-line computer? The simplest way would be to assign two further special registers, say 1 and 2, to provide respectively input and output channels in the manner described in Chapter 3. Even then we would have no method of timing our operations, so let us make location three a special one bit register consisting of a flip-flop which can be set to 1 by an external clock and cleared by the computer writing in a zero.

We can now begin to see what a main program would look like. Let us say that at location 128 we have stored a subroutine which performs a certain action on the contents of the accumulator (e.g. it could by storing the contents of previous entries perform a digital filtering action). Suppose that we wish to allow this process to continue under the control of an external clock, unless the input goes negative, when we would wish to stop the machine. The final order in the subroutine would be 7 0. Then our program if it were stored from location 10 onwards would look like this:

Location	Order
10	0 0
11	1 3
12	5 14
13	4 10
14	0 0
15	3 3
16	1 1
17	5 19
18	4 0
19	6 128
20	3 2
21	4 10

We should remark at this stage that this machine language is not put forward as a likely one for computer use, and it is only devised to illustrate a few simple points. In practice, for example, one would not tolerate the wastage of the unused address field following order 0, and a more likely interpretation for this order would be 'the following address field is to be interpreted as an order'. This would make available a wide range of extra address-free instructions, such as operations on the accumulator (shifts, complementation, reversals, etc.)

We have deliberately left the program unannotated as a reminder of the obscurity of an unfamiliar language and even at this simple level it is beginning to look rather difficult to unravel. A flow diagram would help, as we shall see later in this chapter, but we would probably have originally written the program in an assembler language, which would make it a little more comprehensible. In an assembler based on alphabetic mnemonics, assuming it is to be loaded from location 10 onwards, it would look something like this:

```
CLA
ADA      3
JAP     14
JMP     10
CLA
STA      3
ADA      1
JAP     19
JMP      0
ENT    128
STA      2
JMP     10
```

while with an algebraic mnemonic and a few improvements it might look something like this:

$$
\begin{array}{ll}
[10] & V4 = 0 \\
& V4 = V3 \\
& \rightarrow 14,\ V4 > 0 \\
& \rightarrow 10 \\
[14] & V4 = 0 \\
& V3 = V4 \\
& V4 = V1 \\
& \rightarrow 19,\ V4 > 0 \\
& \text{STOP} \\
[19] & \rightarrow \text{SR } 500 \\
& V2 = V4 \\
& \rightarrow 10 \\
\end{array}
$$

Here we have replaced the accumulator by V4, used $\rightarrow$ for jump and the comma for IF. We have assumed that the subroutine is numbered 500, and also labelled the destination of the jumps. These changes enable the compiler to locate our program anywhere in the store.

We have found such an algebraic language very useful in explaining basic programming techniques to students, and propose to use it in the remainder of this book. Although it is based on languages used in certain commercial machines, we shall ignore the restrictions that go with application to a real machine, and assume that it is being used in an ideal three-address machine (the like of which, as far as we know, does not exist). At the end of this section we give sufficient examples of some orders and their interpretation to make the remaining examples, we hope, self-explanatory.

The advantages of using an idealized three-address code are that it will shorten the length of our examples, and leave them uncluttered by house-keeping orders, such as the clearing of accumulators, yet retain the lowness of level which is advantageous in the discussion of real-time computing.

V is used to represent 'the contents of' and is followed by an address which is either a number for direct addressing or N followed by a number for indirect addressing, in which case the number represents an index register; $=$ means 'replaced by', e.g.

$V4 = 1$ set the contents of location 4 to unity

$VN3 = V4$ set the contents of the location whose address is found in index register 3 equal to V4

The ordinary arithmetic operators are used, but for clarity we shall avoid examples with multiplication and division, which require further action to deal with the implied double-length result; e.g.

$$V3 = V3 + 1$$
$$VN1 = VN2 - V3$$

In addition we make use of the operator & which implies a direct AND operation between the binary digits of the two numbers; e.g.

$$V1 = V1 \ \& \ 31 \qquad \text{zero all but the last five bits of } V1$$

The index registers can be assigned numbers and combined in simple operations; e.g.

$$N1 = 4096$$
$$N1 = N1 + 1$$
$$N3 = N1 + V3$$

IF is represented by the comma, and the non-equivalence operator $\neq$ is useful for comparing two numbers. Also the arrow represents the instruction 'jump to' and if followed by a number refers to an instruction labelled with that number; e.g.

$$[1] \rightarrow 1, V1 \neq V3 = 0 \qquad \text{loop if } V1 \text{ and } V3 \text{ are equal}$$

Other tests which may appear in jump instructions instead of a simple equality are $\geq$, $>$, $<$ and $\leq$; e.g.

$$\rightarrow 2, V1 + V2 \geq 0 \qquad \text{jump to instruction labelled [2] if } V1 + V2 \text{ is positive}$$

The unconditional jump (cf. GOTO) to labelled instructions is in the simple form $\rightarrow 1$. A subroutine jump is written $\rightarrow$ SR999, where the number is unique to the subroutine and is not a direct reference to the address at which it is loaded. Note that the subroutine jump implies storage of a link which is the destination of the jump which terminates the subroutine, i.e. RETURN.

4.7 Programs

The concept of a computer program is so familiar that we need not dwell on it overlong, but there are some ways in which this concept varies slightly when one transfers to the on-line mode of operation. Then the program is not just the manifestation of a calculation, but is rather a prescription for the behaviour of a conveniently flexible part of a system. There are constraints imposed on an on-line program, especially a real-time one, which are largely non-existent in conventional computing. These are constraints of time, storage, input/output formats, etc. The implications of variations of approach and actual errors are much wider in the on-line case, particularly when the overall system may be effectively a closed-loop one. This criticality is also extended to the construction of general software aids such as compilers and executives.

We are obliged to dwell on the various pitfalls which are peculiar to on-line programming, but would hope that this does not engender in the reader a morbid obsession with the difficulties of the subject. In fact it is not very much more difficult than ordinary programming, but it does require a more disciplined approach. An example of this is the treatment of subroutines.

4.8   SUBROUTINES

When one is first learning to write programs for execution off-line, one learns various aspects of good practice which are well worth instilling as a routine. The same precepts apply to on-line computing, but more so. One of the most important of these precepts is the recommendation that all programs should be constructed in a modular or segmented form, i.e. they consist of a *master segment* and a number of *subroutines*. The master segment should be short and simple, and, indeed, it usually needs to be little more than a string of subroutine calls. The reasons usually advanced for this form of modularization in programs are:

(1) It prevents wasteful repetition of sequences of instructions.

(2) It marks the natural conceptual boundaries within a program, thereby making it easier to understand.

(3) It makes debugging more simple and effective by providing small stand alone segments which can and should be compiled and tested separately.

(4) It enables a number of programmers to write different parts of a large program.

(5) The same procedure can be used in a number of different programs.

(6) It enables the software related to a particular investigation to grow in a disciplined way by increasing the number of useful basic building blocks, rather than by proceeding from one discarded program to another.

(7) It sometimes permits the combination of pieces of program which had their origin in different source languages.

(8) Each segment can be written with regard only to its specification, thus eliminating the mental gymnastics required to keep an idea of the whole program in one's head.

We have implied that such considerations are even more important in on-line and real-time application than in off-line ones; this is because there are further advantages of modularization.

(9) It can cope with the greater variability of input/output mechanisms found in on-line applications.

(10) It permits the accurate timing of important pieces of sub-program, especially those which have to be repeated many times, say between samples.

(11) It facilitates the idea of presenting a new input/output channel in terms of a combined software/hardware package.

(12) The idea of a program interrupt, which is one of the more powerful concepts in on-line computing, presumes the existence of dedicated sub-programs.

Furthermore some of the earlier advantages are reinforced. For example, (3) above becomes extremely important when the program controls the behaviour of only part of a complex system, *especially* if the system is a closed-loop one.

A program can, of course, be segmented by chopping it up into sequential blocks, but this is a fairly trivial exercise compared with the method of subroutines. The essence of the idea of a subroutine is embodied in the link-storing jump (or CALL or ENTRY instruction). This is an instruction which transfers control to a remote location in the store, but also stores (or saves) in a special register the address of the instruction immediately following the jump instruction, by a method we have discussed in Chapter 3. Its partner is the *restore link* (or RETURN or EXIT) instruction which *normally* marks the end of a subroutine, and returns control to the address stored by the original jump instruction. There is also a slight complication in low-level programming which is concealed by high-level languages. This is the requirement that normally, on exit, *a subroutine must leave the computer in the state in which it was found* on entering. In other words, if it uses any accumulators, registers or index registers, or contains any instructions which imply a change in the state of staticizers, etc., it must store their states on entry and restore them on exit. The important exception to this rule arises, of course, from the fact that some registers must be used to convey input and output information to and from the subroutine, and also the contents of some store locations may be altered if such action is specified for the particular subroutine.

We are getting to the point where life could become very complicated, but for the existence of a special concept which we must now discuss. The reason that it could become complicated is the familiar fact that subroutines are often (even usually) *nested*. That is to say, the master program might call subroutine A, which would call subroutine B, which would call . . . etc. Thus by the time we get to subroutine N we have stored a lot of information which has to be unravelled for restoration. The device which overcomes this difficulty is the *push down store* (or *link-nest*). It is similar in concept to those mechanisms one sees in cafeterias for storing plates without having vulnerable piles around. These consist of a spring loaded base which is adjusted to sink into a hole in the counter by a depth equivalent to one plate for an increment of load equivalent to one plate, thus allowing the plates to be stored and unstored sequentially on a *last-in, first-out* basis. Such a system is easily realized in the computer by using an index register as a pointer, which also has the advantage that nothing actually has to move its position as in the mechanical model.

This concept as applied to the subroutines means that each subroutine removes as many items on exit as it stored on entry, so the subroutine which called it can rely on the next item being the last one stored by itself. It is evident that the items have to be restored in the reverse order to that in which they were stored. The scheme is illustrated diagrammatically in Figure 4.1.

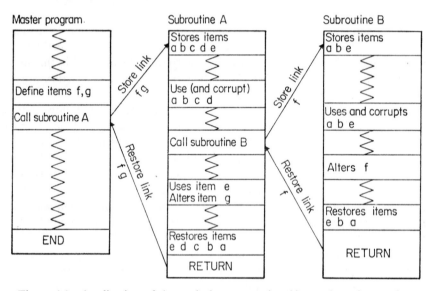

Figure 4.1   Application of the push-down store (stack) to subroutine nesting

The push-down store is used in this way by high-level compilers, but the off-line programmer does not need to know anything about it, so it is a concealed automatic process. The on-line programmer, however, may need to retain control of the process, as each store or restore instruction increases both storage requirements and run time. For this reason the on-line programmer may have to learn to be much less prodigal in his use of variables than he may have been as an off-line programmer. *The onus is always on the author of a subroutine to ensure that it does not cause any undeclared corruption of any register, staticizer state, store location, etc.* Neglect of this duty can produce one of the most insidious forms of fault condition possible, since the effect of an undeclared corruption may manifest itself at a point in the program so remote from the call to the offending subroutine that the actual cause is one of the last possibilities considered. Also, the subroutine may have been used in many different programs over a long period before one particular program reveals a sensitivity to the particular corruption that has occurred.

Before we leave the subject of the push down store let us examine the way in which it is realized in terms of elementary instructions. Imagine that we have written a subroutine which makes use of N1, N2, V4 and V5, and we have reserved N3 as the pointer to the push down store. The beginning and end of the subroutine would contain orders something like this:

$$N3 = N3 - 1$$
$$VN3 = N1$$
$$N3 = N3 - 1$$
$$VN3 = N2$$
$$N3 = N3 - 1$$
$$VN3 = V4$$
$$N3 = N3 - 1$$
$$VN3 = V5$$

$$- \quad - \quad - \quad -$$
$$- \quad - \quad - \quad -$$

Main body of subroutine
(corrupts N1, N2, V4, V5)

$$- \quad - \quad - \quad -$$
$$- \quad - \quad - \quad -$$

$$V5 = VN3$$
$$N3 = N3 + 1$$
$$V4 = VN3$$
$$N3 = N3 + 1$$
$$N2 = VN3$$
$$N3 = N3 + 1$$
$$N1 = VN3$$
$$N3 = N3 + 1$$
$$RETURN$$

The net result of the subroutine is that N1, N2, V4 and V5 have the same values as they did on entry and N3 points to the original position in the push down store. Obviously, there will be some change somewhere, otherwise the subroutine call would have been pointless. Note that the return link address could have been saved in the same store as the other variables, or it could have been allocated its own separate area. Under this system, the increment of depth of the push down pointer is an important constituent of the specification of the subroutine, and the total storage required for this purpose for any program is determined by the summation of all such increments at the point of maximum nesting of subroutines. Provided that the subroutines are well documented this is easily determined. The compiler for the assembler language may provide a means of condensing the sequence of storing and restoring instructions, by generation of a macro-program, but the user should take note of the number of basic instructions thereby implied.

Let us return to item (3) in our list of advantages of modularization: the facilitation of testing procedures. It is good practice to test every subroutine separately as soon as it has been written. There is a convenient way of doing this which allows the test program to be written and punched as paper tape at the same time as the subroutine itself. The tape would then carry a program laid out as shown in Figure 4.2.

The blocks marked OPTIONAL represent a special subroutine which may well be worth writing for the particular machine. On entry 0 it records the values of all the important registers, etc., and on entry 1 it compares the

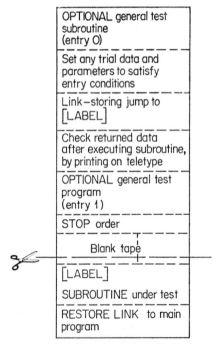

Figure 4.2   A general test procedure for new subroutines shown in terms of a paper tape layout

present values with the stored values and points out the values of any that have been changed. If the subroutine successfully passes its test the tape can be cut at the point indicated, and the leading part discarded, so that whatever leader is required by the compiler can be attached. A great deal of effort can be saved if one develops the habit of writing the subroutine and its test program in parallel, setting up each piece of data in the test program as soon as its need arises in the subroutine. We cannot overemphasize the importance of using fully tested subroutines in on-line work, a single lapse at this stage can waste many man-hours at a later stage.

A final important aspect of the use of subroutines is the fact that they allow the whole program to be written in a relocatable form, i.e. one that is not, as in our simple example of Section 4.6, confined to a particular area of the store because it contains absolute addresses. This means that one is able to rearrange and expand programs via the compilation and assembly process and place them in any part of the store. For this reason there is also another type of subroutine, the *data subroutine*, which contains no program, but is a relocatable block of storage. This block is allocated a number (or name) which can be presented to the compiler in lieu of an absolute address.

Note that a subroutine call is nearly always a link-storing jump, but there are occasions when this is not so. We may for example wish the subroutine to return to a previously stored address rather than the instruction following the call. An example of this occurs in our discussion of flags in Section 4.13.

4.9   FLOW DIAGRAMS

One of the techniques of programming that everyone learns, and unfortunately many subsequently abandon, is the construction of a flow chart [CoMeLaFa]. This is again something which assumes an even greater importance in on-line computing; for it then becomes a detailed part of a larger system diagram. It can be annotated with extra information (e.g. timing) and can be used to trace out patterns of behaviour that are much more complicated than they are in the off-line case, since they are conditioned by external stimuli. Various flow chart symbols may be defined to represent the various forms of input and output device, but the only really important ones are the rectangular box, which denotes a self-contained process, and the lozenge, which denotes a branch instruction. Let us take as a simple example the program we developed for our mythical restricted-repertoire machine in Section 4.6, shown in Figure 4.3.

Note that this flow diagram is uniquely of a real-time type, since the question asked in the first lozenge relates to the occurrence of an external stimulus, and the operation of the whole loop is invalidated unless a suitable

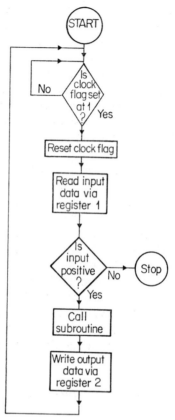

Figure 4.3   A simple flow diagram: on-line use of the mythical machine of section 4.6

connection is made. It is also an on-line type through the fact that the input and output variables are numbers, as opposed to symbols, with an external source and destination. The flow diagram has the merit that it is easily understood, which could not be said for the original version in our artificial language, or indeed any other. One reason for this clarity is that the loops are clearly mapped, the other being the fact that the instructions are in the common tongue.

Obviously, with such a crude control system, our mythical machine would have a greatly restricted capability, but it would be quite capable of performing a simple simultaneous input/output process such as that described by the flow diagram, and since the subroutine is undefined this would include a wide range of signal processing techniques. The flow diagram allows us to see that, apart from any external hardware limitation, there is an upper bound to the speed of operation of the system which is determined by the total time round the major loop, and this is easily determined by annotating each block with its execution time and summing round the loop. These times could be culled from a table of instruction times, but, in practice, for any significant process the total would be determined by the subroutine execution time, which would most conveniently be measured directly by embedding it in a special program (this would either time it accurately by reference to an on-line digital clock, or call the subroutine say 100 times so that the run time would be measured and divided by 100).

A more complicated flow diagram with several alternative loops and sub-loops would facilitate extension of the technique to include worst-case analysis of a critical-path type. We should not, however, lose sight of the importance of the flow diagram as a prelude to the coding stage of programming. A great deal of optimization of program structure can be carried out by tackling it with a pencil and eraser so that the disposable parts of the program can be effectively placed with respect to the immutable parts (prescribed subroutines, hardware interactions, etc.). Once settled, the flow diagram can then be retained as one of the most important elements of the documentation of the process.

We have purposely left ill-defined the specification of the elements in the flow diagram. This allows different diagrams to be drawn for different levels of decomposition of the system. The only constraint upon a rectangular block is that it has only one entry and one exit. Internally, it can have many loops and sub-loops, but provided these all start and terminate within the block it is still valid, and it would have a flow diagram of its own. There is, of course, scope for the use of common sense in deciding on sensible divisions into contiguous blocks so that they represent coherent processes.

The concept of the flow diagram is built upon the fact that the computer is a sequential machine, so that at any given time during the running of the program its activity can be identified with a unique point on the diagram. This concept is complicated slightly in on-line programming by the fact that there are mechanisms by which the computer can suddenly be diverted to a completely different activity, but in this event care is taken to ensure that it always returns to the original program at the point from which it emerged. Thus the integrity of the concept is preserved, but the timing deductions could be erroneous if they are made without reference to the whole system and the priorities built into it. This is a good reason, however, for ensuring that such diversions are of minimal duration. Such diversions or *interrupts* also give rise to a special type of flow diagram which starts at a point determined by an external stimulus and finishes with a link storing jump, so, though it looks like an open-loop diagram, in practice it starts and finishes at the same arbitrary point in a separate program.

4.10   Documentation

This is another aspect of computing which assumes an enhanced importance in on-line work. In off-line computing it is something which can be treated informally by the individual, but this is not entirely satisfactory for the present purposes, because:

1 On-line computing is more likely to be a co-operative effort.
2 Low-level programming is more common.
3 The overall system is likely to be in a permanent state of growth.
4 The type of investigation promoted by on-line facilities tends to be a continuing one.
5 There are greater possibilities for the duplication of effort on straightforward tasks.
6 Knowledge of many factors is more critical; e.g. timing, storage, depth of nesting, incidental corruptions, subroutine entry conditions, permitted ranges of variables, etc.
7 Complicated faults can become apparent at a late stage of development, or during use, and unless the facilities for tracing these are backed up by comprehensive accessible information, they can cripple the work for a long period.
8 The modular approach is indispensable and the free interlocking of modules can only be achieved by the imposition of standardization supported by comprehensive descriptions.

The essential module of software is the subroutine, and the essential document that goes with this is the *subroutine specification*. This should be a standardized document of one page, supported if necessary by notes on how the subroutine can be used and what restrictions apply to it. There is a number of necessary items which must appear on the specification. These will vary slightly with the type of computer concerned, but they would include typically:

> Title and reference number
> Author
> Date and issue number
> Result and/or description of method
> Entry points and conditions
> Exit details (including details of any corruption of store location)
> Storage used
> Other routines called
> Accuracy or timing details.

The first move in writing a subroutine or a suite of subroutines should be the drawing up of draft specifications so that at least the entry and exit conditions are established. This can be done with reference to a flow diagram for the whole program or suite. In support of the specification, which will ultimately be filed, it is worth while to preserve flow diagrams, and essential to preserve the original coded form of the subroutine. Presumably the machine code version would be available in relocatable form on a subroutine library tape, but in the event of queries or necessity of modifications this would be almost useless. Furthermore the assembler (or higher-language) version must be adequately *annotated*. There is usually a method provided for parenthesizing comments so that they are ignored by the compiler but appear on any print-out from the punched tape or cards. One feels a great temptation to save time and effort by omitting the explanatory remarks from a piece of program, but if one succumbs it is almost invariably eventually regretted, sometimes bitterly.

Another vital aspect of documentation is the notification and recording of modifications. As the system develops it is often more convenient to modify existing software rather than indulge in continual rewriting, and, if the suggestions above have been adhered to, this is usually a simple matter involving additions or substitutions on the annotated tape. As a first step all extra or changed lines should be indicated in the annotation (or line numbering, etc.) by inclusion of M or MOD or some other appropriate mark. Then for serious modifications a new specification should be written, while for minor modifications the original specification should be amended. 'Dead' specifications ought to be preserved, and if storage is available it may be worth while preserving tapes of old versions of subroutines, since one occasionally finds it desirable to retrace one's steps and branch off in another direction with new modifications.

The effort of cultivating a system of documentation that is thorough and eventually automatic is well worth while. It may all sound very pedantic to the uninitiated reader, who is consulting this text with reference to a few simple problems and does not foresee the sort of growth we describe, but experience suggests that this is the way it happens, and, if one does not take a disciplined approach, at best one carries on inefficiently with a good deal of wasted effort, while at worst the whole structure collapses in a tangle of unrelated and unidentified paper tape.

4.11 SETTING UP PROCEDURES

The importance of setting up procedures is yet another aspect which is peculiar to on-line computing. When an interaction occurs with the real world, the computer must have been completely forearmed with the necessary information and procedures to deal with it. This sort of programming is usually standard for a particular input/output channel and so tends to become part of the software/hardware package related to it. The user may, however, wish to vary some of the details of operation , and would usually be expected to do this when he performs the essential first stages of initiating the set up. This he would do by calling a special subroutine, or preferably calling a special entry of the subroutine which is ultimately used with the channel for the transfer of information. The sort of questions which are asked implicitly whenever an interrupt occurs, and for which an answer must have been previously supplied, are:

1 Where must the data go (or come from) in the store?
2 How many data must be transferred?
3 Where is the piece of program to deal with this interrupt?
4 What control information is there for the peripheral and where is it?
5 What is to be done if this interrupt goes wrong?

The only answer that the general user might wish to have a say in is the one to the second question, and he would be accommodated simply by an indication (in the appropriate subroutine specification) of where the count should be placed. The entry conditions might also allow him to vary the answer to question 4, but probably in an indirect and simplified way. *Control words* are typical of the sort of software entities whose format is conditioned by the nature of the hardware channel and the desirability of simplifying it. In general, it is unnecessary and undesirable for every user of the channel to have to unearth the specification of such formats and study them. Provided the first person to do so does it with his mind on the common good, he should with very little extra effort be able to produce a standard subroutine or suite which will serve his own and most other users' purposes in the future. He would normally be the designer of the channel.

Nevertheless, it remains a necessity for each user of a channel to initiate some sort of setting up action, even if it is only a single call to a special entry of a subroutine, and this action would best be performed at the beginning of the master program. An alternative procedure might be to allow the set-up to be performed on the first call of a subroutine after which a *flag* is set which causes a jump round the setting up part, but this has severe disadvantages. Firstly the timing would be degraded, and secondly, in the event of a fault occurring, the program would not be self-starting, as the set flag would prevent the setting up procedure from being carried out. The program would then have to be reloaded, or a cumbersome sequence of manual orders carried out. This is a good example of a *clag* being provoked by the careless use of a flag.

This observation leads us to another variant of setting up procedure that is peculiar to on-line programming. The program may need to be re-started several times during an experimental run, something which would be pointless in off-line computing where there is no external source of change, and it is unsafe to make any presumptions about the state of any stored entity other than the program after the first run. This applies particularly to those entities, such as flags, which condition branch instructions in the program. Thus besides the public setting up procedures the programmer must take steps to cancel any flags, zero any critical data areas, and carry out any other initiating procedures which constitute the private requirements of his program.

The surest programming technique to avoid neglecting this task is to have a separate sheet of paper to hand on which all the initializing instructions are written as the need for them becomes evident during the main programming task. This subsidiary sheet of instructions then becomes part of the beginning of the completed program or constitutes a separate setting up routine.

One advantage of treating the setting up instructions in a block form like this is that they also act as a *reset* facility which is useful in the event of a fault or during program testing. This is particularly true when the setting up is done in a subroutine, as a link-storing jump to it can be substituted for any other unimportant instruction at an appropriate place (or performed manually on handswitches). The set-up procedure, however, usually involves resetting data pointers and data areas, so data will usually be lost when this is done, and it is usually best reserved as a last ditch effort to get some basis for diagnosis out of an obstinately faulty program.

Needless to say, all set-up procedures are performed without reference to absolute addresses, apart from the special case of a block of store being dedicated to interface control data, as is often done for the sake of fast and efficient transfers. Thus flags and data will be stored in data subroutines, whose addresses will be used by the initializing instructions. Only instructions intimately concerned with the interface block will refer to absolute locations, and these would normally be approached via a standard subroutine which forms part of the package for a particular channel.

4.12 GROUP ACTIVITY

It will have become evident to the reader that in our view experimental on-line computing, like a football match or an orgy, is essentially a game for more than one player. This is not to say that it is impossible for the individual to do valuable work in this field, but rather to say that when several people work together in a properly organized way their contributions combine, so that the whole is greater than the sum of the parts. Some of the reasons for this are rooted in the nature of computing in general, others are peculiar to the on-line variety.

One of the general factors is the nature of the growth of software. One could rather foolishly begin each stage of development anew starting from the primitive material provided by the machine and its basic instruction code, but almost invariably software grows from the totality of what exists at a particular time. It feeds upon itself, so that the rate of growth is proportional to what already exists, and is therefore potentially exponential. An extreme example of this is the writing of a new high-level language compiler in an existing high-level language (ALGOL 60 was written in ALGOL) which not only makes the task easier than going back to low-level forms but also makes it more machine-independent. In the more restricted field with which we are concerned, the process begins with the development of basic subroutines which relate either to the type of hardware being developed or to the theoretical concepts on which the class of work is based. At a later stage more advanced subroutines obviate repetition of this groundwork by containing calls to the basic ones.

This introduces one of the special aspects of experimental on-line computing. The on-line computer (ignoring the dedicated process variety) is usually situated in a laboratory, which implies that some at least of its users have common interests and goals, since for the sake of efficiency laboratories and their equipment are usually specialist in nature, be they industrial or academic in affiliation. The off-line computer, on the other hand, is much more likely to be a central facility shared by a diverse group of users. Furthermore, these on-line interests and goals are more likely to diverge from those of dissimilar groups than in the off-line case, so the workers can rely less on the pressures of a global demand to produce desired developments in software. It is therefore desirable that their work should be organized in such a way that the 'bootstrap' effect is maximized in the growth of their stock of software.

Another factor is *machine-independence*, which we have just mentioned as a desirable feature of general purpose software. This is not on the whole within reach of on-line work. Each machine configuration in this field is specially adapted for its particular rôle. The type of machine will probably have been chosen largely on the grounds of suitable hardware features, rather than its software handling capability. Thus we have another factor tending to isolate a group and turn it inwards to its own resources. Let us not exaggerate the point, however, there will be many points of common interest with other workers in the field and other users of the same class of machine, which will provoke fruitful cross-fertilization and must be encouraged.

Our main point, however, is that the rate of progress of a group of people working in this field is largely conditioned by the way in which the group organizes itself. This can be optimized by paying attention to the 3D's of successful on-line computing, which are:

Dialogue: If each new development is carried out in full consultation with co-workers it can be moulded to give the greatest common benefit.

Documentation: A well organized pool of information on the current state of the art is the only reliable platform from which to launch the next development. This requires

Discipline: which can ultimately only be self-discipline.

There will always be rogue members of any group who insist on going their own way. In this field they will come and go and the result will be as if they had never been (unless they manage to leave behind a small legacy of chaos).

4.13 FLAGS

Occasionally in off-line computing one wishes to record the fact that a certain condition has occurred in such a way that the fact can be used to determine the direction taken in a branch instruction later in the program, and some compilers have included such a facility under names such as SENSESWITCH, though it is easy to simulate this effect in terms of ordinary algorithmic language. In on-line computing this is a procedure of great importance. It is often the only efficient way that a fact such as the prior arrival of suitable data (or its failure to arrive) can be communicated to the relevant part of the program. The on-line central processor does not follow a program in a unique inevitable sequence as does its off-line counterpart, but proceeds in fits and starts and diversions which are conditioned by the occurrence of various interrupts. In an advanced operating system, an occurrence in one program may require the running of a completely separate program, and the request for this must be issued and maintained until it is complied with.

By an obvious analogy the entity which provides this facility is called a *flag*. It is essentially a bit of binary information and this is one of the reasons for the inclusion of bit operations in our list of desirable features of an on-line computer in Chapter 2. If bit testing and setting operations are available as part of the basic instruction code of the machine, flagging can be a simple and efficient operation. A single word can hold as many flags as there are bits in it, and this would be enough for most programs. Furthermore, the important setting up and resetting procedure is carried out simply by equating the word to zero, and the existence of unsatisfied flags is indicated by a non-zero value of the word. If single-bit operations are not available the bit-testing procedure might become a little cumbersome, in which case it will be preferable to sacrifice a whole word to each flag.

It is important to remember that there are three stages in the use of a flag— *initializing, setting* and *cancelling*. While flags can lend great elegance and simplicity to an on-line program they can also, if abused, cause chaos and clags. One of the commonest forms of clag is where the program remains looping on a flag which is never cancelled. We used such a looping method to convert our mythical simple computer of Section 4.6 to an on-line one, and it provides one of the basic methods for dealing with interrupts. In a simple one-loop program, failure of the flag cancelling mechanism implies failure of the whole system, and therefore it is immaterial that it results in a permanent loop, but in more complex systems this is not necessarily so. An unsatisfied flag can prevent the salvaging of a whole program even after a fault has been cleared. The authors have been in the past presented with a problem by a faulty public subroutine, which, once a fault had occurred, persisted in setting the flag on which it was looping, even though the fault was cleared and the flag reset by a manual sequence of orders.

One way of organizing a program is to build it up round a flag testing routine, so that the quiescent state of the computer is one of looping on a flag word or words. Such a scheme is illustrated in Figure 4.4. Typically of an on-line flow diagram, this does not represent a self-contained process, i.e. without the setting of flags via program interrupts, the program would remain in its minor loop. The behaviour of the program once a flag becomes set can be quite complex, for one subroutine could flag others. There might appear to be no advantage in this over a direct call to the subroutine, but it is, for example, possible in this way to introduce a priority system of dealing with flags, as indicated in Figure 4.4. (This would, of course, operate at a level much lower than any hardware priority assessment associated with the input/output channels.) The communication between subroutines would then take place in common data areas.

As an example of the application of such a system, the first flag might be set by the teletype interrupt program, indicating that an *unsolicited* message has been received. The flag controlled loop of Figure 4.4 would direct control to a subroutine which would examine the message and set appropriate flags to initiate the actions requested, and any relevant quantified information would be stored in an appropriate data block; for example, the teletype input message might request that 1000 samples be taken via the A–D converter (ADC). This would flag a subroutine which would set up the count and the data pointer and initiate the transfers. Meanwhile, if no other flags were raised, the control program would return to its quiescent minor loop until a program interrupt from the ADC channel signified that the data had all been acquired. This could be used to flag an output teletype message asking 'What next?' etc.

There are a few points worth noting about this system. Firstly, it is purely a method of software organization and does not interfere with the progress of data transfers to and from the peripherals. Secondly, the flag is cancelled as soon as it is tested. This is important as it avoids ambiguous treatment of

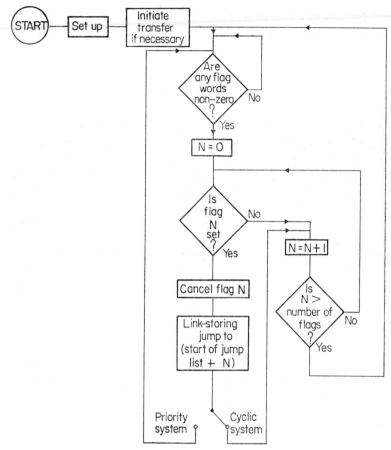

Figure 4.4   A flag-testing basis for organizing programs

consecutive flags, and where a combined bit test and cancel instruction was available this would be used. Thirdly, the priority status of flags can be predetermined by their rank in the order of testing, though this would have to be treated with great care if anomalous behaviour were to be avoided. Fourthly, the jumps to subroutines in the list referred to in Figure 4.4 would be of the special *non-link storing* kind, so that the control would return to the control loop rather than to the next jump in the list.

Obviously such a system is fairly crude, but it does help to illustrate the use of flags in such a way as to avoid some of the grosser errors which may be associated with them. It also serves to introduce some of the ideas behind the concept of an on-line supervisor, of which this might be considered an elementary example. To achieve more advanced control it is necessary to extend the idea of a flag to cover more than just binary information and to provide for a queue-based treatment rather than the simple one described here.

4.14   OPERATION OF PROGRAMS

Before the program as conceived by its author can achieve consummation as a prescribed pattern of behaviour in a machine, it has to undergo certain processes such as *compilation* and *assembly*, and except in the simplest systems it will act only under the control of a higher software authority, the *supervisor* or *executive*. The off-line programmer needs to know little about these complications, other than the fact that he has to conform with any limitations of language and provide certain control cards to steer the execution of his program.

The on-line programmer, however, is more intimately concerned with the relationship of his program with its hardware environment, and he needs some knowledge of how these processes affect that relationship. Let us therefore examine these processes a little further.

4.14.1   COMPILATION

The only form of program which requires no further treatment before being obeyed is one in raw machine code. This is very rarely used for other than direct engineering work on the system since:

(1) It does not offer any mnemonic aids to the programmer and is therefore difficult to write and interpret.

(2) It lacks the advantages of relocation, especially in respect of subroutine calls, so that the absolute address of every subroutine has to be known before programming is commenced.

The next stage in the language hierarchy is the *assembler* language which, apart from its considerable mnemonic aids, also, as its name implies, facilitates the *assembly* of programs with relocatable subroutines. Although the assembly process is separated conceptually from compilation it is important to note that even an assembler language will have a compiler associated with it to perform translation and organizational functions. In order to understand what is meant by compilation it is useful to examine it in terms of a high-level language, as this requires all the features of the process, but we will restrict our discussion to a particular mode of compilation in which it is completed before execution of the program, noting in passing that there is an alternative dynamic procedure in which some interpretation occurs during execution.

Some of the main stages of the compilation process are:

(1) *Decomposition*—the breaking down of the complex syntactical structure of the algorithmic language into elementary instructions each containing a single operation.

(2) *Translation*—the statement of the decomposed source program in an intermediate language, which for our purpose we shall assume is the assembler language.

(3) *Preparation for assembly*—the tabulation of various lists of jumps and calls which are at this stage incomplete because they refer to addresses which are as yet unallocated, e.g. public library subroutines.

(4) *Optimization*—the reorganization of the program to remove any redundancies and inefficiencies which may have been introduced by a combination of compiler and programmer action.

(5) *Diagnostics*—a very variable facility which is designed to assist the programmer to detect errors before and during execution.

Each of these stages contributes to the prime function of the high-level language—to act as an interface between two very different systems of organizing a numerical procedure, the intuitive, wayward, generalizing, creative method of the human brain and the punctilious, subordinate, step-wise approach of the machine. Each stage, however, also disturbs the rapport between man and machine, and inhibits the human brain in its most telling rôle of acting on the basis of a global appreciation of a problem.

Decomposition is on the whole a straightforward process, especially for a limited-repertoire machine. It will always produce a result which conforms to the intentions of the programmer, but it is quite possible for this to be done in a grossly circumlocutory way. For example, a procedure which is basically one of dealing with a number of binary flags might be realized with a few direct bit operations in machine code, but could involve many times the number of operations and amount of storage if realized via a high-level language which is not equipped to deal with such problems efficiently. In some cases the penalties in loss of speed can be enormous. Even in off-line computing it is not uncommon for the crucial inner loops (i.e. the ones most often repeated) to be written as an insert in machine or assembler code. The basic reason for such difficulties is that the definers of languages and writers of compilers are producing a facility for *all* users, and cannot allow for exploitable peculiarities of particular cases.

Decomposition does not in itself imply a change of language, and it is not unknown for a language to be decomposed into a subset of itself (boot-strapping) before *translation* into a form more amenable to assembly in the computer. *Preparation for assembly* also includes processes beyond the simple transliteration of instructions. The program will contain various address-dependent orders such as jumps and calls to subroutines which are not at this stage included or located. In the case of the subroutine itself, the compilation process must have it in such a form that it can be absorbed into any program at any address (relocatable binary). Thus the compiled program contains a number of unsatisfied tags, which during the final assembly stage will be satisfied by the allocation of an address.

Optimization is a very variable and, from our point of view, questionable process. Basically it consists of an examination of the overall procedure produced by the compiled program with subsequent modification if the performance can be improved without a change in the overall logic. Its main aims are the minimization of storage and time. The inherent difficulties are illustrated by the fact that the total machine time consists of compilation time plus the run time multiplied by the number of runs. Optimization may reduce the run time but will increase the compilation time. Optimization is feasible in off-line work as the computer knows the whole story once the program is stored. This is not true of on-line, real-time work, and the procedure therefore carries much more danger in this field.

Diagnostics are often the most important measure of a compiler as far as the mathematical programmer is concerned, and he is inclined to leave worries about inefficiency to the managers of the computer system. It is possible to compile programs in a dynamic mode so that they are interpreted while they are being executed, but while this maximizes the diagnostic facility it so degrades the efficiency that we shall not consider it here. Normally for our purposes we have to make do with a simple syntax-checking facility, which does not normally carry overheads of time and storage during execution.

Thus we see that there are many ways, apart from its basic one-to-many nature, in which the high-level compiler can interfere with our control of the situation at run time. The only process which does not interfere with this control (and then only if we are provided with certain extra information) is preparation for assembly. There are therefore strong grounds for our commitment to an assembler language for at least a major part of the work.

Nevertheless, there are higher languages with a claim to on-line real-time application areas, including *dialects* of the main programming languages FORTRAN, ALGOL and COBOL, and they form a family tree of some complexity [TaSof 71]. Now, in some of these variants there is capability of interaction with hardware events such as interrupts, but in general the relevance to on-line, real-time work is more one of the philosophy of data handling. We will mention briefly one of these languages which originated in the military field.

CORAL (Computer On-line Real-time Applications Language) is descended from ALGOL via JOVIAL (Jules' Own Version of the International Algebraic Language) [ProLaSe]. Unfortunately, it shares its acronym with a contemporary (Class Oriented Ring Association Language) [ProLaSe]. The emphasis in the structure of the language is on the efficient speedy handling of variable blocks of data, which are packed into tables. There are provisions for the handling of individual bits and bit-strings, switches, overlays, text-strings. The logic operations are available under the names MASK, UNION and DIFFER in addition to arithmetic operations, and interconversions are possible between FIXED, INTEGER and FLOATING forms of operand. All of these features are relevant to the real-time situation, but they do not help to solve the basic problems of handling novel input/ output channels, which are our main concern and are not defined in the language. For laboratory applications, the best approach to using one of these high-level languages is through a compiler which allows it to be combined with segments in assembler code, so that each language can take care of that part of the problem best suited to it. Real-time high-level compilers tend to delegate input/output activity to the *operating system*, which is not entirely suited to many laboratory installations. Languages like CORAL and EXTENDED FORTRAN will no doubt become more important as the degree of procedural complexity in laboratory calculation increases, but at present the assembler language provides the best approach to most problems.

It is important to note that even the program in assembler language requires some sort of compilation process. This would consist of

1 Syntax checking
2 Translation
3 Preparation of jump lists and subroutine tags;

and there is a possible fourth point which one must watch out for—the generation of macro-programs. This represents a possible breakdown in the one–one nature of the process, and is particularly common when one assembler language serves a family of machines of differing hardware characteristics. It may also be provided in the form of an extra optional set of instructions. There might for example be FIX and FLOAT instructions available in the language which at the compilation stage generate some half dozen machine orders instead of one. Further instructions may generate calls to subroutines in the public library without their being specified by name by the programmer.

For an assembler language the process of compilation is usually combined with assembly in one controlling program. After the compilation stage, the program (or subroutine) will be complete in machine code except for a number of blanks which need to be filled in with addresses when the complete program is assembled in store. Each of these blanks must be represented by an item in a jump or tag list which will be erased as soon as it is possible to fill the blanks.

4.14.2 ASSEMBLY

This is the process of gathering together the master program with all the subroutines that it calls and all the subroutines that they call, and so on. As each subroutine becomes available its address is used to fill in the appropriate blanks in the calling instructions and the tag list pointers are decremented accordingly. When the lists are all reduced to zero the process is complete and the program, if free of errors, is capable of being run.

For convenience the subroutines are grouped together in libraries on paper tape or backing store in relocatable binary form. The time for assembly from paper tape can be very long indeed, and it soon begins to dominate the activity of a small system with a number of users, which is a major reason for the pressure that usually develops for the addition of backing store as an early enhancement to the system. The presence on a library of perhaps hundreds of subroutines each of which calls several others is also a potential source of difficulty; for if the order of the library is arbitrary, the need for a subroutine might arise after it has passed through the reader via a call from another assembled subroutine, and several passes of the tape might be necessary before assembly can be completed. We shall have to examine this point further.

4.14.3 LIBRARIES

There are two possible ways of obviating the necessity for multiple passes of a library tape—by *hierarchical structure* or the *directory* method. In the hierarchical structure the subroutines are placed on the library in a carefully chosen order which is based on the rule that no subroutine is to be preceded by one which it calls itself. The directory is simply a compressed catalogue of the library which occupies the first part of the library tape. It is small enough to be taken into store, so that during assembly the ramifications arising from the subroutine calls in the program can be mapped out and a *complete* tag list prepared before the library itself is read.

Both of these methods cause complications when a new subroutine is added to the library. In the hierarchical structure the new subroutine has to be inserted at exactly the right spot, while a directory has to be remade every time a new subroutine is added. All of these problems are, of course, greatly eased by the availability of backing store, which allows complete automation of the handling of both existing and new subroutines. Several different libraries will usually be in use with a given system. There will be a public library of general purpose subroutines developed by the manufacturer, a local library of general purpose subroutines developed by the team, and several special purpose and personal libraries. Each user should organize his work so that he uses at the most four libraries, otherwise assembly becomes too complicated. Any small special purpose libraries will be stored on paper tape and will not have a permanent place in a backing file. If assembly is not complete after passes of all the library tapes, action has to be taken to initiate output of a list of unsatisfied subroutine tags, which allows the user to make provision for them to be provided.

Obviously development of the local public library is an important *group activity* which depends strongly on good supporting *documentation*. There is one further variation which is very useful if provided—the possibility of different subroutines of the same name or number but in separately numbered versions. This allows, for example, a program to be developed with a version with output on a channel such as the teletype which is convenient for monitoring, and then finally assembled with a different version to output to a more appropriate channel. There might be separate fixed point and floating point versions of, say, a fast Fourier transform subroutine, or one version might be a dummy of one instruction—restore link—which is included during the testing of another part of the program to ensure that the particular tag is satisfied during the test assembly. When two or more versions of the same subroutine exist in a library, the one required will have to be specified.

4.14.4 LOADING

The most basic software operation is *loading*, i.e. entering the program into the machine. Initially we have a paradoxical situation in which the computer store is empty, and therefore contains no instructions which it can follow to allow itself to be filled. The device to overcome this is called a *bootstrap*, which may be conveniently divided into a *primary* and a *secondary bootstrap*. The primary bootstrap consists of the *minimal* set of orders required to read in a program in special reduced format and relinquish control to it. It is entered by a sequence of handswitch orders, by rotating a multiple content switch or by activating a special hard-wired unit (for example, a ROM). The program that is loaded in this special reduced format is the secondary bootstrap which can perform the function of reading in ordinary binary program and relinquishing control to it. It is conveniently used in the form of a special tape leader for the first basic program fed in.

The first program is a *loader* or some other program such as a compiler or supervisor which has the load function built into it, and once it is in store the operation of bootstrapping can be forgotten (unless it is corrupted either accidentally or deliberately). With a very small system, storage can be conserved by bootstrapping in programs directly, while in a very large system the loader will be a large subsystem of the supervisor program, and it monitors and allocates storage for the various programs.

4.15   Dictionaries

A very important class of subroutines contains those concerned with the comprehension of input keyboard messages. They are very important and powerful, and if they are not supplied in suitable form by the computer manufacturer, one of the first tasks should be to set about writing some. There are many ways of approaching this problem and as an illustration we shall describe a simple scheme that we developed as a basis of the programming philosophy of a small system.

The scheme consists of a program MAKE DICTIONARY and a user subroutine CONSULT DICTIONARY, and they each make use of a common subroutine CONSOLIDATE MESSAGE. This latter subroutine is based on the need to compress messages to conserve storage and utilizes the fact that most of the information in the message is contained in its consonants (and numbers if present). The vowels and spaces, being more probable, contain less information. The subroutine therefore takes the first six significant characters of a message (i.e. eliminates vowels and spaces) and packs them into consecutive words (two 24 bit words or three 16 bit words, etc.).

The programmer as an early step in writing his program decides what input messages he is going to need, and with the program MAKE DICTIONARY in the computer, types them on the teletype as a list, using a new-line to terminate each message and one of the control characters to signify an error. He finishes the list with an agreed terminating character and the computer immediately outputs a tape which is in fact a data subroutine, containing the list of compressed messages. Thus a stored list of single word messages might look like this:

> STRT
> BRT
> TRNSFR
> PLT
> DSPLY
> PNCH
> CNTN
> STP

These are all more or less readable, though the second message ABORT is difficult as it begins with a vowel. An important point to note is that ambiguities are possible with such a system, so if the third word is TRANSFORM one cannot use TRANSFER in the same list.

The subroutine CONSULT DICTIONARY is used in the main program and, if it is used as the key to the whole program, the quiescent state of the program will be one of looping on a flag within it. The address of the dictionary subroutine is supplied as a parameter so any number of separate dictionaries can be incorporated in the same program. The flow diagram of this subroutine is shown in Figure 4.5. The action of the subroutine is to wait for an input message, and when it arrives compare it with each of the stored messages one by one. When it finds a match it exits with an output parameter set to an integer value equal to the rank of the message in the list. This parameter can be

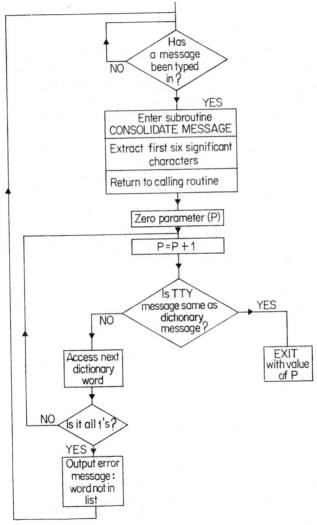

Figure 4.5   Flow diagram of the subroutine CONSULT DICTIONARY

used in a switch jump instruction (or if this is not available, a group of instructions) which causes a jump down a list of instructions which are non link storing jumps to appropriate subroutines which carry out the desired actions. Note that this leaves the returning subroutine without a link to return to, so a special entry is provided to CONSULT DICTIONARY which stores a link to itself, otherwise the programmer must take steps to store a link to a desired final destination.

4.16   Systems of operation

There are two extremes of regime under which the experimental on-line computer system can operate. The first is the simple arrangement, normally associated with small systems, in which each user has a period of sole occupancy, and is able to start and stop the machine, step through programs under manual control, etc. The second is a more dynamic organization, associated with more highly developed systems, in which the computer itself never stops physically although it may mimic such an action to satisfy a particular program.

The simple system is in many ways ideal for the individual experimenter, since it gives him a chance to make optimal use of the machine facilities, and in the laboratory environment it will no doubt always be reserved as an option to cope with the tasks which are most demanding on the capabilities of the system. There are, however, a number of factors which eventually tend to favour the second form of operation, e.g.:

(1) As the system develops it represents an increasing investment of capital and there is greater pressure for it to be put to the maximum use.

(2) As the power of the system becomes apparent it begins to attract the attention of a greater number of potential users.

(3) The variety of tasks tends to increase, so that it ranges from short intensive runs to long ones which demand only occasional action and therefore do not make economic use of the facilities.

(4) Program development becomes an increasing load which is not dealt with very expeditiously under a simple regime.

The ultimate development of such trends is the institution of a full *operating system* which would provide facilities for *multiprogramming* under control of an *executive* with such facilities as *peripheral allocation* and *buffering, background* and *foreground programs, multi-access*, etc. We shall discuss the meaning and implications of some of these terms later. They represent the normal way of doing things in a large non-real-time computer installation, which exists only to process customers' mathematical programs with maximum speed and efficiency. There are many phases of on-line, real-time computing which have features similar to this sort of activity, program development being a prime example. There are other phases which are totally different; for example, the development and testing of new hardware input/output channels, which would usually demand a more intimate access to the machine, and would therefore have to be allocated special periods of use.

The point we wish to emphasize at this stage is that it is most important to recognize the possibility that such developments may take place, and to write programs in such a way that they will not have to be rewritten on a large scale in that event.

Let us take a simple example which may or may not apply to a particular machine but which serves to illustrate the point. If, in the early stages, programs are written to include machine-stop orders, they will be capable of arresting the whole system and will defeat later attempts to install a continuous operating system unless they are weeded out one by one. A much better scheme is to nominate a standard subroutine which serves to provide the STOP function, and ensure that each programmer uses a call to this subroutine to obtain a stop. In the early stages this subroutine could contain only a simple machine-stop order, but later on a new version could be instituted which caused a return to the executive program. Thus the user programs would never have to be rewritten, but they might need to be re-assembled.

This example is only included as an illustration, and there are other ways around the particular problem. For example, in the mythical computer we dreamed up in Section 4.6, to convey the idea of a function repertoire, we avoided the existence of a machine-stop order, and in that particular case the problem would be solved by storing in location 0 a jump to some form of supervisor program. Alternatively, many computers can be provided with special hardware which will *trap* destructive orders and allow the executive to replace them with appropriate actions. Other examples of destructive orders are those which refer directly to the operation of the standard interface thereby by-passing, or perhaps colliding with, instructions from the controlling program.

We shall discuss the control system problem in terms of the growth of a computer installation from small beginnings to a medium-scale fully equipped system, as this is what tends to happen in laboratory systems in our experience. This treatment may, however, also be useful to the reader who has by-passed the small system stage, as it helps to put the larger system in an understandable context. In many ways the smallish computer with a minimal operating system is the most ideal for the purpose we are concerned with here, and the economic considerations which go with the availability of larger systems tend to detract from their value to the experimenter.

4.16.1 OPERATION WITHOUT A SOFTWARE SYSTEM

It is common for a start to be made on the automation of a laboratory or group of experiments through the installation of a minimal set of computer hardware. Indeed, there is a lot to be said for this approach, whether it is dictated by financial considerations or not, as it allows the development of the system to be conditioned by experiences in the particular environment, and not constrained by one's first hasty thoughts. In this initial state, storage will be at a premium and there is a reluctance to sacrifice some of it to a permanently resident control program, besides which the repertoire of programs will not be large enough to justify it. Any extra money available will be directed towards the realization of input/output channels appropriate to the experimental activity.

Control instructions at this stage will probably be communicated to the assembler program by means of tape leaders, and it will produce assembled programs in binary format which can be bootstrapped in so that virtually the whole store is available to the program at run time. Compilation and assembly will be viewed as activities distinct from operation, and the programs that perform these functions will be overwritten by user program and data as soon as their usefulness is finished.

This form of operation gives the user absolute control over the machine, but the advantage is offset by an absence of certain labour-saving devices and provisions for versatility. One example is the treatment of character strings which are the main vehicle for man–computer communication.

A clearly defined group of peripherals handles signals which represent strings of alphanumeric characters. They are tape reader, tape punch, teletypewriter, magnetic tape cassette, visual display unit and incremental plotter. The last two, however, will also deal with other types of signal. Character strings will also be associated with the various types of backing store—drum, disc or tape—particularly in an advanced system where all input/output strings will tend to be handled via backing store files. One of the prime requirements of a successful software system is that the basic user subroutines are independent of the source or destination of these character strings, so that these sources and destinations may be chosen and varied at will before, or even during, execution of the program.

Most modern on-line computer systems are to some extent modular, so that they are likely to expand to cope with new requirements, and it is the user of a small system who is most subjected to the temptation to write subroutines dedicated to one peripheral, as this is certainly more economical in storage. Such a policy is almost sure to be regretted at a later date. The computer manufacturers will (or should) have developed a policy in the form of a standard software interface which the on-line programmer should understand and adhere to. Then the software will be able to grow with the hardware system up to the point where it is large enough to support a full real-time operating system.

4.16.2 PROGRESSION TO A MINIMAL SUPERVISOR

As activity on a machine increases, the priorities begin to change. The preparation and handling of paper tape begin to consume an annoying proportion of the time available, compilers and programs are being read in and overwritten with greater frequency, and a few of the programs begin to require increased storage. At this stage it is natural for the computer storage to be increased, though some laboratories may be fortunate enough to start off with excess storage capacity. In either instance it will be found that the majority of programs do not occupy a major share of the available storage, and it becomes feasible to have some of the utility programs such as loaders and assemblers in semi-permanent residence. It also becomes possible to think in terms of an elementary operating system designed to cut down the wasteful activity between runs and eliminate the necessity for the user to fiddle with the main computer console (in jargon, 'hands-on' operation). The facilities required of such a system are:

(1) No true computer stops, so that interrupts can occur even when there is no program activity, and the computer has a recognized quiescent state.

(2) Control by simplified messages via a keyboard without the preparation of special tape leaders, etc.

(3) Elimination of duplication of software to operate the common input/output channels if more than one program is resident in the store.

(4) Flexibility, so that desirable features may be added to the system as required.

(5) Minimal sacrifice of storage.

The method of implementation of such a scheme is very machine-dependent, and it may already exist as a software provision of the manufacturer. If it is not available in suitable form, however, it should not prove too daunting a task to produce one, and the effort is well repaid. As an illustration from outside the range of manufacturers' software, we shall briefly describe one such simple scheme, which was developed by the authors as a basis for running their installation when it was too small to warrant a full operating system. The basic features are, briefly:

(1) All the character input/output subroutines on the public library are replaced by dummies which contain only a link-storing jump to an absolute location where the operating system input/output subroutines are held.

(2) The utility programs, such as assemblers, are also 'doctored' to use this common character route.

(3) The central organizing program is the subroutine CONSULT DICTIONARY, and the quiescent condition is one of looping in this subroutine on the teletype input flag (see Section 4.15).

(4) Standard addresses are nominated for the utility programs which are in general use (loader, assembler, etc.) and their addresses are stored in the DICTIONARY jump list (see Figure 4.5), so that they are activated simply by typing in a verbal instruction (such as LOAD, ASSEMBLE, etc). These, with the operating system subroutine, tend to be located at the end of the store, so that they are only overwritten when the longest programs are loaded, though the loader itself is placed before the normal *program start address* so that it is never overwritten. The normal program start address is accessed by typing PROGRAM, while programs at other addresses are accessed by typing ADDRESS which causes a jump to a subroutine which permits the address to be nominated via a teletype message.

(5) The *stop subroutine* is replaced by one which types out STOP (followed by a number, where applicable) and jumps to CONSULT DICTIONARY for further action.

(6) The bottom address in the push down store of links is always the entry to CONSULT DICTIONARY, so that control is always ultimately returned to it.

(7) All tape input control messages are 'diverted' to be received from the teletype.

(8) Features can be added by extending the dictionary.

This system reduces the user's activity at the computer to loading tapes and typing control messages. More than one program can be housed in the store and accessed at any time and, although full multiprogramming is not possible, interrupts initiated by one program are not interfered with by another, so that it is possible to have a long term data acquisition process going on while a separate program is running. The system is simple, but effective, and its scope could be enlarged by the adoption of a binary flag system as discussed in Section 4.13, though this would involve a larger scale of software re-organization.

4.16.3 ADVANCED OPERATING SYSTEMS

A higher level of organization becomes possible, and to some extent imperative, when a substantial amount of backing store becomes available. Virtually all manufacturers provide such systems, and many of the features are extremely elegant, though often of somewhat doubtful value in the laboratory context. When the manufacturer has the wisdom to develop his systems in a fully modular form, it becomes possible to select a suitable subset, possibly with minor specialized additions. The concepts of *multi-programming* and *multi-access* are only really important in the laboratory when there exist experiments which require extended periods of measurement with long intervals which could be filled with some other activity, though low grade activities, such as program development, are so undemanding that it is good economics for several users to be accommodated simultaneously.

In this field usage varies a great deal, but we are using the term *operating system* to mean a group of programs which are resident in the computer and exercise control over the loading, operating and cancelling of the user programs. They would include an *executive* which deals with software/ hardware interactions and/or a *supervisor* which performs a purely software organizing function. Without going into too much detail, we list below some of the functions performed by the operating system software:

1 Job control
2 Routing of character streams between input/output devices and the backing store
3 Scheduling of use of the main store
4 Organizing of files on the backing store
5 Aids to program development (e.g. text editing facilities)
6 Interpreting the user's program (so that it appears to him that he has sole occupancy)
7 Error handling (including a new range of trespass errors)
8 Protection of valued stored program from overwriting.
9 Accounting.

This activity is made possible and desirable by the provision of large amounts of information at moderate rates through the backing store. It allows, for example, the relatively slow character stream peripherals to be fully *buffered* so that they do not hold up the central processor. The existence of a master program means that all other programs, including compilers, etc., effectively become subroutines. The organizing program will activate or suspend all other programs, and as the running of one program often implies the need for another, it maintains a system of *flags* for the programs. An example of such an occurrence is the one where a program outputs a character stream which is directed to a buffer on the backing store; at the same time another program is flagged whose function is to pass the stream out through the requisite peripheral when it becomes available. Obviously a priority system is necessary, and the operation is something like that outlined in Figure 4.4, but here the flags are not simple binary ones and they have to be handled on a queue basis with special provision for urgent programs. As in that case, however, there is a quiescent condition in which the organizing program is in a base-loop waiting for a program to be flagged.

In some modular, general purpose operating systems, the concept is expanded to include the subsystems of Languages, Program Development and Utility programs. Laboratory work requires the greatest flexibility of all applications, and one finds that features of many real-time supervisors are inapposite as they are directed towards the optimization of a relatively fixed system. One of the great assets of an operating system is that it can be used to compress the time dedicated to the subsidiary activities, such as program development, leaving more of the full power of the machine available for difficult measurement problems.

Chapter V

Hardware–Software Interaction

5.1 INTRODUCTION

The subject of this short chapter is at once the most important to our present purpose and the most difficult to deal with. It is important because it embodies the whole point of the exercise of laboratory on-line computing and determines its main strengths or weaknesses. It is difficult to present because it is highly machine-dependent in its realization and concerns random concatenations of events which are peculiar to each computing task. Thus again we have to tread a path between delivering either a series of lofty generalizations or specific examples of narrow interest. Because it is such a machine-dependent activity, the computer user must rely on the manufacturer for the provision of a simple and efficient system and for the provision of clear instructions on its use.

As with the modular approach to hardware and software, the most productive approach to the interaction problem is to avoid duplication of effort by providing a once and for all solution to a specific sub-problem, which can be used as a basis for building up techniques for tackling particular tasks of measurement and control. In this case, the basic module which provides the sub-problem is the specific input/output channel, and our object is to provide a coherent hardware–software entity straddling the standard interface, which offers a simple 'plug-in' facility from the hardware or the software side, whatever its internal complications may be. Such basic building blocks can then be assembled in various combinations of channels to produce a scheme of instrumentation appropriate to any particular task in hand, and we discuss this further in Chapter 8.

Software deals only with numbers, in which description we include the logical entities *true* and *false* which are represented by *one* and *zero*. Hardware deals with currents and voltages, and indirectly with a wide range of other physical variables. The interface package of hardware and software has the basic function of providing a *mapping* between these two different assemblages of entities, so that each variable on the hardware side of the interface has its *image* on the software side and vice-versa. The most fundamental problem of interaction is therefore concerned with the essential imperfection of this mapping. We tend to treat it as unique and linear, but it is only approximately so, and 'pathological' situations can occur in which its defects assume over-riding proportions. The more difficult problems, however, tend to be con-cerned with *organization* and *timing*, and these are what tend to preoccupy us in the design of the interface package, to ensure that as little of the complexity as possible leaks out into the surrounding areas of software and hardware.

The organization problem is one of achieving compatibility between two sets of rules—those governing the operation of programs and those governing the operation of the external devices—and furthermore we are obliged to work for this compatibility through a third rather restrictive set of rules—those governing the operation of the standard interface. The standard inter-face itself has two quite separate descriptions or images, one as seen from the software side and one from the hardware side, and it is often convenient to preserve the distinction by altering one's mode of thought according to which side of the problem one is dealing with, thereby avoiding the complications of a global approach. Thus, having specified, with reference to the nature of the peripheral device and its appointed task, the sequences of transfers which are to take place across the standard interface, one is left with two residual problems, one of programming and one of electronics, which can be tackled independently.

Another common aspect of the interaction problem is that there may be a minor form of data processing to be performed somewhere along the software–hardware chain that goes to make up the channel. This leads us to a character-istic feature of on-line measurement—the existence of a choice between software and hardware solutions of problems. To take a simple example, in the issuing of an alphanumeric character stream to a VDU, the task of the main program with regard to each character is finished once the character is *specified* in the form of an 8 bit word, but the character cannot be considered to be *produced* until it is in a format suitable for direct display, e.g. a dot matrix of 30 or more bits. There is a one-to-one correspondence between the elements of the specified and produced sets, which emphasizes the high degree of redundancy in the latter, so the task of proceeding from one to the other is relatively simple. It can be achieved either as a piece of program, using a stored table, or as a piece of electronics using a ROM, and these two processes may be thought of as images of each other on either side of the interface. As long as it occurs somewhere along the chain, the conversion process will produce the desired result, but there may be reasons for preferring one method to the other in a particular case. In general, software solutions are more versatile and more quickly achieved, but hardware solutions have the distinction that they do not load the central processor and they also have a higher speed capability. This is why there is often some element of pre-processing in the operation of an on-line instrument, for as we shall see, during on-line operations there are good reasons for relieving the computer of unnecessary tasks; one of the most important is concerned with the aspect of timing.

Timing in this field of computing is of unique importance, particularly in *real-time* work. It is a dominant consideration in all aspects from the operation of the standard interface to the operation of a complete program. If approached wrongly it could make the whole task one of impossible complexity. The secret of mastery over it is the total avoidance of *critical timing*.

In order to discuss timing it is convenient to consider the elementary sequential operations of data processing as linked sources and sinks of data, so that for each stage which has the function to *create* data there is a subsequent stage which is designed to *use* those data. Furthermore each create stage stands as a use one in relation to a preceding stage, and each use stage serves as a create stage to a following one. Now, in the general run of computing, there is no difficulty associated with the concatenation of such *create–use* links to form the overall program, but in on-line computing the endmost links of the interconnected chains are conditioned externally. The peripheral devices in many cases create or require to use data at their own particular rates and times and cannot be constrained by the exigencies of instantaneous computer loading. The instantaneous creation of or demand for data passes along the chain, like the shock passing down a train of wagons in a shunting yard, and at the end of the chain it has to be satisfied. If it is not satisfied before the next one arrives the system has broken down. Critical timing occurs when the endmost create and use links are exactly synchronized so that any variation in the chain delay causes a collision and consequent breakdown; and only in a single-channel, single-task system could it be tolerated.

In general, the way to avoid critical timing is to provide some element of *elasticity* in the create–use chain. The first ingredient is high-speed computer hardware to reduce the contribution of computational delay to the possibility of collision, and the second is the idea of *buffering*, which is of paramount importance in on-line work.

Like a mechanical one, the computer buffer provides elasticity by introducing a storage element in the chain of action, and this takes the form of a *pool* of data interposed within one of the create–use links. When the chain is in operation, the pool is continually being emptied by the use stage of the program and replenished by the create stage. It is important to realize that the pool only converts the requirement of *instantaneous* matching of input/ output rates to a requirement for *average* matching, a point we pursue further in the following section, and it is necessary to monitor the pool contents to avoid adding data to a full buffer or taking them from an empty one, as shown in Figure 5.1. In either of these events it is necessary to inhibit the flow of data, and if the flow on either side is subject to external requirements,

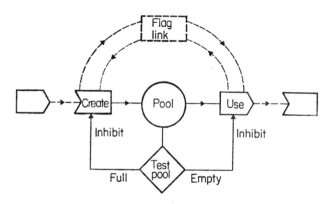

Figure 5.1   The buffer as a data pool in the create–use link

blocking that side will produce a pathological condition. Such a condition, which implies a system breakdown, is a result of either the pool not being large enough or a fundamental inconsistency in the prescription of the computing task.This subject of buffering is so important that we shall examine it more deeply with the aid of a simple mathematical model.

5.2   BUFFERS

There is a wide variety of problems, from domestic plumbing to electronic power supplies, in which it is necessary to compensate for the differential fluctuations between the input and output rates of a process. In the examples mentioned, one would employ a storage tank and a storage capacitor. In the on-line computer one employs a storage buffer. This buffer has in the past usually been a section of the core store of the computer, or for slower channels a section of the backing store, but increasingly it is also becoming feasible for it to be an external store dedicated to a particular channel.

Consider a digital process in which the source provides data at a fluctuating rate, ω_i [this may be represented functionally by an irregular train of impulses $\omega_i = \Sigma\, \delta(t - t_i)$] while the output demands data at a different fluctuating rate, ω_0. Then obviously a quantity of data, say s, must be stored, and

(5.1) $$\frac{ds}{dt} = \omega_i - \omega_0 \quad \text{or} \quad s = \int_0^t (\omega_i - \omega_0)\,dt$$

Obviously, s must be bounded—one cannot store a negative amount of data and there is not an unlimited amount of store available. Hence,

$$0 \le s \le \hat{s}, \text{ say}$$

Familiarity with continuity equations would lead us to expect the following result for average rates.

(5.2) $$\bar{\omega}_i - \bar{\omega}_0 = \underset{t\to\infty}{\text{Lt}} \left(\frac{1}{t}\int_0^t (\omega_i - \omega_0)\,dt\right) = \underset{t\to\infty}{\text{Lt}} \left(\frac{s}{t}\right) = 0$$

hence $\bar{\omega}_i = \bar{\omega}_0$.

Now, while the restrictions on ω_i and ω_0 may vary greatly from case to case, we must never forget this obvious fact, that *on average* they must be the same. Furthermore, the amount of their differential fluctuation is governed by:

(5.3) $$0 \le \int_0^t (\omega_i - \omega_0)\,dt \le \hat{s}$$

For an input process, ω_i would possibly be a constant sampling frequency ω_s, while ω_0 would depend on the time T, say, required for the intersample computation, interrupts from other channels, etc., which might vary up to some maximum delay $\hat{T}$, say. Thus the highest possible sampling speed is controlled by the average requirement that $\bar{\omega}_s \le \overline{T^{-1}}$, but it is also conditioned by the fluctuations of T and the size of the buffer, so that

(5.4) $$\int_0^t (\omega_s - T^{-1})\,dt \le \hat{s} \quad \text{for all } t$$

Now, T is to some extent a stochastic function of time, of which we have limited knowledge. One could play safe by making $\omega_s < (T)^{-1}$, if $\hat{T}$ could be determined, and this would correspond to the unbuffered mode. One of the reasons for buffering is the wide variation of T in a complex system which causes its maximum value to exceed greatly its average value.

Sometimes ω_i and/or ω_0 are not critical, so that input can be suspended if the buffer is full and/or output suspended if it is empty, so that the restriction implicit in equation 5.3 is preserved. Consider for example a simple peripheral, the tape reader. Tape information will be used in a variety of ways, so that the intervals between the requirements for consecutive symbols vary greatly. Hence in the unbuffered mode, the reader needs to be stopped to ensure that each character is dealt with by the computer and the reader would dominate the machine activity. In the buffered mode the worst that can happen is that the reader must stop each time the buffer is completely filled. The electronic computer being so many times faster than the mechanical reader, this would rarely occur while the need existed for the characters being input. Even with a relatively heavy load of input/output from other devices and consequent computation, it is unlikely that the reader would be held up. Furthermore, once a block of characters has been taken in for processing, the reader can carry on putting the next block in the buffer, so that when needed they are available from a high-speed rather than a low-speed source. In systems with backing store, slow character streams from sources like the reader would almost invariably be *spooled* onto the backing store so that they can be unspooled when required at the high rate appropriate to computer operation. Thus the backing store acts as a large subsidiary buffer, thereby greatly enhancing the efficiency of the system.

Undoubtedly, the only efficient way of organizing an on-line system is to provide each input/output channel with its own buffer, but there are several possible variations in buffer organization. An output buffer to a tape punch for instance would be made self-emptying as far as the user is concerned, so to output a character he simply requires to call a subroutine which inserts the character in the buffer, and he is not interested in the mechanism by which his action subsequently initiates the output transfers. The presence of such a mechanism is shown in Figure 5.1 in the form of the dotted path marked FLAG LINK, which may in fact take many forms depending on the machine organization. In a simple system the flag link might consist of the setting of a staticizer which initiates the output transfers, while in an advanced system it might mean the flagging of an independent program which unspools the data from backing store to the peripheral. A tape input buffer might only initiate transfers when the buffer is full, so input and output buffers have the contrasting quiescent conditions of full and empty. This can have practical consequences, such as the need to provide a length of blank tape at the end of a data tape so that the condition is satisfied by the provision of a buffer full of blank characters before the reader actually stops. Also at any stage in the program it is important to realize that the next block of characters to be operated on is probably in the buffer and not on the current portion of the tape.

This last remark leads us to observe that as with all things there are disadvantages in these techniques, and buffering, particularly when it is linked with *interupt mode* operations, as it invariably will be in on-line work, greatly complicates the debugging process by invalidating the simple procedure of stepping through the program by manual operation.

Two further variations of buffer technique which are worth discussing are the *dual buffer* and the *cyclic buffer*, which are shown in diagrammatic form in Figure 5.2. The dual buffer comprises two separate buffers, and at any stage

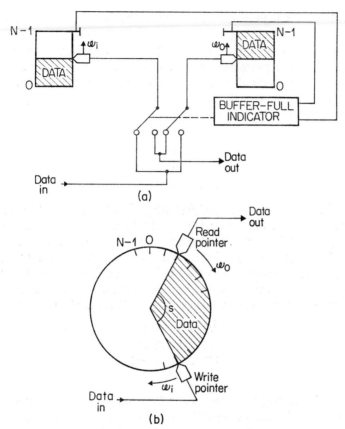

Figure 5.2   Two variations of buffer technique (a) the dual buffer (b) the cyclic
buffer

one is in the process of being filled while the other one is being emptied. When
these processes are completed the buffers exchange rôles. The reader who is
only familiar with off-line computing may at this stage be wondering how the
computer, contrary to his experience, appears to be doing two things at once.
The answer is in the powerful concept of *data interrupts* which we shall
shortly discuss. It will be evident that there is an inconsistency in the operation of the simple dual buffer system illustrated in Figure 5.2(a) for the case
where one of the data rates is critical, since the switching over process can
only occur when both pointers are at the end of the buffer. A solution would
be to allow the critical pointer to switch over before the other has completed
its passage, but this then becomes a variation of the cyclic buffer technique.

The cyclic buffer may be thought of in terms of a clock face with two hands,
one representing the *read pointer* and the other the *write pointer*. The quantity

of data stored s is represented by the angle between the hands, and the data rates ω_i and ω_0 by their angular velocities. The average and peak restrictions embodied in the simple mathematical model discussed earlier emerge as a single rule that the pointers are not allowed to pass each other, and $\hat{s}$ is represented by an angle of $2\pi(1 - N^{-1})$, where N is the buffer length.

How can we realize a cyclic data pointer? Very simply indeed, by modulo-N arithmetic. Consider the following lines of program:

$$V1 = V1 + 1$$
$$V1 = V1 \& 31$$
$$N2 = N1 + V1$$
$$VN2 = V2$$

N1 is the base address, the start of the buffer, and N2 is the cyclic data pointer. 31 represents the binary number 11111 so that the second order masks off the bottom five bits of V1, which can therefore never exceed 31 and must return to zero if incremented beyond this. We have thus made N2 a data pointer which causes the current value of V2 to be written into the cyclic buffer, so that the 33rd value overwrites the first, and so on. Obviously cyclic buffers of length 2^n are very convenient. Data read is similarly achieved,

$$V3 = V3 + 1$$
$$V3 = V3 \& 31$$
$$N3 = N1 + V3$$
$$V4 = VN3$$

and the cyclic pointer N3 causes a value from the buffer to be written into V4.

These pieces of program are still incomplete as we have yet to build in the mechanism which stops the pointers passing each other. The exact nature of such a pointer depends very much on the circumstances. We are obliged to provide some means by which the computer can temporize while the laggard pointer moves ahead, either by returning to the supervisor program, or another subroutine, or by going into a loop until there is some form of interrupt indicating that further data have been supplied or extracted. If one of the above sections exists in modified form as part of an *interrupt program* the pointers are automatically separated, in which case we could write something like

$$V1 = N2 - N1$$
$$V1 = V1 + 1$$
$$V1 = V1 \& 31$$
$$V1 = V1 + N1$$
$$[1] \rightarrow 1, V1 \neq V3 = 0$$
$$N2 = V1$$
$$VN2 = V2$$

where V3 represents the output data pointer which is made cyclic and checked by means of an interrupt program regulated by a *word count*, which is in turn conditioned by the relation between V3, N2 and the end of the buffer (these terms will be discussed in Section 5.4). Once V1 caught up with V3 the machine would loop until V3 was changed by interrupt. If neither pointer is part of an interrupt routine, then we have to provide alternative action by placing label [1] elsewhere, remembering always that there are circumstances in which the buffer-full or buffer-empty condition is pathological.

One of the most powerful uses of cyclic buffers is in the provision of delayed versions of data sequences, and they are useful as purely software entities for purposes such as the realization of recursive digital filters. As an extension of the above example, let us suppose that we require in V6 a version of the sequence appearing in V2 which is delayed by ten samples in addition to the undelayed sequence in V4. We merely require to modify the data read routine (omitting the pointer coincidence check for clarity):

$$V3 = V3 + 1$$
$$V5 = V3 - 10$$
$$V3 = V3 \ \& \ 31$$
$$V5 = V5 \ \& \ 31$$
$$N3 = N1 + V3$$
$$V4 = VN3$$
$$N3 = N1 + V5$$
$$V6 = VN3$$

Thus in addition to the data write pointer we have provided two data read pointers which are rigidly fixed together. This could be used for example for recursive smoothing by the running mean (see Section 6.7), but in general, ordinary digital filtering would require the equivalent of more read pointers closer together.

By their very nature buffers introduce delay into a system, and this delay is reduced in proportion to the speed of the computer, which is one of the reasons why we seek fast computers for on-line work. The existence of the delay is particularly important in closed-loop systems, where it has to be included in any considerations of stability.

5.3 DATA CORRUPTION

We have referred elsewhere to the general problem of corruption of data in the overall experiment, but it is particularly in the traversal of the software/ hardware boundary that this is likely to occur. At a minimum there is likely to be a problem of range compression, since it is rare for the effective word length to be the same on both sides of that boundary. It is commonly on output that the problem arises, since the computer word tends to be longer than the D–A converter word, though the analogous situation occurs at the input to the A–D converter where the excursions of the signal may exceed the full scale amplitude; so the input/output process tends to behave as a constriction in the signal pipeline. Now, there are two basic ways of getting objects through a constriction, squeezing them or chopping bits off. What we have to avoid is the loss of bits from the most significant end of the word since it would then lose all meaning (Figure 5.3).

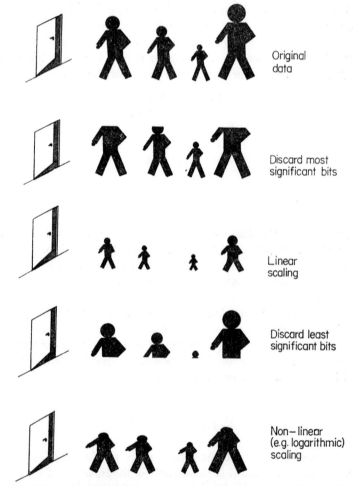

Figure 5.3   Ways of getting objects through a constriction, illustrating the various possibilities for data compression

It is important, however, to realize that there are some statistical types of calculation in which it is possible to make allowance for data which have been lost or *censored* even when these are the extremes. This facility is provided by the methods of *order statistics* in which *best linear unbiased estimators* are available for samples corrupted by censoring. Such estimators are valuable because many of the useful amplitude distributions (e.g. Gaussian) are theoretically unbounded and cannot therefore be treated practically without censoring.

Nevertheless, in general, loss of most significant bits represents a corruption of the data of a particularly severe form. It is far worse than, for example, limiting in an amplifier, which at least preserves some information about the signal amplitude and only produces a slope discontinuity in the output signal. This leaves us with three more acceptable choices of treatment for our data to get them through the constriction—discarding some least significant bits, linear scaling down and non-linear scaling. The first two are similar in effect since the excision of r least significant bits is equivalent to multiplying by 2^{-r} without rounding. The general form of scaling down corresponds to attenuation on the analogue side, while digitally it is multiplication by a fractional constant. The dominant form of non-linear scaling is the logarithmic one, and this is easily realized in both continuous and digital forms. In many applications logarithmic representation is a natural form of the data; it is quite common for the relative accuracy of the data to be more relevant and constant than the absolute accuracy.

The actual method of scaling used will depend on some prior knowledge of the data (or at least their amplitude distribution) and one of the constraints upon the design of a real-time procedure is that as a signal process it should be of known gain, or at least produce signal amplitude of known bound. An exception is the sort of process where data are acquired in real time but are output en bloc after acquisition in a form which allows scaling to be applied as an afterthought, e.g. through a digital plotter. In simultaneous input/output processes, however, the process gain is a very important factor, so digital filters for example tend to be synthetized to provide unity gain in the passband.

The translation of signals from the continuous form to the discrete form is inherently a non-linear corruption, but it is most conveniently treated in terms of a noise problem as we shall see in the following chapter. The reverse process, D–A conversion with zero order hold, is actually a linear one [it can be represented in terms of linear operators as $(1 - z^{-1})s^{-1}$, see Section 6.4]. The total corruption effected by these processes is relevant to the software–hardware interaction problem in that its severity is governed by the utilization of the available accuracy in the computer word. In particular, the sort of erroneous fixed point programming which causes loss of definition by allowing the numbers at an intermediate stage to become too small will cause the gross intervention of alien signal components which at worst might produce system instability. Similarly, some signal processes such as time differentiation can cause amplification of the corruption, and this again can lead to a situation where hardware and software stages work when tested independently but fail when interacting. Such situations are always more difficult in closed-loop systems.

Aliasing due to faulty choice of sampling conditions is also a potential source of trouble, which can produce most complex and unpredictable behaviour. This is a case in which the whole of the reasoning behind the software procedure design can be invalidated by the introduction of irrelevant signals through improper use of the hardware. It is, of course, easily avoidable if the constraints due to the sampling theorem are taken into account within the systematic approach to the measurement problem, but it is in the sudden ill-considered change of experimental tactics that such spurious effects can enter surreptitiously.

The actual hardware fault is also something which can be heavily disguised through interaction with the software. The commonest form, the loss of one of the bits in a channel unprotected by parity checks, can produce effects ranging from a slight noise increase to complete disruption of the information in the signal: but while it is easily recognized by examination of the acquired data, after even the simplest processing its origin is completely obscured. Checking the D–A converter is one of those habits of fault finding which are acquired the hard way after wasted hours of checking through programs and test rigs which appear to be faulty. In some cases, e.g. a scanning channel which serves several peripherals, it is found worth while to send across the interface test numbers (e.g. the integers 0 and -1) to check that all the bits are valid, and an individual test program is an important accessory to any peripheral.

Other forms of corruption, which have more of a software origin, may occur during interaction. Excessive and variable delay in a calculation loop may go undetected during the testing of a program by software, but in combination with the exigencies of hardware operation in real time it will cause the loss of data words, or, depending on the organization of the system, other faults ranging up to a complete stoppage.

The question of how important the loss of data is, be it in the form of bits or complete words, is relative to the processing being applied. Spectrally, it takes the form of leakage between the sinusoidal components of the signal, and since such leakage is generally present anyway, the fault may go unrecognized in spectral processing. In other cases the loss of one bit could invalidate the whole experiment, and it could conceivably be physically dangerous, though in such a case one would incorporate extra precautions. As a rather artificial but not impractical example imagine a computer being used to move a large mass at low frequency through a powerful actuator. The loss of one bit, say through failure of a gate in the parallel interface, would suddenly introduce high frequency components into the driving signal, which would in turn produce large and possibly destructive accelerations. An obvious precaution in such a case would be low-pass filtering of the output signal, which would also mitigate the effects of possible software errors.

5.4 INTERRUPTS

The most important development in computer techniques for on-line use is the concept of interruption. We shall speak of two kinds of interrupt to avoid the wider variation in terminology which occurs—*data interrupts* (also known as data breaks, cycle stealing, etc.) and *program interrupts*. They are alike in that they involve a temporary diversion of the computer from the task in hand.

The data interrupt involves suspension of the current program for one (or very few) clock cycles while a transfer takes place between the main store and an input/output channel. It requires no programmatic action and (providing critical timing has been avoided) interferes negligibly with the program execution—in fact the central processor is not cognisant of its occurrence. It provides a means of exchange of large amounts of data between peripheral and computer at great speed without interfering with the current activity. It is not self-sufficient and the occurrence of a group of such interrupts implies the subsequent occurrence of an interrupt of the other type.

The program interrupt involves suspension of the current program for several instruction times while a completely independent program is performed. It allows such facilities as informing the central processor of the presence of data previously supplied via data interrupts and asking for more data, warning of fault conditions, intervention by the user in the progress of a program, initiation of actions at intervals timed by a peripheral clock, etc.

There is a number of important operations that the *interrupt program* must encompass. It is entered by a link storing jump which occurs between instructions in the main program, and the *interrupt address* is specified by the contents of a store location which is permanently allocated to the particular channel which initiated the interrupt. Its first task is to set a staticizer which blocks all further interrupts from other channels until certain important actions have been carried out. It is very important not to abuse this facility, so the staticizer must be reset to allow further interrupts at the earliest possible stage in the interrupt program. Next it is necessary to store the contents of any registers which will be used, and therefore corrupted, by the interrupt program. Then the reason for the interrupt must be ascertained, usually by inspection of the contents of a *status word* sent across the standard interface from the peripheral controller, following which the appropriate action can be initiated in the main body of the interrupt program. Penultimately the original contents of the registers are restored, and the final instruction is a return-to-link jump which re-activates the original program at the point at which it was interrupted.

Interrupts of both kinds require careful setting up instructions before they are allowed to occur. Data interrupts require a *data pointer* to be set to the address which is the source or destination of the first word, and a *word count* to be set equal to the negative of the number of data words to be transferred. These can both be incremented by unity each time a data interrupt occurs, in which case when the word count reaches zero a program interrupt occurs to permit the data to be used and the channel to be reset. The program interrupt requires the interrupt address to be set up, i.e. the start address of the interrupt program to be put in the place where the hardware expects to find it.

There are variations in the means of handling *multiple interrupts* [CoOrgFlo], which are bound to occur in a laboratory system of any complexity, but the method most suitable to our application, because of the wide variation of peripheral requirements, is one in which interrupts can occur within interrupt programs on a strict priority basis. Such a system of nested interrupts minimizes the delay that any channel may cause to one of higher priority.

Figure 5.4 shows a combination of data and program interrupts which might occur if one channel were in operation during the running of a main program. Data are transferred by data interrupts which occur during the execution of the instructions of the main program. In this case a program interrupt occurs because the word count has reached zero. The interrupt program takes appropriate action to ensure that the data are used (or more created for an output channel) and resets the word count for more data. Note that data interrupts from all other channels could occur during the instructions of the interrupt program, and that program interrupts from *higher priority* channels may be allowed to occur after the unblocking operation.

Obviously program interrupts are somewhat disruptive, and as much channel activity as possible is carried out by means of data interrupts. For the same reason, interrupt programs are made as short as possible, and this applies especially to those parts for which further interrupts are blocked. The idea of buffering is very closely associated with the idea of data interrupts, since the incrementing of the data pointer means that the data are effectively being loaded into or out of a buffer area whose size is determined by the setting of the word count.

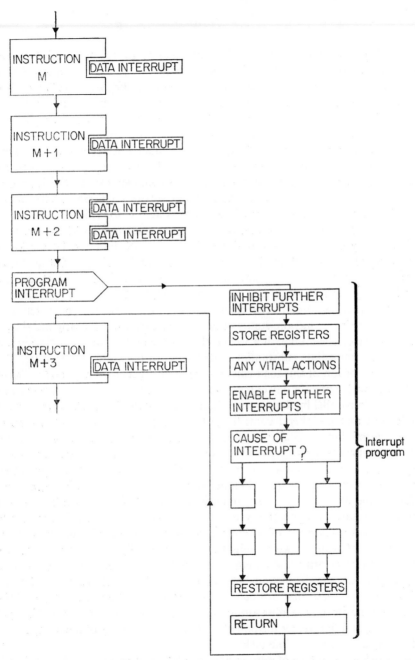

Figure 5.4 A sequence of interrupts from a peripheral in the course of a main program

5.5   AUTONOMY

The ideas we have discussed so far—modular software, buffers, interrupts, peripheral controllers, etc.—all contribute to the concept of autonomous operation of peripherals, and a good measure of the effectiveness of an on-line system in a complex environment is the degree to which the main program can *delegate* tasks rather than *control* them (a remark which applies equally to human organizations). The crucial element in this autonomous operation is the hardware organization of the computer interrupt system, and though deficiencies of hardware can be compensated by extra software, such an arrangement would carry considerable time penalties due to the increased processor loading, which is characteristic of software solutions. This is one of the reasons why the choice of computer system is so critical.

Typically, when writing an on-line program one would wish to say to a channel, by means of a subroutine call, 'Acquire N data and let me know when you have done it' or 'Dispose of these N data' or simply 'Let me know if at any stage you have any data which require processing.' It is not relevant to the program how these data would be timed, be it by manual pushbutton or high speed A–D converter clock, and even a controlling computer real-time clock simply has the status of another channel, but the original simple subroutine call will unleash a welter of software and hardware action which makes an immediate substantial contribution to the computer loading. The software portion of this load can only be handled sequentially, as this is the mode in which present day computers work, but the hardware portion can be handled in parallel by the separate channel hardware circuits. This is why the interrupt and peripheral control mechanisms play such a decisive part in pre-determining the efficiency of an on-line system; so, while any two computers can carry out any given task, one may perform it more efficiently and quickly than another, and this may not be indicated by the usual published performance figures, such as add time. The only ways of comparing computers for on-line work is in the performance of on-line tasks, and while one does not often have an opportunity to make such comparisons, it is possible to make some assessment of where the software–hardware boundary occurs. Examples of features which might lie on either side of the boundary are word count; priority assessment; data pointer increment; identification of type of interrupt; distinction between control, data and status words; etc. The more of these that are accommodated within the specification of the machine hardware, the more autonomous is the operation of the input/output channels, and the greater the potential speed and efficiency of the computer in tackling a complex on-line task.

A further advantage of autonomous operation of peripherals is the simplification of program organization that it permits. Besides easing the load of the programmer, the reduction in number of instructions required for a specific task means a saving of storage space and execution time. The only possible disadvantage is the potential loss of versatility that, as we observe elsewhere, is characteristic of the hardware as opposed to software solution of problems, but for our application it is negligible in comparison with the advantages.

The most significant benefit offered by peripheral autonomy is thus the increase in capability of the computing system, i.e. the ability to deal with more data from a wider variety of sources. The benefit most immediately noticed by the user, however, is the easing of the programming task, especially when this concerns the treatment of an unpredictable sequence of demands for data processing. The onus, of course, remains upon the programmer to utilize whatever system the hardware manufacturer presents him with in a sensible way, mainly by efficient communication within the programs by means of *flags*, etc., and it is very easy to throw away the potential advantages of a system. The idea of making the best of a system is worth discussing further in general terms.

5.6 MAKING THE MOST OF A COMPUTER'S FACILITIES

Having plumped for a particular computing system, the essential thing is to immerse oneself in the philosophy concomitant with that system. It is fatal for the laboratory worker to be a Jack of all computers and master of none. It is particularly when changing from one system to another that an immense effort of will is required. A factor very easily underestimated is the degree to which one's attitude to programming is imprinted with the behaviour imposed by experience of a particular machine. We have found in the training of students to use a multiple-address machine effectively that the task is easier with students of no previous experience than it is with those who have had extensive experience with single-address machines.

The optimum program for a particular task on a particular machine can only be realized through consciousness of the *whole* repertoire of instructions, their mode of execution and their relative merits. For two different machines optimum programs for the same task may be totally different in conception and construction. The existence of a special feature in the repertoire, or the provision for rapid execution of a particular type of order, will distort the distribution of frequencies of occurrence of all instruction types so as to favour the occurrence of such features. To quote an earlier example, in a machine with a fast-shift facility, this would be used for many applications, including multiplication by powers of two. If in contrast, fast multiplication hardware were provided, the shift order would be realized as multiplication by a power of two and would tend to disappear as a separate entity.

Furthermore, such considerations extend beyond the superficial intentions in the provision for various types of instruction. For example, suppose that double-length arithmetic were provided as a hardware facility. This would still be utilized even though one were only involved with single length numbers. Thus, a store area for single length numbers could be zeroed more rapidly by treating them in pairs and using a double length assignment order, and similarly numbers could be fetched out of store more rapidly in pairs by the appropriate double length instruction. Attention to such possibilities results in a reduction of the length of stored program and an increase in speed of execution, but because of the indirectness of the procedure careful annotation of the programs is essential.

The existence of certain hardware facilities will condition the whole approach to a problem. For example, floating point arithmetic would be avoided in most real-time programs if it were realized by software, but should it be included as a fast hardware facility it would immediately become a favoured form. The provision of bit-handling instructions (i.e. setting and resetting particular bits of words, and also using them as jump conditions) will completely alter the conception of a real-time program and greatly enhance its speed and economy.

The software provided with a machine is also an important, if secondary, part of its make-up in this context. The contents of the library of standard subroutines will have a great influence on the way any particular job is tackled, and it is important for the programmer to be aware of them. If a high-level compiler capable of *efficiently* coding real-time programs is available (e.g. CORAL), then it may be worth while to conceive the program in high-level terms, though a compiler can never match a good programmer. An even more valuable alternative is the compiler which allows critical segments to be included in assembler form (critical segments would be such things as inner loops and input/output subroutines).

Above all, it is the hardware–software interaction which is most critically conditioned by the nature of the particular machine involved, and in on-line work the organization of the whole program will be founded (or will founder) on this aspect. Again, consciousness of the whole repertoire is the chief ingredient of efficient use of the machine. This means having full knowledge of what hardware staticizers can be set by program, making full use of automatic increment of word count and data pointer, maximum exploitation of data-interrupt facilities combined with a conservative approach to program interruption, etc. For any optimum way of performing a task there will be dozens of less efficient ones, and on the whole those will tend to be the ones which substitute software action for a facility which is implicit in the hardware.

There can be a slight complication in the identification of the optimum method. Often, it is sufficient for it to be the best *on average*, but in some critical applications it may be necessary to aim for the best solution in the *worst case* of accidental circumstances. The latter case might occur, for example, in a closed-loop system where one instance of an excessive computation delay might invalidate the whole operation, and one might then be prepared to accept an increase in the average delay to pay for a reduction in the scatter of delays. The supreme example is the input/output buffer which in a multiple-interrupt system smooths out the variations in delay at the expense of an increase in the average delay. The minimization of this average delay will depend not only on the efficiency with which the directly relevant loop is programmed, but also on the depradations due to any interrupting programs which happen to be active. There is thus an inescapable mutual interaction of coexistent programs, including supervisors, and the need for good programming using all the tricks of the trade peculiar to the particular machine is ever present. Of course, any experiment which requires maximum operating speed will need sole occupancy of the machine for its program.

5.7   HOUSEKEEPING

Housekeeping is a very useful jargon word with important implications in both the internal hardware organization of the computer and the organization of the user's software. It is a factor which is often disregarded in the assessment of the potential speed of a system, and which tends to result in a somewhat painful re-appraisal. It is also one of those features which present a choice between software and hardware solutions, and the computer manufacturer is able to bestow considerable benefits by including as much of it as possible in the hardware design. Housekeeping, by analogy with those domestic chores which burden the lives of all but the most affluent of us, covers those tasks which, while not being directly part of the job in hand, are implied by and essential to its proper execution.

Consider, for example, the simple process of acquiring a block of data. Housekeeping operations have to be performed both before and after the acquisition, but it is the ones that have to be performed *during* it that are important since they impose a significant overhead which affects the maximum speed of acquisition. There are three essential operations—*increment the data pointer, increment the word count* and *check the word count.*

Now it is quite possible to perform these tasks by software instructions using program interrupts, but this would be very cumbersome for any but the slowest channels, such as the teletype. More commonly they would be accomplished by automatic hardware options which form part of the data interrupt cycle and are not at the disposal of the programmer. In this case the housekeeping duties of the programmer would lie mainly in the setting up stage of the acquisition process, and would consist of setting the initial values of the data pointer and the word count. Note that these values may be obtained indirectly by calculation, as for example in a cyclic buffer where the number of words to be acquired by data interrupts alone is determined by either the value of the read pointer or the address of the end of the buffer, whichever is less.

The concept of housekeeping goes right through the art of programming, and neglect of its duties is the most frequent cause of errors, because it covers the more indirect and easily forgotten tasks. The prime example is the common error of forgetting to zero a location which is to be used for accumulating data by addition. The setting up process requires particular care in on-line work, as, unlike off-line programs, the subsequent action is often executed by hardware and may not appear explicitly in terms of program instructions. However, the subsequent 'tidying up' housekeeping is also important, and in the case of the block acquisition it is mainly carried out in the interrupt program. The essential features of this part are checking the validity of the data and ensuring that the procedures which make use of them are initiated.

In advanced operating systems with backing store the housekeeping activities are quite extensive. Files must be allocated and maintained, programs must be dealt with in turn on a queuing basis, but with due regard to priority, and the surrendered store areas tidied up for re-allocation, etc. But housekeeping is also an essential part of even a simple program, and it represents a significant proportion of the overall computing load. One of the most important concepts in on-line computing which comes within the housekeeping orbit is *priority* assessment, and it merits further discussion.

5.8 PRIORITY

The variations between the potential speeds of the peripherals connected to a computer are enormous, and consequently the degrees of urgency with which it should respond to them are also widely different. As we have observed in Chapter 3, the *interrupter* in an on-line computer is just as important as the central processor, and one of the reasons for this is its rôle in dealing efficaciously with the various demands of the peripherals through their controllers. *Priority* is a most important concept in this context, and it is essential that, for example, a high speed disc store is not kept waiting while a keyboard is being serviced. In some systems priority assessment is covered by software routines, but while this has the usual advantage of versatility it also has the usual disadvantage of slowness. Hardware priority assessment has the advantage of speed, which makes it applicable to both kinds of interrupts, and for modern laboratory applications it is an essential feature.

When the *assessment* of priority during interrupt operation is automatically performed by the hardware, the *allocation* of priority, which is a human prerogative, must be undertaken with great care. It is not simply a question of relative speeds. Consider, for example, the *transient recorder*, which we discuss elsewhere, in comparison with a conventional A–D converter, and let us say that the former has a maximum sampling speed of 100 MHz while the latter has a maximum sampling speed of 100 kHz. In this case it is the slower device which requires higher priority since it does not possess the advantage of the other of having its own internal hardware buffer store. A computer-controlled high-voltage supply is a very slow device, which would be right at the bottom of the priority hierarchy were it not for the fact that it is required to react quickly to an alarm condition. Thus the arguments leading to the establishment of the priority structure can be quite subtle, and may include peculiar local considerations (see for example Section 9.2).

Priority becomes important as soon as the system is concerned with multiperipheral operation, and as the system grows the next stage at which it is important is when multiprogramming is instituted. In this case the priority decision is essentially a software one delegated to the supervisor, and the program priority arrangements are in a continual state of flux as various programs are entered and withdrawn. New computer designs are increasingly recognizing the multiprogram role of central processors, which means that more hardware support is becoming available to speed up these processes. In the laboratory, however, by far the most important aspect of priority is the one concerning the input/output channels, and as it is the more difficult and important measurements which tend to push the computer to its limits of performance, it is essential that the inclusion of other desirable, but less important facilities (such as the handling of unsolicited keyboard messages) does not in any way degrade this performance. Of course, priority assessment itself is a form of housekeeping with a corresponding overhead of processing time, but the only faster alternative would be restricted single channel operation.

Chapter VI

Mainly Mathematical

The mathematical background to on-line computing includes most of the material relevant to off-line computing [CoMeLaFa, NuMeHam] *plus* certain other aspects. The most important of these are *control, signal processing, and the identification and modelling of systems.* Each of these has been developing as a study over a number of years. Control, in particular, has produced a vast literature and has become something of a speciality. It is greatly enhanced by the availability of on-line computing but not essentially changed, and since laboratory problems in this field tend to be comparatively straightforward we shall omit reference to its more advanced aspects in favour of more urgent topics. Signal processing, on the other hand, has been greatly enhanced but also greatly changed by on-line methods, and its theory provides some of the most important tools of the trade, so we shall examine this topic more closely. The identification and modelling of systems have tended to reside in the camp of the control theorist, but it also represents a powerful approach to physical measurements whose benefits have hardly been tapped. A significant proportion of laboratory measurements is directed towards evaluating the response of a physical sample and determining the origins of the response, which is precisely the rôle of system identification techniques.

6.2 SIGNAL PROCESSING

The term *signal* is generally taken to mean any quantity which can be represented as a function of time (though the methods of signal processing can often be applied effectively to functions of other variables) and it is usually considered to convey information. The signal function should be single-valued, but it may be either continuous or discontinuous. Examples of

136

signals are—The Financial Times Ordinary Share Index; EEG potential; air temperature; orientation of the eye; traffic passing a monitoring point; pH of a solution in a chemical process plant, etc.

Signals are conveniently classified in various ways (e.g. whether they are continuous or discrete, bounded or unbounded, random or deterministic) and there are further possible subdivisions (e.g. deterministic signals may be periodic or unperiodic while random signals may be stationary or non-stationary, etc.). These classifications tend, however, to be chiefly conceptual and therefore rather variable. Thus, for example, a television signal from a static scene could be argued to be determined, but the determination is so complex that a random approach to it would be much more fruitful. Indeed, since a wholly determined signal essentially conveys no information, it is of restricted value, and the probabilistic approach to signals has proved to be the most powerful [ProPap].

Signal processing is the treatment of signals to produce further signals or functions or numbers which epitomize that aspect of the information content of the signals sought. The availability of digital methods has produced two distinct types of processing. The first type is the *simultaneous input/output* operation in which the rates of data entering and leaving are, like water in a hosepipe, equal at a given time. The second is the *total storage* type in which all the data are acquired before output commences, as with a watering can. The prime examples of the two types of processes are, respectively, *digital filtering* and *fast Fourier transformation*.

Before the digital era, signal processing was based almost wholly on the application of *continuous linear* devices, such as resistors, capacitors, inductors, amplifiers and delay lines. These were assembled to form linear systems which were designed to give the closest possible approximation to a desired form of behaviour. For reasons we discuss below the design procedure was rarely carried out in the *time domain*, and the *complex frequency domain* was of considerable importance. The behaviour of systems could be reduced to ratios of polynomials in complex frequency, and, since a polynomial can be completely represented in terms of its roots, *poles* and *zeros* become important entities for the characterization and design of systems.

A linear system is one which is additive and homogeneous. Thus if a system produces output y_1 from input signal x_1 and output y_2 from input signal x_2, it is linear if for any constant a and any signals x_1 and x_2 it produces output $(y_1 + ay_2)$ from input $(x_1 + ax_2)$. No real system is totally linear, but within a certain range of signal magnitudes it can be very nearly so. Digital signal processing is based on the use of non-linear devices such as magnetic cores, saturating amplifiers, etc., which are assembled to form systems capable of quasi-linear operation in that they are additive and homogeneous *within certain quantization approximations*. We should remark however that recently non-linear processing has begun to emerge as an important technique, and the previous emphasis on linearity probably arises from the existence of a powerful linear algebra [LinAlgMir] which has no non-linear counterpart of equal generality.

The essential operation of a linear system is represented in mathematical form by the operation of superposition convolution [ProPap], which for a causal system relates output $y(t)$ to input $x(t)$ by means of an integral operation represented by $*$,

$$(6.1) \quad y(t) = \int_0^\infty x(t - \tau)h(\tau)\, d\tau = \int_{-\infty}^t x(\tau)h(t - \tau)\, d\tau = x(t) * h(t)$$

Here τ is a dummy variable and $h(t)$ is the impulse response of the system, since $\delta(t) * h(t) = h(t)$. The operation is actually easier to understand in the discrete form necessary for digital realization, since it follows from the definition of linearity

$$(6.2) \qquad y(nT) = \sum_{m=0}^n x(nT - mT)h(mT)$$

$$= \sum_{m=0}^n x(mT)h(nT - mT) = x(nT) * h(nT)$$

Here m is the dummy variable, T is a sampling interval and $h(nT)$ is the unit-pulse response [DiSiGoRa], which unlike $h(t)$ is dimensionless. Any reader to whom this operation is not thoroughly familiar is advised to investigate it further by examining graphically the process of reversal and summation involved.

6.3   THE THREE DOMAINS OF SIGNAL PROCESSING

As we have seen, both signals and system responses can be conveniently mapped as mathematical functions of time, but there is of course another mapping which is in many ways more convenient, i.e. as a function of frequency. It is important to realize that these are two different ways of looking at the same entity. Neither form *is* the signal, but each is a representation of it. Furthermore we can proceed from one form to the other directly via the Fourier transform and its inverse:

$$(6.3) \qquad X(\omega) = \mathscr{F}[x(t)] = \int_{-\infty}^{+\infty} x(t) \exp(-j\omega t)\, dt$$

$$(6.4) \qquad x(t) = \mathscr{F}^{-1}[X(\omega)] = \frac{1}{2\pi} \int_{-\infty}^{+\infty} X(\omega) \exp(j\omega t)\, d\omega$$

The main reasons for adopting the ω domain are that convolution is simplified, filtering is generally more understandable and applicable, in linear systems a component at one frequency cannot interact with any other frequency (this is not true in time), and other advantages accrue from the mathematical fact that the sinusoidal functions form an *orthogonal basis*.

In the Laplace transform, the Fourier transform is extended into the complex domain, by the inclusion of a convergence factor σ to yield a complex frequency $s = \sigma + j\omega$. Three basic reasons for this are

1 to overcome certain convergence problems, thereby including, for example, the step function
2 to remove a separation between the treatments of natural and forced responses
3 to take advantage of the complex frequency plane as a vehicle for the analysis and synthesis of systems.

The Laplace transformation can be defined in terms of the Fourier transform by

(6.5) $X(s) = \mathscr{L}[x(t)] = \mathscr{F}[\exp(-\sigma t)x(t)]$ where $s = \sigma + j\omega$

but note that there is a restricted domain of convergence [FouBra, WidLap] and the half range $[0, \infty]$ integral form is usually used. With regard to convolution, it is easy to show by application of the transform definitions (equations 6.4 and 6.5) that equation 6.1 is transformed to

(6.6) $Y(\omega) = H(\omega)X(\omega)$

(6.7) $Y(s) = H(s)X(s)$

so that the operation becomes a simple multiplication of functions. Figure 6.1 illustrates the position of the two transforms as links between the time and frequency domains.

In digital signal processing we have to consider a third domain which is peculiar to discrete-time systems and provides a most powerful tool in synthesis and analysis. The z transform is in fact no more than the sampled version of the Laplace transform, but it transpires that the transformation between the time and z domains is particularly easy.

First let us consider the sampling functions for unit sampling period $ш(t)$ or $\alpha(t)$ [FouBra, ZTraHelm] which are defined by

(6.8) $ш(t) = \dfrac{d\alpha(t)}{dt} = \displaystyle\sum_{n=-\infty}^{n=+\infty} \delta(t - n);$ $n = \ldots -2, -1, 0, +1, +2, \ldots$
$$\alpha(0) = 0$$

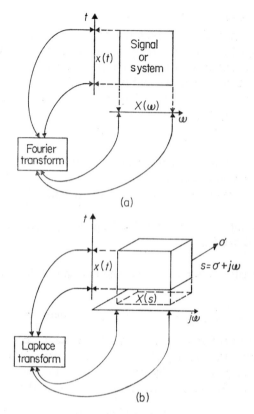

Figure 6.1 (a) the Fourier and (b) the Laplace transform as links between the time and (complex) frequency domain representations of a signal or system

where δ is the unit impulse function; both are shown in Figure 6.2. ɯ (t) is consistent with the more common treatment of sampling through the properties of the impulse function $\delta(t)$, but $\alpha(t)$ has the advantage that it can be used in the Stieltjes integral form which is powerful for discontinuous functions and has the property that it demonstrates the convergence of continuous and sampled forms. A signal $x(t)$ sampled at intervals T apart may be represented by the product $x(t)\,ɯ(t/T)$, but this form only has meaning within an integral. Thus the Laplace transform is represented by

$$(6.9) \qquad X(s) = \int_{-\infty}^{+\infty} x(t)\,ɯ\left(\frac{t}{T}\right) \exp\left(-st\right) \mathrm{d}t = \int_{-\infty}^{+\infty} x(t) \exp\left(-st\right) \mathrm{d}\alpha\left(\frac{t}{T}\right)$$

Note that the latter (Stieltjes) form is characteristically converted to the

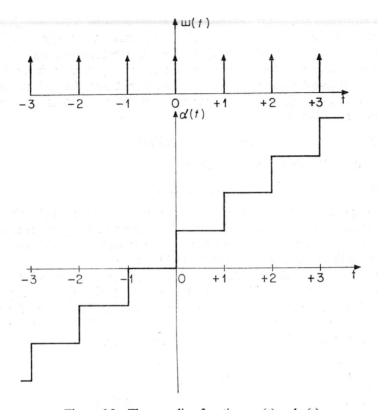

Figure 6.2   The sampling functions ɯ(t) and α(t)

continuous form by the substitution of t for α. The integral is reduced by the sampling property of δ to

$$(6.10) \qquad X(s) = \sum_{-\infty}^{+\infty} x(nT) \exp(-snt)$$

and the defining substitution $z = \exp(sT)$ is made to give

$$(6.11) \qquad X(z) = \sum_{-\infty}^{+\infty} x(nT)z^{-n}$$

The transform of the response of a causal system is given by

$$(6.12) \qquad H(z) = \sum_{n=0}^{\infty} h(nT)z^{-n}$$

Thus all signals and linear systems can be represented by polynominals in z, and the transformation is simply achieved by setting the coefficient of z^{-r} equal to the rth sample ordinate of the signal or response function.

Another feature of the z domain which offers simplification is the form taken by the shift theorem. In Laplace transform terms, the shift theorem, which arises directly from the definition (equation 6.5) tells us that if $y(t) = x(t - rT)$ then

$$(6.13) \qquad\qquad Y(s) = \exp\left(-srT\right)X(s)$$

and in the z domain this becomes simply

$$(6.14) \qquad\qquad Y(z) = z^{-r}X(z)$$

so the operation 'delay r sample-times' is represented by multiplication by z^{-r}. Hence each term of the polynomial in equation 6.12 represents a combined delay and weighting operation, which is consistent with the rôle played by the function h in convolution with a signal.

The operation of *deconvolution* is rather inaccessible in the time domain since it demands the solution of an integral equation, but it is relatively simple in the z domain. We shall examine the important linear operations of differentiation and integration later, but at this stage we tabulate the mappings of the important operations between the three domains.

t	ω	z
Addition	Addition	Addition
Multiplication by a constant	Multiplication by a constant	Multiplication by a constant
Convolution	Function multiplication	Polynominal multiplication
Deconvolution	Function division	Polynominal division

The first two lines of the table tell us that the mappings are linear. The last two lines show that the unravelling as well as the ravelling of signals with system functions is feasible in digital form.

The mapping between the z and s domains is embodied in the defining substitution $z = \exp(sT)$, and it is rather important to understand its implications, which are summarized in Figure 6.3. The important features to note from this figure are

  The ω axis is mapped into the unit circle;
  ω is naturally expressed as a fraction of the sampling frequency $\omega_s = 2\pi/T$;
  The left hand half plane (of stable poles) is mapped to the inside of the unit circle;

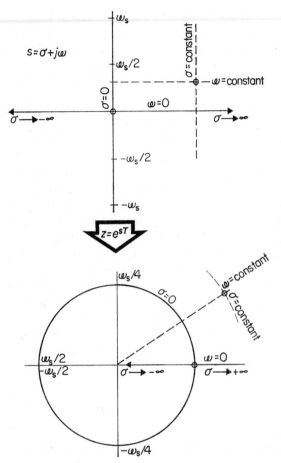

Figure 6.3 The z transform mapping

The mapping from s to z is many-to-one;

The mapping is unique only if all $\omega \leq \omega_s/2$;

Any $\omega > \omega_s/2$ has an indistinguishable *alias* in the range $0 \leq \omega \leq \omega_s/2$;

$\exp[\sigma T]$ and ωT become respectively the magnitude and angle of z.

6.4 INPUT

As with any electronic system the stage of input to a digital system is the most critical, since it affects all subsequent stages, but in the digital case we have an extra process of conversion to contend with, and this gives us a slightly more complicated noise situation. Furthermore, the very process of sampling, which is fundamental to a digital method, imposes its own restrictions, as we have seen in our brief glimpse at the z transform. It therefore behoves us to consider the theoretical background to the input stage more fully. In particular, we must examine the concept of noise, especially in relation to the fundamental processes of quantization and sampling, and also expand our discussion of the theoretical implications of the sampling process.

For a computer dealing with analogue signals it is important to distinguish between the input and output stages in respect of their defects as signal processes. A–D conversion is *essentially* non-linear because the quantization prevents it from being additive or homogeneous (in other words the exact result of adding two signals or multiplying by a constant will be dependent upon whether it is performed before or after conversion). Non-linearity is difficult to deal with, and we actually tackle the problem of analysing A–D conversion in an indirect way by treating it as a noise problem.

D–A conversion, on the other hand, is essentially a linear process: so, apart from actual component defects, in a system consisting of an A–D converter followed by a D–A converter all the damage is done by the former. There is, of course, a further consideration in D–A conversion; the question of *hold* (i.e. the interpolation necessary to produce or restore a continuous signal from a discrete one). The simplest form is zero order hold, in which the output signal is set at the value of the last sample until the new sample arrives. As one might expect, this process can be represented in terms of a mixture of discrete and continuous operators,

i.e.
$$(1 - z^{-1}) \cdot \frac{1}{s}$$

Here s is the normal Laplace operator and z^{-1} is the discrete operator meaning delay by one sample. Note that though $z = \exp(sT)$, the above has not precisely the same implication as $[1 - \exp(-sT)](1/s)$ which is a continuous operation representing the transform of the block function $b(t) = U(t) - U(t - T)$. Both parts of the above operation are, however, linear.

There is a very important lesson here which must not be forgotten. The most damning part of the whole operation occurs at the point where the signal enters the computer system. Obviously the implication of this, and the precise meaning of the operations used in its description, require further study.

6.4.1   NOISE

The definition of noise is rather subjective, in that the meaning of the word depends on the intentions of its user. Similarly used is the word *weed*—a rose by any other name is a weed in a bed of carrots. Thus noise is strictly any *unwanted* signal. *Random* noise is an important special case, and it is perhaps unfortunate that the adjective is often dropped in the literature so that we are left to assume it. The important property of random noise is that it is uncorrelated. So the cross-correlation of a noise signal $n(t)$ with another signal $s(t)$ is zero, i.e. the average $\overline{n(t)s(t)}$ is zero (or more strictly $\bar{n}.\bar{s}$). $s(t)$ can be any signal other than $n(t)$, it could be $n(t + \tau)$ for example. Total uncorrelation is never found in practice as it requires infinite bandwidth, so there is always a value of the constant τ below which the autocorrelation $\overline{n(t)n(t + \tau)}$ is always positive. This limiting value of τ is of the order of the reciprocal of the highest frequency present. As we shall see later in this chapter, it is this very property of absence of correlation which enables us, under certain restricted conditions, to eliminate the random element from a measurement.

It is important to distinguish between noise which is present in the signal as received by our system and noise which is *inevitably* introduced by our processing.

The former is largely outside our control, and it is only in particular circumstances where there is redundancy of information in the signal, for example where it is repeated many times or we have prior knowledge of its form or time of incidence, that we can take steps to eliminate the noise component. The latter is to a large extent disposable, down to a lower limit characteristic of the equipment used, but without care it can under certain conditions assume a dominating magnitude.

Of course, the conventional sources of noise, such as thermal agitation, shot-effect, interference, non-linearity, etc., can be of great importance and must be fully understood, but we are constrained by considerations of space to treat only those sources peculiar to on-line computing.

6.4.2 TRUNCATION AND ROUNDING NOISE

In texts dealing with mathematical computing [e.g. CoMeLaFa] we find these terms referred to as truncation and round-off *errors*, and they can be exceedingly important, especially in such applications as the numerical solution of differential equations. The substitution of the term *noise* for *errors* is an important clue to the basic difference of philosophy in on-line, real-time computing. For here all our variables are treated as *signals*, i.e. varying currents or voltages etc., which can be treated in their convenient mapping as *functions* of time. The difference can be illustrated by considering a simple mathematical statement

$$y = a \sin(\omega t)$$

A mathematical programmer will write in FORTRAN

$$Y = A * SIN(WT)$$

being aware that the computer will probably calculate SIN(WT) as a series in terms of the variable (WT) and as the summation must stop somewhere it will be in error by an amount, say ε_t, which represents the negative sum of the remaining infinite sequence of terms; thus actually SIN(WT) $= \sin(\omega t) + \varepsilon_t$. Also the process of multiplication will produce an error term ε_r since the product will essentially occupy a double-length word which has to be rounded to single length to be accommodated by the computer register, hence a good programmer will continually bear in mind that the calculated value Y will be related to the ideal value y by $Y = y + \varepsilon_r + \varepsilon_t$, second order errors being neglected. Normally these terms can be safely ignored, but if for example, later in the calculation, we wish to find the difference between this value of Y and one calculated for a slightly different value of ωt, the error terms would become larger than the result.

The real-time programmer must always be aware of these and further sources of noise. In his case the variable t is related to time in the real world (albeit a temporarily frozen version to allow time for the calculation to be made), so that he could, for example, route the result y through a D–A converter to observe on an oscilloscope that his result is $y(t) = \sin(\omega t) + n_r(t) + n_t(t)$, where ε_r and ε_t have now been replaced by random functions of time, $n_r(t)$ and $n_t(t)$. Indeed, these noise components may well be obscured by further error signals more peculiar to the on-line technique, which we must now discuss.

6.4.3 SAMPLING AND QUANTIZATION

These processes, which are fundamental to on-line computing, must also be considered as sources of noise. They are illustrated in exaggerated form in Figure 6.4. Consider an original source signal $f_1(t)$ upon which we have to perform some digital operation. In order to do this we must sample the signal at regular intervals which are widely spaced enough to allow our longest sequence of calculations to be sandwiched between two samples. Thus the sampled form $f_2(t)$ consists essentially of a series of discrete points, coincident with $f_1(t)$ at the sampling instances. Obviously such a form is useless in the real world, so if we wish to observe the sampled signal on an oscilloscope we must do something about the amplitudes between samples. Having discarded this information in the original signal we must therefore make some reasonable assumption. Usually one assumes that the signal remains constant between samples and applies the mechanism known as zero order hold to achieve this, producing the result $f_3(t)$.

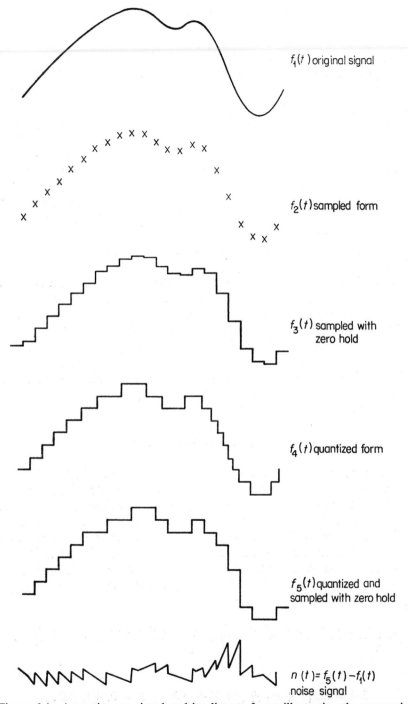

$f_1(t)$ original signal

$f_2(t)$ sampled form

$f_3(t)$ sampled with zero hold

$f_4(t)$ quantized form

$f_5(t)$ quantized and sampled with zero hold

$n(t) = f_5(t) - f_1(t)$ noise signal

Figure 6.4 A continuous signal and its discrete forms illustrating the conversion of the non-linearity problem to one of additive noise

Even without sampling problems, the digitizing of the signal must produce some distortion because the A–D converter must have a finite number of stages, so increments smaller than that represented by the least significant bit cannot be accommodated, and the signal must be *quantized* in steps of this magnitude, producing version $f_4(t)$.

In practice, both these effects must occur together giving the final form $f_5(t)$. Now one way of looking at this problem is to consider $f_5(t)$ as a non-linearly distorted version of $f_1(t)$, but a much simpler way is to imagine that $f_5(t)$ has been produced by adding a certain signal to $f_1(t)$. This signal $n(t) = f_5(t) - f_1(t)$ is shown at the foot of Figure 6.4. Thus, in effect, the input process has added a noise signal of wide bandwidth to the original source signal. Obviously, such noise is minimized by making the quantization interval small compared with the expected signal amplitude, and the sampling frequency large compared with the highest frequency present in the signal.

It should be evident from inspection of the noise waveform $n(t)$ that it covers a wide spectrum. Indeed, in most analyses of such noise in digital processes it is assumed to be totally uncorrelated (white). Awareness of the existence of such spurious components throughout the relevant spectrum is important, especially as all digital processes have frequency-domain implications, and some common ones, as we shall see, cause significant amplification of part of the spectrum. It is quite possible for noise which is negligible at one stage of a process to be dominant at a later stage.

6.5 The sampling theorem

We have already seen that the sampling theorem arises directly from the many-to-one nature of the mapping from s domain to z domain. In order to emphasize the result we shall now derive it by means of a simple trigonometrical manipulation. What we wish to ascertain are the precise conditions under which two sinusoids of different frequency and phase produce the same result when sampled at a certain rate. Let the times of sampling be nT (where $n = \ldots -2, -1, 0, +1, +2 \ldots$) and the respective frequencies and phases be Ω_1, φ_1 and Ω_2, φ_2. Then we have $\cos(n\Omega_1 T + \varphi_1) = \cos(n\Omega_2 T + \varphi_2)$ for all n which can be rearranged to give

$$\sin\left(\frac{n\Omega_1 T + \varphi_1 + n\Omega_2 T + \varphi_2}{2}\right) \sin\left(\frac{n\Omega_1 T + \varphi_1 - n\Omega_2 T - \varphi_2}{2}\right) = 0$$

or

$$2\pi k = n\Omega_1 T + \varphi_1 \pm (n\Omega_2 T + \varphi_2), \quad k = 0, \pm1, \pm2 \ldots$$

This is true for $n = 0$, and we may restrict φ to the first cycle, so

$$\varphi_1 = \varphi_2 \quad \text{or} \quad 2\pi - \varphi_2$$

and since it is true for all other integral values of n, assuming Ω_1 is a low frequency

$$|\Omega_1 \pm \Omega_2| = \frac{2\pi k}{T}; \quad k = 0, 1, 2, 3 \ldots$$

then $k = 0$ makes Ω_2 equal to the signal frequency Ω_1 itself, but $k = 1$ with the plus sign represents the *first alias*, i.e. the lowest frequency which cannot be distinguished from the signal frequency. In fact, there is an infinite number of aliases (*alias*—an assumed name, Latin for otherwise), so the only way of ensuring a unique representation for a general waveform is to predetermine that none of its sinusoidal components is of frequency greater than a certain critical frequency. That frequency is the one which is its own first alias i.e. π/T ($= \omega_s/2$ where ω_s is the sampling frequency). Any frequency slightly higher, say $(\pi/T) + \Delta$, will be indistinguishable from a lower one $(\pi/T) - \Delta$.

Thus, if the spectrum of the source signal is fixed, we must set the sampling frequency to at least twice the maximum frequency present. Alternatively, if the sampling frequency is set we must prefilter the signal with a low-pass filter to ensure that the spectral content above half the sampling frequency is negligible. It should be said that in some applications of digital encoding in telecommunications aliasing may be deliberately exploited to transfer a signal from one band to another, but here ambiguity can be obviated by the prescribed frequency relationships. Another example of deliberate aliasing occurs in the sampling oscilloscope. In general, however, aliased signals can never be unravelled, and rigorous prefiltering should be the rule unless prior knowledge of the signal shows that to be unnecessary. Even then it must be remembered that, without filtering, high-frequency noise will be aliased into the observed band.

Diagrammatic illustrations of aliasing can be found in many texts [e.g. SigProBeau], so we will not reproduce them. Instead at this stage we wish to draw attention to a related problem which arises from the tendency of the eye to associate dot patterns in a way which can be positively misleading. This is illustrated in Figure 6.5(a) in which a 2 kHz signal sampled at 10 kHz is plotted in the form of individual sample points. Note the optical illusion of interlaced sinusoids of low frequency. In Figure 6.5(b) the program has been changed to cause consecutive points to be joined. Although this removes the ambiguity, it carries its own form of deception in the form of an apparent periodic variation of the envelope. Obviously such effects will be less predictable with complex waveforms, but needing to watch out for them is one of the penalties of trying to use the whole range of $\omega_s/2$ efficiently.

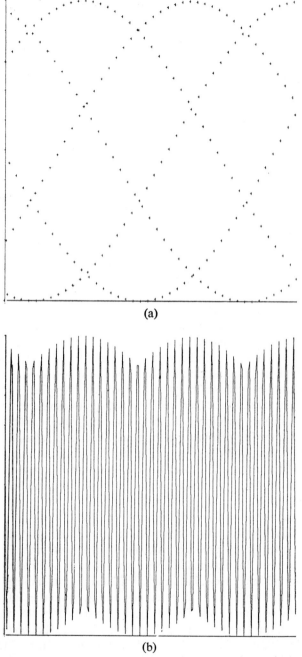

(a)

(b)

Figure 6.5   Two of the less frequently illustrated hazards of the visual interpretation of sampled data. A 2,002 Hz signal sampled at 10,167 Hz with (a) sample points plotted and (b) linear interpolation (*realization by Terry Hewish on FM* 1600*B*)

6.6   Some simple processes

Having dealt with some of the theoretical implications of the signal input stage we now turn our attention to the sort of processes which can be applied to the digitized signal. It is not necessary or desirable in a text of this nature that we review the entire field, and what we propose to do is select a few illustrative examples. Firstly, we consider two processes which appear simple but which are difficult to realize in digital terms—differentiation and integration. Then we look at an example of a process which seems easy to realize but whose implications have often been overlooked, smoothing by the method of running mean. These discussions conveniently lead to the much more powerful concept of digital filtering. Throughout, the emphasis is on time as the independent variable, and we try to show the link between classical computer methods [CoMeLaFa] and the signal processing approach [DiSiRaRa].

6.6.1   Differentiation and integration

Differentiation is a noisy process which should be avoided if possible. This frequently heard statement, while not strictly true, is well worth inscribing indelibly on the mental tablet, because attempts to perform numerical differentiation on real-time data can produce serious errors. A more accurate version of the statement would be: *Differentiation tends to amplify high-frequency noise while integration tends to amplify low-frequency noise.* Our discussion of noise sources early in this chapter shows that we unavoidably introduce high-frequency noise in all conversion and arithmetical operations. We must not forget, however, that very low-frequency noise, or drift, may be present in the source signal.

It is a simple matter to obtain the equivalent of these two operations in the frequency domain by applying partial integration to the Laplace transform, and substituting $s = j\omega$, thence

$$\frac{\mathrm{d}}{\mathrm{d}t} f(t) \leftrightarrow s\mathscr{F}(s) \leftrightarrow j\omega\mathscr{F}(j\omega)$$

$$\int_{-\infty}^{t} f(t)\,\mathrm{d}t \leftrightarrow \frac{1}{s}\mathscr{F}(s) \leftrightarrow \frac{1}{j\omega}\mathscr{F}(j\omega)$$

Thus, if as in Figure 6.6 we plot the magnitude of each operator as a function of frequency, it is obvious why differentiation emphasizes high frequencies, while integration emphasizes low frequencies. In the present context, noise amplification in differentiation is likely to be the more serious problem, as it normally occurs over a wider proportion of the usable frequency range and the introduced noise is roughly white.

It is worth while to examine the operation of differentiation further, to see how it can be realized in the discrete scheme, but without the full panoply of digital filter approximation techniques, which would only serve to obscure the basic point at this stage. We have seen that d/dt becomes s in the complex

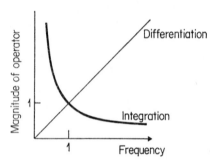

Figure 6.6   The magnitude of the differentiation and integration operators as a function of frequency

frequency domain, so what does it become in the z domain? We can answer this question by inverting the defining relation $z = \exp(sT)$, then

$$\frac{d}{dt} \leftrightarrow s \leftrightarrow \frac{1}{T}\ln(z)$$

There are three basic reasons why this result is not as simple as it looks. Firstly, the logarithm of a complex variable is infinitely valued [FuncTitch]. This is a direct manifestation of aliasing, since

(6.15) $\ln(z) = \sigma + j\omega T + j2\pi k; \qquad k = 0, \pm 1, \pm 2, \pm 3$

and, as we have seen, it is impossible to distinguish between ω and $\omega + 2\pi k/T$. We shall set $k = 0$, thereby forbidding aliasing, and take the principal value. Secondly, our main interest is in the Fourier components ω, which means we are primarily interested in the unit circle on the z plane which is the transform of the $j\omega$ axis. Thirdly, and most importantly, we are restricted to real powers of z in our realization of the process (*i.e.* only delays or advances by multiples of T in the time domain). Thus the best we can do is form a series, which to be practicable must be truncated.

It is beyond our present task to examine the methods for developing a series approximation for a function of a complex variable, so we shall restrict ourselves to the best known—Taylor's series. This gives a form for a function $f(z)$ which is analytic in the region of a point z_0 [FuncTitch] in terms of its derivatives

$$(6.16) \qquad f(z) = \sum_{n=0}^{\infty} \frac{f^{(n)}(z_0)}{n!}(z - z_0)^n$$

Thus expanding $\ln (z)$ in the region of $z = 1 + j0$ we obtain

$$(6.17) \qquad \ln (z) = \sum_{n=1}^{\infty} \frac{(-1)^{n+1}}{n}(z - 1)^n$$

so one form for the differential operator is

$$(6.18) \qquad \frac{d}{dt} \rightarrow \frac{1}{T}\sum_{n=1}^{\infty} \frac{(-1)^{n+1}}{n}(z - 1)^n$$

This form will be found in text-books of numerical analysis under the guise of the Newton Gregory forward difference formula [CoMeLaFa]. Thus the crudest approximation to differentiation can be made by selecting the first term only

$$\frac{d}{dt} \rightarrow \frac{1}{T}(z - 1)$$

or in terms of samples x_i

$$(6.19) \qquad \left(\frac{dx}{dt}\right)_i \doteq \frac{1}{T}(x_{i+1} - x_i)$$

Two terms give a better approximation

$$(6.20) \qquad \left(\frac{dx}{dt}\right)_i \doteq \frac{1}{T}\left(-\frac{1}{2}x_{i+2} + 2x_{i+1} - \frac{3}{2}x_i\right)$$

The first order approximation in equation 6.19 is an obvious intuitive form for the differential coefficient, which is often used without regard to its limitations. Note, for example, that the series was derived for the region on the unit circle near $z = 1 + j0$, which corresponds to $\omega = 0$, so we should expect it to be accurate only for low frequencies.

It is convenient to examine the frequency dependence of the whole formula here, as it is a useful introduction to the idea of filtering. The question we now ask is—how good an approximation is $(z - 1)/T$ to the desired operator $j\omega$? We can establish this by substituting $z = \exp(j\omega T)$, so that our approximation function is

$$(6.21) \qquad H(\omega) = \frac{1}{T}[\exp(j\omega T) - 1] = \frac{1}{T}[(\cos \omega T - 1) + j \sin \omega T]$$

which seems very different from $j\omega$ until we note that as $\omega \to 0$, $\cos \omega T \to 1$ and $\sin \omega T \to \omega T$, so that $H(\omega) \to j\omega$. The magnitude, obtained from $H(\omega)$ in equation 6.21 or from the useful identity

$$|F(z)|^2 = F(z)F\left(\frac{1}{z}\right)$$

is

$$|H(\omega)| = \frac{1}{T}[2(1 - \cos \omega T)]^{\frac{1}{2}}$$

and again we see that $|H(\omega)|$ only approaches the desired form (ω) as $\omega \to 0$.

In passing, observe that we have established that the iterative differencing scheme $y_i = (x_{i+1} - x_i)/T$ is exactly equivalent to a filter whose amplitude/frequency characteristic is given by equation 6.21. Although this in itself may not be a particularly interesting or useful characteristic, the idea of a one-to-one correspondence between an iteration scheme and a filter characteristic is extremely important, giving rise to the powerful technique of digital filtering. In Figure 6.7 we show how well the first and second order forward difference formulae fit the desired form by plotting $|H(\omega)|$ against ω. Note

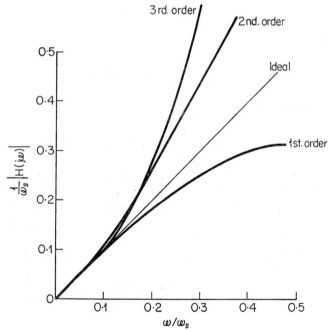

Figure 6.7 Frequency domain behaviour of the Newton Gregory forward difference formula for differentiation. Note the restriction of validity to low frequencies

that in order to obtain a convenient base we normalize ω by expressing it as a fraction of the sampling frequency $\omega_s = 2\pi/T$. All digital filter characteristics are presented in this way to present a unique curve, and it is a characteristic property that particular points (e.g. the cut-off frequency) are proportional to the sampling frequency.

The Newton Gregory forward difference formula has been chosen as a simple illustration. It is not the best for real-time work as it implies a knowledge of the future, and from this point of view the equivalent backward difference formula would be preferred

$$(6.22) \qquad \frac{d}{dt} \leftrightarrow H(z) = \frac{1}{T} \sum_{m=1}^{\infty} \frac{1}{m} (1 - z^{-1})^m$$

There are many other classical forms using forward, backward and central differences, but the reader should note that for our purpose they have been made redundant by the more powerful modern methods based on digital filter synthesis, which yields forms accurate in both frequency and phase up to 90% of $\omega_s/2$ [DiSiRaRa].

Consideration of integration leads us to another important filtering concept, *recursion*. Since integration and differentiation are reciprocal operations, an obvious crude form for integration is the reciprocal form of equation 6.19 which is $T/(z - 1)$.

Now, transforming

$$y(z) = \frac{T}{(z - 1)} x(z)$$

to the time domain gives

$$y_{i+1} - y_i = Tx_i$$

or

$$y_{i+1} = y_i + Tx_i$$

which gives us the simplest scheme of integration—the rectangular approximation. A slightly better scheme is the equally familiar trapezoidal one, corresponding to

$$y_{i+1} = y_i + \frac{T}{2}(x_{i+1} + x_i)$$

or the filter function

$$(6.23) \qquad H(z) = \frac{T(z + 1)}{2 \, z - 1}$$

This last form is the one we would have derived if we had used one of the simpler digital filter synthesis techniques, *bilinear transformation*, to approximate to $1/s$ [DiSiGoRa]. Note that these schemes, regarded as digital filters, are fundamentally different in that they utilize previous output signals as well as the input signal. These are called *recursive* schemes, whereas in the discussion of differentiation we restricted ourselves to *nonrecursive* schemes. Each has its own particular frequency response, the trapezoidal rule above, for example, being

$$(6.24) \qquad H(j\omega) = \frac{T}{2j} \cot \frac{(\omega T)}{2} \doteq \frac{1}{j\omega}$$

It must be emphasized that the foregoing treatment of approximate differentiation and integration is far from complete, but this is a well documented subject, and we have confined the discussion to real-time aspects, using it to develop the digital filtering approach to processing.

Though it is very important to us, time is far from being the only variable with respect to which we may wish to perform these operations. The conditions are similar with other variables and parameters, and though the ideas of noise and frequency are then less precise, they are still very useful. In general, we have more freedom to choose intervals, etc. when time is not the differential variable involved, but the real-time programmer must always be conscious of the time lapse implicit in each calculation, and this always tends to be a limiting factor.

It may appear from the foregoing that a high sampling frequency, much higher than the highest signal frequency, is the complete panacea, for then ωT (or ω/ω_s) is always small, but there are usually other constraints, such as the amount of computation needed to be performed between samples. This is a factor limiting the number of terms of a serial formula that may be used. Another factor is the transient nature of the response of such a formula. For it has to begin with one data point, giving an estimate which is very awry, but which slowly converges in an oscillatory or damped fashion towards a more accurate estimate as more data become available. This sort of behaviour, familiar in the use of linear networks, is typical of a digital filter type of iteration, as is an inherent propagation delay. Thus once again in our real-time calculations we have the problem of how much to trade speed for accuracy and vice-versa.

6.7   Smoothing

Consider another process which was around long before the idea of a digital filter began to gel—the smoothing of data sequences. A method often used is the *running mean*, whereby a new smoothed sequence is formed from the original one by making each new data point equal to the unweighted average of several consecutive points in the source sequence, i.e.

$$(6.25) \qquad y_k = \frac{1}{n} \sum_{r=0}^{n-1} x_{k-r}$$

Until the filtering interpretation began to penetrate general texts [e.g. NuMeHam], n was apparently chosen by a combination of faith, hope, trial and error. The method appeared to be successful, perhaps more so with some forms of periodic process than others, but as intuition would suggest, it certainly reduced short term fluctuations of data, and one never seemed to find time to question the exact implications of the procedure. The development of techniques such as the z transform has made this fairly easy, for the iteration of equation 6.25 is obviously a non-recursive filter of the form

$$(6.26) \qquad H(z) = \frac{1}{n} \sum_{r=0}^{n-1} z^{-r}$$

The important conceptual advance is the understanding that the operation is independent of k. This is a good example to illustrate the greater efficiency often obtained by changing to a recursive scheme, since we may rewrite the geometric progression of equation 6.25 as

$$(6.27) \qquad H(z) = \frac{1}{n} \frac{1 - z^{-n}}{1 - z^{-1}}$$

The inverse transform is

$$(6.28) \qquad y_k = y_{k-1} + \frac{1}{n}(x_k - x_{k-n})$$

which obviously yields the same result as equation 6.25. The single delay of n places is most simply obtained by a form of cyclic buffer technique (Section 5.2) with read and write pointers separated by an interval of $n - 1$ words. We are led to wonder how much computer time has been wasted in the past by the computation of the redundant central terms in equation 6.25. Such profligacy is certainly not tolerable in real-time work.

How does the operation treat the different frequency components of the signal? We can find out by examining it on the unit circle by substituting $z = \exp(j\omega T)$ whence equation 6.27 becomes

$$(6.29) \qquad H(\omega) = \frac{1}{n} \frac{1 - \exp(-nj\omega T)}{1 - \exp(-j\omega T)}$$

$$= \exp[-(n-1)j\omega T/2] \cdot \frac{\sin(n\omega T/2)}{n \sin(\omega T/2)}$$

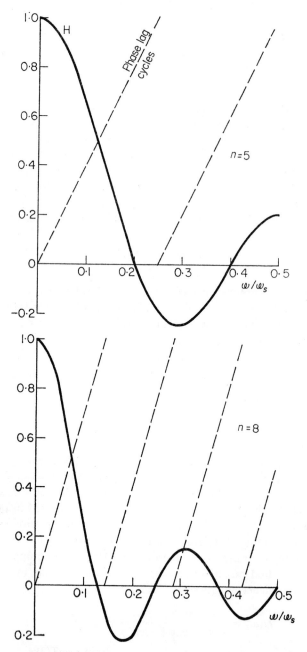

Figure 6.8 Amplitude and phase characteristics of the Running Mean smoothing formula for $n = 5$ and $n = 8$, compare with Figure 6.13

and since the exponential term has unit modulus, the effect on the amplitude is given by

$$(6.30) \qquad |H(\omega)| = \left| \frac{\sin (n\omega T/2)}{n \sin (\omega T/2)} \right| = \left| \frac{\sin (\pi n\omega/\omega_s)}{n \sin (\pi \omega/\omega_s)} \right|$$

Examination of this function shows that $|H(\omega)| \to 1$, as $\omega \to 0$, so that zero and low frequencies are unaffected, and the behaviour in the rest of the domain is conditioned by zeros of ω/ω_s at $1/n$, $2/n \ldots (n - 1)/2n$, when n is odd, and $1/2$, $2/n \ldots 1/2$ when n is even. While the numerator is periodic, the denominator steadily increases as $\omega/\omega_s \to 1/2$. Thus we would expect the form of lobes of decreasing magnitude, and we have constructed a form of low-pass filter, but while the elimination of some high frequencies is absolutely efficient, others are not so well suppressed. Examples of $|H(\omega)|$ for this process are given in Figure 6.8.

This is a suitable point to deliver a warning about the dangers of interpreting apparent periodicities in data which have been treated by an iterative process, for the presence of a substantial narrow lobe in the spectrum of the process may well invest even white noise with the appearance of a respectable periodic content. This highlights a major disadvantage of on-line measurement—the ease of producing a beautiful technique to solve a measurement problem. For, unless the implications of the process are fully understood, one is continually in danger of launching into the world a physical theory which

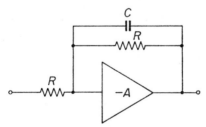

Figure 6.9   The leaky integrator. This simple electronic smoother has a digital analogue

is based on a spurious response in the manipulative scheme. So, in this field of scientific measurement, even more than any other, cries of 'Eureka' should be suppressed in favour of patient checking and double checking.

While on the subject of smoothing, let us see how we can capitalize on our experience of electronic circuits to develop an alternative procedure. One method of smoothing in electronics is to use a leaky integrator as in Figure 6.9. This has the transfer function

$$H(s) = \frac{1}{1 + RCs}$$

or impulse response

$$H(t) = \frac{1}{RC} \exp\left(\frac{-t}{RC}\right)$$

A similar effect would be obtained in a discrete scheme by

$$(6.31) \qquad H(z^{-1}) = K \sum_{r=0}^{\infty} z^{-r} \exp(-art)$$

so we have replaced our former unweighted average by one of continually decreasing weights $\exp(-ar)$, but an infinite sum is of little use. However, we again have a geometric progression, so we can write

$$H(z^{-1}) = \frac{K}{1 - z^{-1} \exp(-aT)}$$

so the smoothing scheme is

$$y_i = Kx_i + \exp(-aT)y_{i-1}$$

To preserve unity gain at $\omega = 0$ ($z = 1$) we have to set $K = 1 - \exp(-aT)$, so in the computer our smoothing scheme would be

$$y_i = (1 - b)x_i + by_{i-1}$$

and we have a simple iterative procedure with known response time

$$-T/\ln(b), \quad \text{where} \quad b = \exp(-aT)$$

Note that we could have obtained $H(z^{-1})$ from $H(s)$ by observing that the pole at $s = -1/RC$ is mapped to $z = \exp(-T/RC)$ so $a = 1/RC$.

6.8   DIGITAL FILTERS

Having approached the idea of digital filtering from an interpretation of the established processes, let us take the opposite point of view, which we have implied is the more effective, and start from the digital filter, to see how it can be adapted to provide a desired process. A digital filter is simply an iterative scheme either of the non-recursive type

$$(6.32) \qquad y_i = \sum_{k=0}^{n-1} a_k x_{i-k}$$

or the recursive type

$$(6.33) \qquad y_i = \sum_{k=0}^{n-1} a_k x_{i-k} - \sum_{k=1}^{n-1} b_k y_{i-k}$$

These can be represented by polynomials in z^{-1} in which the weighting factors a_k, b_k become the coefficients

(6.34)   e.g. $$H(z^{-1}) = \frac{a_0 + a_1 z^{-1} + a_2 z^{-2} \cdots + a_n z^{-n}}{1 + b_1 z^{-1} + b_2 z^{-2} \cdots + b_n z^{-n}}$$

The problem of synthetizing a digital filter is one of choosing the coefficients a_k and b_k so that the characteristic response is a best fit *in a certain sense* to a given ideal. The problem in classical linear-continuous processing is similar, and it is worth while to remark upon why in that case we resort to the s domain. The great manipulative power of the s domain arises from the fact that the linear elements of networks can be represented by differential operators

$$v = \frac{L\,di}{dt}, \qquad i = \frac{C\,dv}{dt}, \qquad v = iR, \qquad v_0 = Av_i$$

Hence, through their linear combination via Kirchhoff's laws, input and output signals can always be related in the form of a linear differential equation characteristic of the system

(6.35) $$\left[\sum b_i \left(\frac{d}{dt} \right)^i \right] y(t) = \left[\sum a_i \left(\frac{d}{dt} \right)^i \right] x(t)$$

Now we can show by partial integration that

(6.36) $$\mathscr{L}\left(\frac{d}{dt} x(t) \right) = sX(s)$$

so that any linear lumped system can be completely represented by a ratio of polynomials in s:

(6.37) $$Y(s) = \frac{\Sigma a_i s^i}{\Sigma b_i s^i} X(s)$$

Furthermore, the *fundamental theorem of algebra* [FuncTitch] tells us that every polynomial of degree n has n zeros, so that a system can also be represented within a constant factor by its poles s_i, and zeros s_k,

(6.38) $$Y(s) = K \frac{\Pi(s - s_k)}{\Pi(s - s_i)} \cdot X(s) = H(s)X(s)$$

The process of synthesis in the main consists of manipulating the poles and zeros so that the surface represented by $H(s)$ at its intersection with the $s = j\omega$ plane produces a curve whose shape is as near as possible to the desired form of $H(j\omega)$. A useful pedagogic analogy is to picture $H(s)$ as a rubber sheet with the zeros as tacks holding it down and the poles as pencils holding it up.

Thus we see that the situation in the synthesis of discrete filters is very similar. In one way it is more difficult in that the target line upon which we wish to establish the desired shape is a circle instead of a straight line. In another way it is simpler in that the correspondence between the z and t domains is more obvious. Because of the historical precedence of linear-continuous methods, digital synthesis techniques are firmly based upon their established principles. We cannot delve deeply into the technique of synthesis, but it is worth while to mention some of them briefly [for further details DiSiGoRa].

6.8.1　IMPULSE INVARIANCE

In this method the pulse response of the digital filter is made to coincide exactly at the sample points with the impulse response of a known continuous filter. We used this method to develop the leaky integrator analogue for a smoothing digital filter in equation 6.31.

6.8.2　DIRECT FROM SQUARED MAGNITUDE FUNCTION

Since $H(z)$ is a rational function of z^{-1}, on the unit circle it is a rational function of $\exp(j\omega t)$, so (as for our running mean formula, equation 6.30) $|H(j\omega)|^2$ can always be represented as a ratio of trigonometric functions of ωT. Conversely, given a suitable filter function in trigonometric form (and these are well known) we can set up the corresponding $H(z)$.

6.8.3　BILINEAR TRANSFORMATION

The simplest rational function which maps the $j\omega$ axis onto the unit circle is the bilinear transformation

(6.39)
$$s \to \frac{z - 1}{z + 1}$$

so if we know a continuous filter function $H(s)$ we can convert it to a digital filter by this substitution. The mapping, however, though unique, produces a non-linear conversion of frequencies ω_c from the continuous scheme to frequencies ω_d in the discrete scheme, for

(6.40)
$$\omega_c = \tan \frac{\omega_d T}{2}$$

This method produces the trapezoidal formula for the integration operator $(1/s)$ which we quoted in equation 6.23 and explains the corresponding cotangential distortion of equation 6.24.

6.8.4 FREQUENCY SAMPLING

This is a rather more complicated technique based on the use of sums of $(\sin x)/x$ functions as approximating forms in the frequency domain. It involves the cascading of a digital comb filter with several digital resonators, producing characteristics close to the ideal at the expense of extensive computation.

The general on-line computer user does not wish to devote his time and energies to problems of filter synthesis, and as a great deal of work has been done by the experts it is not necessary for him to do so. All that he needs is a knowledge of the coefficient of z^{-r} in the polynomial ratio defining a particular type of filter, and he can write a program to realize the filter. It is important to understand, however, that in each case the filter is only an approximation to the ideal. In Figure 6.10 for example we show the ideal forms of the low-pass, high-pass, band-pass and differentiator filters as they appear as functions on the unit semicircle. These functions have to be approximated by the intersection of the unit cylinder with the *essentially*

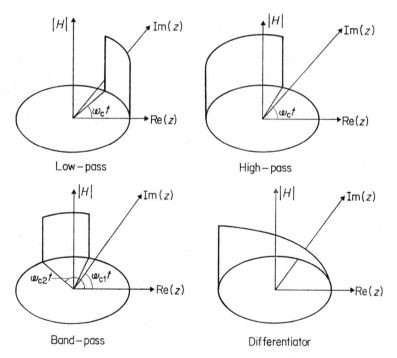

Figure 6.10   Ideal forms of filter function $|H|$ on unit semicircle (there is symmetry about real axis). ω_c, ω_{c1} and ω_{c2} are the cut-off frequencies

curved surface represented by polynomial ratios, so the sharp corners and straight lines of the ideal characteristic are impossible to achieve with a finite scheme. Consequently, the closer they are approached, the higher the order of the filter and the greater the computation load. Furthermore, in a digital system not only are the data quantized, but also the coefficients, so that poles and zeros can only be located on a finite grid whose fineness increases with word length. Round-off noise and the possibility of overflow in fixed point arithmetic can also give stability problems. Thus there are strong grounds for utilizing the simplest filter possible for a particular purpose, especially in real-time work where the question of computation load is paramount.

The literature of digital filtering is extensive, but fortunately most of the major contributions are available in a single collection [DiSiRaRa]. Numerous designs for digital filters can be culled from the literature, and it is fortunate that simple transformations exist to convert a given frequency-selective filter to another type of the same class [Constantinides in DiSiRaRa]. Thus, if say we have a design for a Chebyshev low-pass filter in the form of polynomial coefficients (or pole zero locations), we can convert it to a high-pass, band-pass, band elimination, or a low-pass of different cut-off frequency ω_c by substituting for z^{-1} a given function of z^{-1}. Let us develop the simplest of these transformations, low-pass to high-pass.

Consider that we are given a pulse transfer function $H(z^{-1})$ which represents a low-pass filter of cut-off frequency ω_c. We know that the frequencies in the range $0 \leq \omega \leq \omega_s/2$ are mapped onto the unit semicircle in the z plane, and ω_c will correspond to a particular point on the circle. Obviously, if we can find a transformation which maps low frequencies to high frequencies and vice-versa we could obtain a high-pass filter. A simple mapping with this property is the rotation

$$\omega = \frac{\omega_s}{2} + \omega_1$$

but how does this affect $H(z^{-1})$? On the unit circle we have

$$H(z^{-1}) = H[\exp(-j\omega T)] = H\left\{\exp\left[-j\left(\frac{\omega_s}{2} + \omega_1\right)T\right]\right\}$$

but

$$\exp(j\omega_s T/2) = \exp(j\pi) = -1$$

so

$$H[\exp(-j\omega T)] = H[-\exp(-j\omega_1 T)]$$

and our mapping is $z^{-1} \rightarrow -z^{-1}$, i.e. we simply require to invert the signs of the coefficients of odd delay in the filter. The cut-off frequency of the high-pass filter is $(\omega_s/2) - \omega_c$, so in the general case we would wish to alter this in advance by low-pass to low-pass transformation. This is of the form $z \to (z^{-1} - \alpha)/(1 - \alpha z^{-1})$ [DiSiRaRa].

In order to demonstrate the action of a typical digital filter we take an example of one used in the authors' laboratory in the relatively early days of this technique as an on-line facility. The filter is a low-pass one of the Chebyshev class with the following specification.

ratio of cut-off frequency to sampling frequency = 0.005
maximum passband ripple   = 10%
transition ratio   = 0.7

The sampling frequency was set to 20 Hz, giving a cut-off frequency of 0.1 Hz. This is the order of frequency in which the digital filter is pre-eminent, as here the passive filter is physically enormous and the active filter presents stability problems. The pulse transfer function of the filter when synthetized is given in the form

$$H(z^{-1}) = \frac{K(1 + z^{-1})^4}{Q_1(z^{-1})Q_2(z^{-1})}$$

where $Q_1(z^{-1}) = 1.00477145 - 1.99950878z^{-1} + 0.99571977z^{-2}$
$Q_2(z^{-1}) = 1.01099745 - 1.99985779z^{-1} + 0.98914476z^{-2}$

The filter is realized as a pair of cascaded biquadratics, each of which may be represented by a simple recurrence relation of the form

$$A_3 y_{n-2} + A_2 y_{n-1} + A_1 y_n = x_{n-2} + 2x_{n-1} + x_n$$

where y_n and x_n represent the corresponding elements of the output and input time series. The behaviour of the filter is demonstrated in Figures 6.11 and 6.12, where the output D–A converter of only 8 bits is connected to a plotter. In Figure 6.11 the responses to step and pulse signals are shown. The similarity with continuous filter action is evident, and only the stepwise progression produced by the coarse quantization reveals its digital nature. The selective properties of the filter are shown in Figure 6.12 where the output of the filter is compared with the allpass scheme $y_n = x_n$ for an input comprising the sum of two sinusoids from low-frequency oscillators of frequencies 0.05 Hz and 0.2 Hz.

General points to note about the implementation of this filter are the precision with which the coefficients are specified in contrast to the imprecision tolerable in the data. This is because the former specifies the location of the poles which are close to the unit circle, whereas the latter merely specifies the noise content of the output signal.

The reader will note that we have made little mention of an important filter characteristic—the phase distortion. This is due to the need for brevity

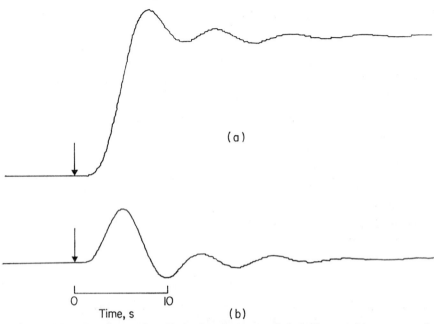

Figure 6.11   Response of a Chebyshev low-pass digital filter to (a) a step and
(b) a pulse input at the time marked by the arrow

rather than any desire to minimize its significance. We shall content ourselves with the remark that one of the constraints upon the design of digital
filters for most purposes is that they should exhibit zero or linear phase
distortion, so that the signal at worst suffers only a delay.

6.9   DISCRETE FOURIER TRANSFORMATION

The alternative to the recursive approach to tailoring the spectral content of
a signal is the equivalent operation in the frequency domain, i.e. multiplication by a shaping function. This method requires transformations to and
from the frequency domain, a rather cumbersome procedure, which, however,
has gained some of its former prestige through the development of fast
Fourier transform (FFT) algorithms. The principal disadvantage of the
method is that it requires storage of all the data before the commencement of
the operation, so it cannot be considered a true real-time operation, though
the FFT does allow it to be used in certain real-time applications in which the
buffering delay can be tolerated. The principal advantage is the fact that the
shaping function can be arbitrary and exact, without the approximation
problem inherent in digital filtering. There is, however, an approximation

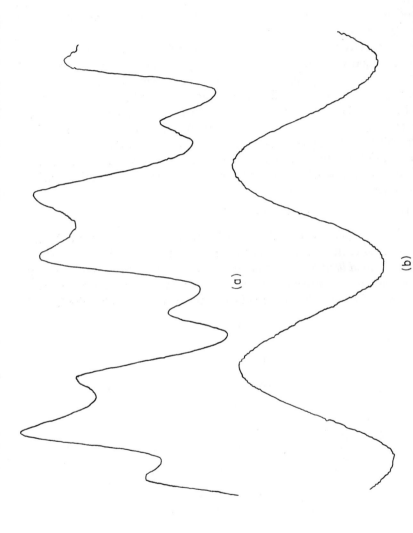

(a)

(b)

Figure 6.12 The output of the computer for an input of mixed sinusoids with (a) an all-pass scheme (b) the low-pass digital filter *(realization by Alan Buttle on Pegasus, reprinted from Electronics Letters, 4, 12, 1968)*

problem in the very idea of the Fourier transform of a process and its determination. The most important application of Fourier transformation lies in the significance of the spectrum as a diagnostic tool, but since the advent of the FFT it has been used for a variety of purposes, including, rather surprisingly until one considers just how great the speed gain actually is, *convolution* and *correlation*, and possibly its potentialities are even greater than we imagine.

Quite apart from the notion of discreteness there is an important conceptual difficulty associated with the experimental determination of Fourier transforms. A stationary stochastic process in general has no Fourier transform [ProPap], so if we wish to examine the harmonic content of a signal which falls into this class, we either have to deal with the spectrum (which is the Fourier transform of the autocorrelation function) or deal with a time-limited block of the signal. Now, *scale factors apart*, the Fourier and inverse Fourier transformations are similar in their effect on the shape of a function, and the most practically important function pair is what we might call the block function

(6.41) $$b(x) = U(x + \tfrac{1}{2}) - U(x - \tfrac{1}{2})$$

and the sinc function $(\sin x)/x$, which are Fourier and inverse Fourier transforms of each other [FouBra]; these are illustrated in Fig. 6.13. Thus if we sharply *band limit* a signal [multiply by $b(\omega)$] we effectively convolve with the oscillating sinc function in the time domain (Gibb's phenomenon). Conversely, if we sharply *time limit* by isolating a block of data, we effectively

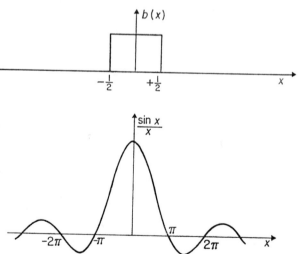

Figure 6.13   The block function $b(x)$ and the sinc function $\sin (x)/x$. The most important Fourier pair in signal processing

convolve with the oscillatory sinc function in the frequency domain. The principal effect of this is *leakage* of energy from each isolated component of the source signal into adjacent frequencies, and the consequent introduction of irrelevant minor lobes in the spectrum. The tailoring of the estimated spectrum to minimize these effects has as much the characteristics of an art as a science, and one of the manifestations of the art is the use of window functions, such as the Hann, Parzen or Bartlet windows [DiSiGoRa, AdSemSpec, SigProBeau], which in the frequency domain smooth the response and in the time domain round the corners of the block function.

Let us examine briefly the simplest of these, the Hann window, which will illustrate the ideas behind the process. Consider the low-pass filter

$$(6.42) \qquad H(z) = \tfrac{1}{4}z + \tfrac{1}{2} + \tfrac{1}{4}z^{-1}$$

Its effect in the frequency domain is

$$(6.43) \qquad H(\omega) = \tfrac{1}{2}(1 + \cos 2\pi\omega/\omega_s)$$

Now the Hann window depends on the reversal of this arrangement, i.e. the smoothing filter of equation 6.42 above is applied to the ordinates of the spectral estimates as though they constituted a time series, which is exactly equivalent to multiplying the time data block function by the cosine bell function of equation 6.43.

A more frequently used version of this technique is to apply the shaping only to the data at the ends of the block, say 10% at each end, and if unity gain is required to multiply by a normalizing factor [SigProBeau]. The various other windows used are all of a similar form, involving low-pass filtering of the spectral estimates, via shaping of the rectangular (block function) window, to blunt the discontinuities. Fundamentally, we have an *uncertainty principle*, and the more precisely we locate a process in time the less precisely we locate it in frequency, and vice-versa. As a result, two different workers will tend to make different spectral estimates from a common set of data. The other complications in computer Fourier transformation arise from its essential discreteness.

The discrete Fourier transform is basically the evaluation of the z-transform on the unit circle, just as the continuous Fourier transform is the evaluation of the Laplace transform on the imaginary axis. For, using the continuous form for a block of signal of duration NT and including the sampling function $\text{Ш}(t/T)$, we obtain

$$(6.44) \qquad X(\omega) = \int_{0-}^{NT-} x(t)\,\text{Ш}\left(\frac{t}{T}\right) \exp\left(-j\omega t\right) \mathrm{d}t$$

$$= \sum_{r=0}^{N-1} x(rT) \exp\left(-j\omega rT\right) \qquad \text{(cf. equation 6.11)}$$

and expressing ω as a fraction k/N of the sampling frequency

$$(6.45) \qquad X(k) = \sum_{r=0}^{N-1} x(rT) \exp\left(-2\pi jkr/N\right)$$

If we assign integral values to k, it can evidently only assume N different values to give independent values of X, since there are only N values of x, and N different exponentials (owing to the circularity of $\exp\left[-2\pi jkr/N\right]$). This is more obvious with the equation written in matrix form

$$(6.46) \qquad \mathbf{X} = \mathbf{Tx}$$

where $\{T_{kr}\} = w^{-kr}$
and w is the principal Nth root of unity, $w = \exp\left(2\pi j/N\right)$, $\mathbf{X}$ and $\mathbf{x}$ are vectors of order N, and $\mathbf{T}$ is an $N \times N$ square matrix. The inverse transform is

$$(6.47) \qquad x(r) = \frac{1}{N} \sum_{r=0}^{N-1} X(k) \exp\left(2\pi jkr/N\right)$$

or

$$(6.48) \qquad \mathbf{x} = \mathbf{T}^{-1}\mathbf{X}$$

The FFT arises from the fact that, though the above equations imply N^2 operations, it is possible by working on a permutated form of T, through partitioning and factoring, to reduce the number of operations. In particular, when $N = 2^n$, the number of operations is $N \log_2 N$, giving a speed increase by a factor of $N/\log_2 N$. This is a dramatic saving of computation (99% for 1024 points), but one must also note that a reduction of the number of operations of this scale also significantly raises the accuracy. We shall therefore assume that the discrete Fourier transform is performed by an FFT algorithm without going into the details of the latter, which can be found in the literature [DiSiRaRa].

The circularity or periodicity implicit in the DFT is of great significance (the reader will have noted the similarity with the Fourier series for periodic functions), and a principal result of this is that the discrete transform of a product becomes a circular or periodic convolution [DiSiGoRa] rather than the normal aperiodic convolution found in the continuous case. Likewise, the shift operator also becomes circular. One may think of this either in terms of the samples lying on a circle, or in terms of the sampled function being extended periodically on either side of the block of samples.

6.10 THE PROBABILISTIC APPROACH

In general, the sort of signals dealt with in laboratory on-line computing can best be described in terms of stochastic processes. A stochastic process may be thought of as a family of functions of time, one of which happens to be the particular outcome we are dealing with as our signal, and the members of this family (which is usually infinitely large) are characterized by certain common overall average properties which are conditioned by their origin and subsequent treatment. These properties, which we can only estimate as we do not have access to the whole family, thus convey information about the signal source, and the retrieval of such information is one of the objects of laboratory measurements. Often we require to extract some number or function which epitomizes some aspect which is important to us. Examples of such numbers are r.m.s. amplitude, bandwidth, dominant periodicity, etc. Examples of functions are those important ones which condense the properties of the signal with respect to amplitude, time and frequency. They are respectively the *distribution,* the *autocorrelation* and the *power spectrum.* Now, though we are obliged to deal rather cursorily with these aspects, we do not wish to minimize the importance of the rigorous probabilistic theory of signals [ProPap] which is one of the cornerstones of the mathematical background, so if the reader finds any difficulty with the rather brief treatment which follows he is urged to consult the reference quoted.

The distribution of a signal is a means of condensing into a single function those properties of a signal which are independent of the time scale. It is defined by

$$(6.49) \qquad F(x) = \text{Prob}\ \{x(t) \le x\}$$

where $x(t)$ is the instantaneous signal amplitude and x is a number, the argument of the function $F(x)$. In non-probabilistic terms it can be thought of as the fraction of time for which $x(t) \le x$. We can use $F(x)$ to define the *ensemble average* of a function $g(x)$ of x

$$(6.50) \qquad E\{g(x)\} = \int_{-\infty}^{+\infty} g(x)\,dF(x)$$

By writing it in this (Stieltjes) form we allow for two convergent interpretations. When $F(x)$ is continuous

$$(6.51) \qquad E\{g(x)\} = \int_{-\infty}^{+\infty} g(x)f(x)\,dx$$

where $f(x) = [dF(x)/dx]$ is the density function, and when $F(x)$ is discrete

$$(6.52) \qquad E\{g(x)\} = \sum_{\text{all } k} g(x_k)P_k$$

where P_k is the jump in $F(x)$ at x_k, i.e. the probability of $\{x(t) = x_k\}$. We can also define a *time average* of $g(x)$.

$$(6.53) \qquad \overline{g(x)} = \lim_{T \to \infty} \left(\frac{1}{2T}\int_{-T}^{+T} g[x(t)]\,dt\right)$$

With stationary signals we are able to make the *ergodic* assumption that $\overline{g(x)} = E\{g(x)\}$.

As we shall see, ensemble and time averages give rise to quite different computer procedures, and it is useful to have the alternatives available.

We have defined two types of average, time and ensemble, but since we assume them to be equivalent is there any practical reason why we should preserve this theoretical duality? Let us examine the computational implications of their evaluation. Consider the calculation of the average $(\bar{x})_n$ of a sequence of n samples, x_i. Note that in order to treat the problem at all we are obliged to abandon infinite limits of the time average as defined; another aspect of the uncertainty principle discussed in relation to the Fourier transform, i.e. the more we locate the average the less accurately we know it [in fact, the variance of $(\bar{x})_n$ is $(n-1)^{-1}$ times the variance of $x(t)$].

In off-line computing we would have no doubt about the way to compute $(\bar{x})_n$ from the equation

$$(6.54) \qquad (\bar{x})_n = \frac{1}{n} \sum_{i=1}^{n} x_i$$

We should certainly not commit the cardinal crime of unnecessarily loading an inner loop by computing

$$(6.55) \qquad (\bar{x})_n = \sum_{i=1}^{n} \frac{1}{n} x_i$$

But in on-line computing the situation may be more complicated. For example, the value of n may not be prescribed, but rather determined by the progress of the experiment, and we might at any stage require access to the intermediate average $(\bar{x})_i$. In such a case we would (through our experience of digital filtering) immediately look for a recursion to fulfil the task, by examining $(\bar{x})_i - (\bar{x})_{i-1}$. This gives rise to the relationship

$$(6.56) \qquad (\bar{x})_i = \left(1 - \frac{1}{i}\right)(\bar{x})_{i-1} + \left(\frac{1}{i}\right) x_i$$

This is *not* a digital filter, as the coefficients relate to the absolute and not the relative incidence of the samples by being a function of i.

On the other hand we might wish to avoid the intersample calculation implied by equation 6.56 above, and resort to the apparently wasteful process of storing all the x_i before computing the average. Such would be the case if we were straining to achieve the highest sample rate possible, or if there were other tasks of computation which could be dealt with while the process of data acquisition via data interrupts was going on.

The above discussion would also relate to the estimation of the average value of any function $g(x)$, as $\{g(x_i)\}$ would form a new sequence which we could treat in the same way as the $\{x_i\}$. However, suppose there were a number of different functions $g(x)$ we might wish to evaluate, perhaps even as an afterthought to the experiment, or the number of data n was very large and the desired sampling rate was high. In such a case, particularly if the distribution itself were significant to the interpretation of the experiment, the ensemble average would be appropriate. Then the real-time part of the procedure would be dedicated to the estimation of the distribution and this would probably be in the form of a stored table of the successive probabilities in un-normalized form, i.e. the values nP_k which go to make up the steps in the un-normalized discrete distribution $nF(x)$. The chief computational difference in ensemble averaging is the fact that the $\{x_i\}$ are interpreted as *addresses* rather than contents of store locations. The basic computational loop on the acquisition of an x_i (which, remember, is quantized at the input) would be

[1] N1 = 'START ADDRESS OF DISTRIBUTION'
[wait for x_i to appear, say, in V1]
N1 = N1 + V1
VN1 = VN1 + 1
→ 1

The distribution storage block would be of size 2^m, where m is the number of bits in the input A–D conversion, though this could be reduced by sacrificing bits via a right shift in the loop. At the end of data acquisition the rth word of the block would contain a number representing the number of occurrences of the sample amplitude signal equal to $(r/2^m)$ of full scale. This is an estimate of nP_k, where n is given by the sum of all the numbers in the distribution block. For the purposes of calculating averages, such as the moments of the distribution, via equation 6.50, and for plotting, etc., $F(x)$ would be required in normalized form, so n would be calculated, saved for future reference, and divided into all the numbers in the distribution block. Note that the basic loop contains a load and two simple fast instructions, unlike the iterative procedure for cumulative averaging in equation 6.56. In a machine where full modification is available as a subsidiary order it could be done in one instruction, but we have of course omitted certain housekeeping orders such as testing to see whether data acquisition is complete. The prime example of the ensemble approach is pulse height analysis, and modern analysers tend to be small dedicated computers which perform the task outlined above.

Now let us define some important averages

The *mean value* $E\{x\}$
The *mean square value* $E\{x^2\}$
The *autocorrelation*

(6.57) $$R_{xx}(t_1, t_2) = E\{x(t_1) \cdot x(t_2)\}$$

This last definition also allows us to define *stationarity* in the wide sense by saying that a process is stationary if the autocorrelation can be expressed as a function of one variable, the time difference $\tau = t_1 - t_2$

(6.58)   i.e. $R_{xx}(\tau) = E\{x(t + \tau)x(t)\}$

We shall, unless otherwise stated, assume stationarity henceforth. The *cross-correlation* of two signals $x(t)$ and $y(t)$ is

(6.59) $R_{xy} = E\{x(t + \tau)y(t)\} = E\{x(t)y(t - \tau)\}$

Some relationships are obvious from these definitions

(6.60) $R_{xx}(0) = E(x^2)$

(6.61) $R_{xx}(\tau) \leq E(x^2)$

(6.62) $R_{xx}(\tau) = R_{xx}(-\tau)$

(6.63) $R_{xy}(\tau) \leq \frac{1}{2}\{R_{xx}(0) + R_{yy}(0)\}$

The *power spectrum* is defined as the Fourier transform of the autocorrelation

(6.64) $S_{xx}(\omega) = \mathcal{F}\{R_{xx}(\tau)\}$

and a *cross spectrum* can be similarly defined from the cross-correlation. Important results emerge when $x(t)$ and $y(t)$ are defined as the input and output signals of a *linear system*, i.e. if we use (∗) to signify convolution, then

(6.65) $y(t) = x(t) * h(t)$

where $h(t)$ is the impulse response of the system, and we can show by a change of order of integration that, among other relationships,

(6.66) $R_{yx}(\tau) = R_{xx}(\tau) * h(\tau)$

and

$$S_{yy}(\omega) = S_{xx}(\omega)|H(j\omega)|^2$$

These are very important to the development of system identification techniques by on-line computer, especially when the input signal is noise-like (uncorrelated) so that $R_{xx}(\tau) \simeq \delta(\tau)$ and $S_{xx}(\tau) \simeq 1$ then $R_{yx}(\tau)$ and $S_{yy}(\omega)$ are estimates of the system functions $h(\tau)$ and $|H(j\omega)|^2$. In the computer, each of these functions must be represented by a set of discrete numbers. The autocorrelation of a sequence $\{x_i\}$ of N samples would, for example, be estimated by

$$R_{xx}(k) = \frac{1}{(N - k)} \sum_{i=1}^{N-k} x_i x_{i+k}$$

but note that for large N the quickest way of calculating it would be via the FFT [DiSiRaRa].

The applications for the probabilistic approach in on-line computing are many, but to give an example we will glance at one particular class of problems, those concerned with the extraction of buried signals. Now, the detection of signals in noise is an important topic and a great deal of theoretical work has been done on it [DetSigWha]. Our discussion of noise earlier in this chapter reminds us that this is in fact the separation of a wanted signal from an unwanted one, but most of the methods rely upon the fact that the unwanted signal is in some sense uncorrelated. Also implied is the fact that we must have some prior knowledge of the wanted signal which defines it and distinguishes it from all other signals. Take three examples which occur as on-line computing problems:

(a) Given the periodicity find the waveshape.
(b) Given the existence of a periodic component find the periodicity.
(c) Given the waveshape detect the occurrence.

Case (a) Given the periodicity find the waveshape. This is one of the most common problems in laboratory measurements, as it is the one which arises when a stimulus is repeatedly applied to a noisy system in an attempt to establish its response. Thus as in Figure 6.14, a stimulus is applied every T seconds so that the input signal $x(t)$ is periodic, i.e. $x(t) = x(t + T)$. The output signal $z(t)$ contains a component $y(t)$, which is the response to $x(t)$ and is therefore periodic with the same period, and a noise component $n(t)$ which is unrelated to $x(t)$ and T.

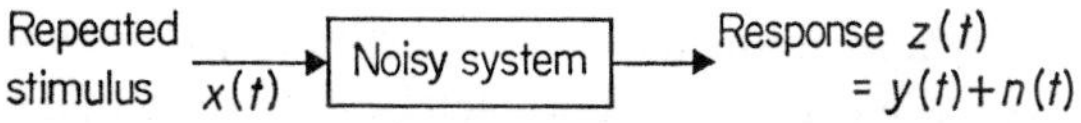

Figure 6.14 Stimulus and response of a noisy system. A common problem in digital signal processing

The problem is solved by dividing $z(t)$ into blocks of duration T and producing a new function by averaging the blocks

$$(6.67) \qquad z'(t) = \frac{1}{k} \sum_{i=0}^{k-1} z(t + iT) \qquad 0 < t < T$$

$$= y(t) + \frac{1}{k} \sum_{i=0}^{k-1} n(t + iT)$$

and since n is uncorrelated with T it is reduced progressively as k increases (in general, in proportion to $k^{\frac{1}{2}}$). Thus, even if $y(t)$ is completely swamped by $n(t)$ in the original signal, it can still be recovered provided k is sufficiently large. We have, of course, assumed that $y(t) = 0$ for $t \geq T$ otherwise a sort of aliasing would occur. This technique is sufficiently important for us to examine its practical computational implications.

Typically, the signal $x(t)$ would be a train of short pulses, whose front edges could be used as a reference for the start of the period T. Each of these periods would by sampling be converted to a block of, say, m data. Now, by the time we have had k repetitions of T we would not wish to have in store km data, yet we would probably wish to have the average response available for monitoring on a VDU so that the process of data acquisition would be terminated when the response is sufficiently well defined. This, following our previous discussion on the computation of averages, would point to a recursive technique, which would have to be modified to account for the fact that we are averaging over k and not t. Let the rth sample of kth block of data be $z_{r,k}$, then the required recursion to produce a current average block $\bar{z}_{r,k}$ would be

$$(6.68) \qquad \bar{z}_{r,k} = \left(\frac{k-1}{k}\right)\bar{z}_{r,k-1} + \left(\frac{1}{k}\right)z_{r,k}; \qquad r = 1, 2, 3 \ldots m$$

Figure 9.6 shows some results obtained (via a digital plotter) for various values of k when this technique was used to obtain the response of a noisy system.

Case (b) Given its existence find the periodicity. An example of the occurrence of this problem is the technique of laser velocimetry, in which the very small amount of light scattered by a moving fluid is used, either by non-linear mixing with a direct beam or by interaction with a fixed fringe pattern, to produce a signal whose frequency is proportional to the velocity. Such a signal is, however, almost always completely buried in noise, so again we have a composite signal $z(t) = y(t) + n(t)$, where $y(t) = y(t + T)$, and $n(t)$ is uncorrelated.

The solution to this problem lies in the fact that, if $y(t)$ is periodic with period T, then so is its autocorrelation $R_{yy}(T)$. Expanding $R_{zz}(T)$ in terms of y and n, we have

$$R_{zz}(T) = R_{yy}(T) + R_{yn}(T) + R_{ny}(T) + R_{nn}(T)$$

and on the right hand side the middle two terms are zero while the last one is rapidly decaying, thereby leaving us with the first which reveals the required periodicity. In a practical estimation, of course, the efficiency with which the terms containing n are eliminated would depend upon the number of samples over which the correlation average was evaluated.

For such a technique to be practicable, fast autocorrelation is necessary, and it is fortunate that we are able to convert to a binary signal to achieve this.

The conversion is valid because passing the signal $x(t)$ through a clipping circuit of output $y(t) = U\{x(t)\}$ causes $y(t)$ to reveal the same periodicities as $x(t)$. This makes it practicable to perform high-speed correlation outside the computer by a system such as that shown in Figure 6.15. Why then do we need a computer? The reason is that $R_{yy}(T)$ can be difficult to interpret, especially if there is more than one periodicity present, whereas $S_{yy}(\omega)$ would exhibit peaks at the relevant frequencies; so by a change of scale it could be converted to a spectrum of velocities. Thus the rôle of the computer would be to perform FFT on the autocorrelation.

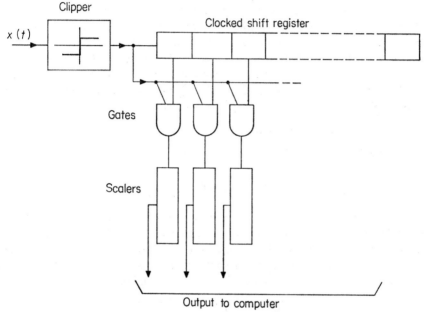

Figure 6.15 The one-bit correlator. Though a complete instrument, it needs the computer for further interpretive processing

The technique of clipping to form a binary function is very important. It is a result of the fact that many of the properties of a signal are exemplified by its zero crossings. If for example the distribution of the signal is of the common Gaussian form, the autocorrelation (hence spectrum) of the input of a clipper is uniquely determined within a constant by that of the binary output through the *arcsine* law [ProPap]. So, as an alternative to correlating externally, one could use the clipping process to boost the maximum transfer rate into the computer by a factor equal to the number of bits in the computer word. This would be achieved by assembling the binary samples for transfer in an external buffer. An example of the application of such a technique would be sound source location by cross-correlation of the outputs of separate transducers.

Case (*c*) *Given a waveshape detect its occurrence*. An example of the appearance of this problem is in electroencephalography where a certain characteristic waveform is a known precursor to an epileptic fit, so the detection of the waveform in the normal EEG signal during constant patient monitoring is a very important research and diagnostic requirement.

Consider the waveform sought to be $g(t)$ of duration T, normalized so that $\int_0^T [g(t)]^2 \, dt = 1$. Further, suppose that an occurrence of the signal of amplitude $Ag(t)$ commences at $t = 0$, so that the input signal is $x(t) = Ag(t) + n(t)$. What we require is a filter $h(t)$ which will give a peak at the first moment the waveform can be known to have occurred, i.e. $t = T$, but will also reduce the contribution of $n(t)$. We shall state without rigorous proof that the required filter is the *matched filter* of impulse response $h(t) = g(T - t)$, i.e. the time reversed version of the waveform. This form arises from the nature of convolution, for the output y is given by

$$y(t) = x(t) * h(t) = Ag(t) * h(t) + n(t) * h(t)$$

which for the matched filter at time $t = T$ is

$$y(t) = A \int_0^T |g(\tau)|^2 \, d\tau + \int_0^T g(\tau)n(\tau) \, d\tau$$

The first term represents a positive peak of amplitude A. The second represents the result of passing the noise component through the filter, and is a reduced noise signal which would be present whether the $g(t)$ signal were present or not. In the frequency domain the matched filter is related to the complex conjugate of the Fourier transformed $g(t)$, i.e.

$$H(j\omega) = \exp(-j\omega T)G^*(j\omega)$$

The above argument assumes white noise, and in the general case $h(t)$ would have to be established from an integral equation involving $R_{nn}(\tau)$ [DetSigWha].

6.11   PSEUDORANDOM METHODS

There are two very important aspects of on-line computing which involve the use of sequences of pseudorandom numbers. The first of these is *simulation*, where the modelling of systems and signals is extended to include a treatment of the stochastic elements. The second is in the use of *test-signals* which are chosen to be pseudorandom because of the correlation (and spectral) properties they then possess. In both applications a dominating consideration is the fact that a register of m bits can hold 2^m different numbers (or, excluding zero, $2^m - 1$), and the basic device is an iterative scheme which produces a *maximal length* sequence of numbers, i.e. one which includes all possible numbers without repetition. Furthermore, it is essential that the sequence be *uncorrelated*, a word of simple meaning in our signal processing sense, but rather more complicated for some mathematical applications. A typical generating formula for sequences of numbers is

(6.69) $$x_{n+1} = kx_n \text{ modulo } m$$

where k and m are carefully chosen integers [ArtSimToc]. It is convenient to treat the sequence of numbers as though they were fractions for they then have a uniform distribution in the range $(0, 1)$, and this leads to techniques for generating sequences of any given distribution. One of the most useful is the method of *analytic inversion*. This arises from the fact that if we have a sequence of numbers x_i whose distribution is a known function $F(x)$, then a new sequence of numbers u_i formed by $u_i = F(x_i)$ will exhibit a uniform distribution in the range $(0, 1)$. Thus if we can invert the function $F(x)$ analytically and have available the uniformly distributed sequence u_i we can generate the desired sequence from $x_i = F^{-1}(u_i)$. Take for example the important exponential distribution $F(x) = 1 - \exp(-ax)$, with $x \geq 0$, equating $1 - F(x)$ to u and inverting

(6.70) $$x = -\frac{1}{a} \ln(u)$$

so we can generate exponentially distributed numbers simply by taking negative logs of uniformly distributed numbers. Incidentally, this is a very useful basis for making random guesses of a parameter when one is reduced to a crude trial and error method of solving a problem, as it yields trial increments which are unbounded but of fixed average a^{-1}. If trial increments of both signs are required, the Laplace distribution [ProPap] can be used by setting

(6.71) $$\begin{cases} x_i = a \ln(2u_i), & u_i \leq \tfrac{1}{2} \\ x_i = -a \ln(2u_i - 1), & u_i > \tfrac{1}{2} \end{cases}$$

Accurate generation of numbers of Gaussian distribution requires more complicated techniques [ArtSimToc].

These techniques are the basis of the art of simulation, and while the idea of stochastic modelling has not yet been widely applied in on-line computing, it is so powerful that it is bound to be used more. Of more immediate interest, however, is the use of pseudorandom sequences as test signals. In particular, to test a *linear* system the test-signal only requires two levels, so with the understanding that for non-linear work we would have to revert to multilevel signals, we now examine the important class of *pseudorandom binary signals* (*sequences*), and for a change we approach the topic from the hardware angle.

As previously stated, in a word of m bits it is possible to generate a maximal length sequence of pseudorandom numbers of length $L = 2^m - 1$, zero being excluded. A sort of pseudorandom binary sequence (PRBS) could thence be generated by selecting just one bit, say the least significant, but there is in fact a particularly simple method of generating a PRBS with ideal autocorrelation properties using a shift register with feedback through a modulo-two (exclusive-OR) gate. Consider Figure 6.16 which represents a three stage shift register with such a feedback connection. The reader will confirm that successive outputs from the last stage of the shift register are 1, 1, 1, 0, 0, 1, 0 repeated ad infinitum, given that it is initially in the all-ones state. We exclude the all-zeros state as it is self-perpetuating, so such sequences always contain $(L + 1)/2$ ones and $(L - 1)/2$ zeros. Hence the average value is $(L + 1)/2L$, as is the mean square value. Table 6.1 shows the feedback connections for obtaining maximal length sequences from shift registers up to 10 stages.

Table 6.1 *Feedback connections for maximal length pseudorandom sequence generation*

Number of shift register stages	m-sequence length (L)	Stages from which feedback is derived			
2	3	2	1		
3	7	3	2		
4	15	4	3		
5	31	5	3		
6	63	6	5		
7	127	7	4		
8	255	8	4	3	2
9	511	9	5		
10	1023	10	7		

The PRBS is valued as a test-signal for its noise-like qualities; for if in equation 6.66 we insert $R_{xx}(\tau) = \delta(\tau)$, the system function $h(\tau)$ is given directly by the cross-correlation $R_{yx}(\tau)$. For a discrete sequence $\{x_i\}$ we can redefine the autocorrelation as

$$(6.72) \qquad R_{xx}(k) = \overline{x_{i+k}x_i} = \frac{1}{L} \sum_{i=1}^{L} x_{i+k}x_i$$

and since $x_{i+L} = x_i$ it is periodic with period L. The pseudorandom signal

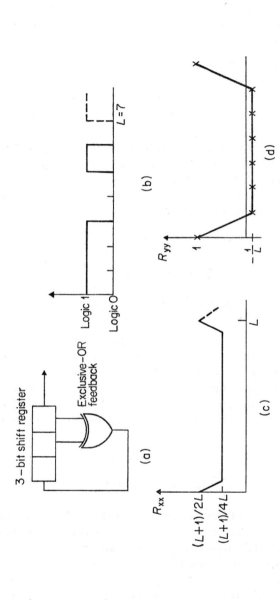

Figure 6.16 (a) 3-stage pseudorandom sequence generator (b) the output sequence (c) the autocorrelation function (d) auto-correlation of the modified sequence

is the sequence subjected to zero order hold, Figure 6.16(b) and its auto-correlation $R_{xx}(k)$ is obtained by joining up the points of the discrete autocorrelation by straight lines, Figure 6.16(c). For zero delay the autocorrelation is the mean square value, and for any other delay it turns out to be half this value, i.e.

$$(6.73) \qquad R_{xx}(k) = \frac{L+1}{2L}; \qquad k = nL; \qquad n = 0, 1, 2, 3 \ldots$$

$$R_{xx}(k) = \frac{L+1}{4L}; \qquad k \neq nL$$

The required form for system identification is a unit spike at the origin and zero elsewhere, and while it is possible to achieve this exactly by a linear transformation of the amplitude, since if $y = Ax + B$ then $R_{yy} = A^2 R_{xx} + 2AB\bar{x} + B^2$, almost always an attractive approximate form is used where the output states are treated at $+1$ and -1, i.e.

$$y = 2x - 1$$

so that

$$(6.74) \qquad R_{yy}(k) = 1; \qquad k = nL$$

$$R_{yy}(k) = -\frac{1}{L}; \qquad k \neq nL$$

This form is shown for the 7 bit sequence in Figure 6.16(d). The computational attractions of the ± 1 sequence are obvious, for they convert the cross-correlation subroutine to one of additions and subtractions only, and the $[-(1/L)]$ offset is usually negligible, though it can be accounted for in the scaling of the cross-correlation function when plotted by plotting $(LR_{yy} + 1)/(L + 1)$. A system response measured by cross-correlation is shown in Figure 9.9.

6.12   OPTIMIZATION

There is a vast amount of literature on the problem of finding the maximum, minimum or zero of a function of one or more variables, and many of the important problems of computer applications can be reduced to such a form. Basically, we can use this formulation whenever we have a set of variables or parameters x_i, $i = 1, 2 \ldots n$, which, through some process, however devious, can be made to produce a number, say φ, whose magnitude is a measure of goodness (or badness) in some precisely defined sense. The problem can be further complicated by the existence of constraints on the range of values that the x_i are permitted to take. The problems are related, since finding the maximum of φ is the same as finding the minimum of φ^{-1} or $-\varphi$, and also related to finding the zero of all the $\partial\varphi/\partial x_i$.

In its crudest form the problem is like the ancient game of hunt the thimble, in which a tentative step in any direction is rewarded by the information 'warmer' or 'colder'. In the latter case we must retrace our steps and try again in a different direction. Success is assured *eventually*, but eventually may take a long time, especially when the thimble is hidden in n-dimensional space.

In on-line computing we must be prepared to face the possibility that hunt the thimble is the only method available. Now the hunt for a *global* minimum (i.e. the smallest of a number of minima in the given space) is usually best conducted by some form of random or systematic search. Even the search for a local minimum can be converted to one for a global minimum if the ideal function is sufficiently corrupted by noise for a number of false minima to be introduced. Let us examine this problem in relation to the most popular method for a directed search.

6.12.1 GRADIENT DESCENT METHODS

For a function of one variable, Newton's formula provides a method of improving approximation x_k to a zero of the function by producing a better approximation x_{k+1} where

$$(6.75) \qquad x_{k+1} = x_k - \frac{f(x_k)}{f'(x_k)}$$

Figure 6.17 shows that this is usually a reasonable procedure on a geometrical basis, but it is no more than a reasonable procedure, and far from being infallible. If the reader has any doubts on this matter he should, before reading further, try this iteration on a function such as

$$(6.76) \qquad f(x) = \text{sig}\,(x)|x|^{\frac{1}{2}}$$

[where $\text{sig}\,(x) = +1$ if $x > 1$,
and $\text{sig}\,(x) = -1$ if $x < 1$, and $|x|^{\frac{1}{2}}$ is the positive square root of the magnitude of x].

Newton's method does not, of course, directly solve our minimum-search problem. There are two possible ways of adapting it to this purpose. Firstly, since a minimum of $f(x)$ represents a zero of $f'(x)$ we can use the method to search for the latter

$$(6.77) \qquad \text{i.e.} \qquad x_{k+1} = x_k - \frac{f'(x_k)}{f''(x_k)}$$

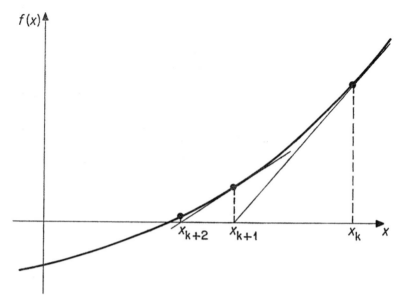

Figure 6.17   Newton's zero approximation method for a well-behaved function

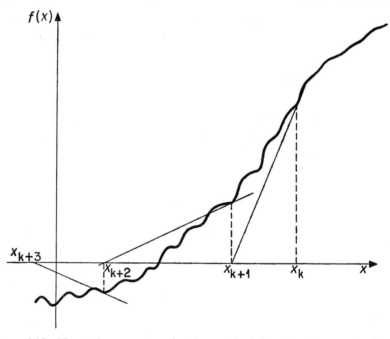

Figure 6.18   Newton's zero approximation method for a function corruption by noise

a method which is very useful when the two differential coefficients can be obtained analytically, as is often the case in mathematical computations, or the function is extremely well behaved and uncorrupted by noise, a circumstance unfortunately rare in on-line work. Remember that the operation of double differentiation applies an amplitude weighting of ω^2 in the frequency domain. In Figure 6.18 we reproduce Figure 6.17 but with a small amount of noise added. Evidently under these circumstances the procedure is not so reasonable.

The second possibility is to use the iteration of equation 6.75 unaltered, with the idea that a step of such a length in the downward direction is probably a good thing. Figure 6.19 shows that this can give a better approach

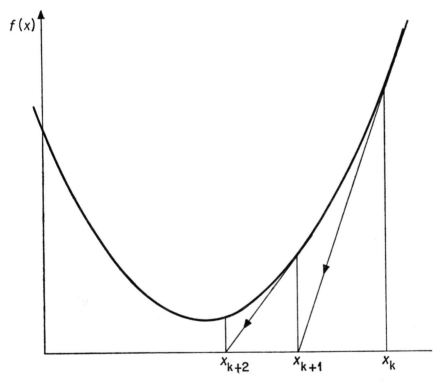

x_{k+2} x_{k+1} x_k

Figure 6.19   Newton's method can also be used to approach a minimum

to the minimum, but Figure 6.20 shows that this is not necessarily so. With a reasonably well behaved function the gradient descent method is an obvious one and the above version of it does at least provide a suggestion for the step length, without which we may become involved in a vast number of steps which are too small or greatly overshoot the minimum in one step.

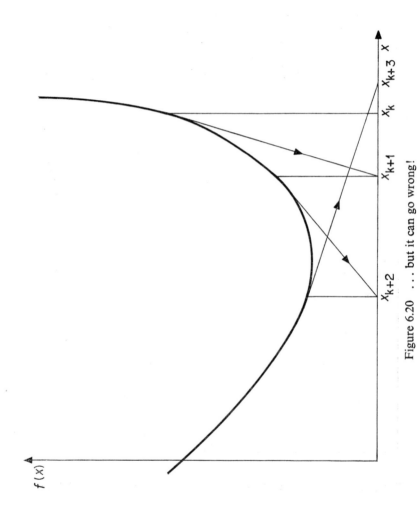

Figure 6.20   . . . but it can go wrong!

It is important to note that we are not obliged to accept the result of an unsuccessful attempt, and it should be an invariable rule that such a method should be mixed with another so that in the event of failure the routine does not enter an unstable condition, as would occur with a function behaving like equation 6.76.

We have so far only considered a one-dimensional form of the problem, and it is the essence of the gradient descent method that it translates each problem locally into such a form. If, for example, we have the problem of a criterion function of two variables $\varphi(x_i, x_j)$ we can imagine φ as a surface plotted above the (x_i, x_j) plane, then we can consider the one-dimensional function of a new variable x represented by a vertical cut through the surface in the direction of the steepest gradient of φ. We achieve an increment δx in the direction of this new variable by incrementing x_i by

$$\frac{\delta x}{[(\partial\varphi/\partial x_i)^2 + (\partial\varphi/\partial x_j)^2]^{\frac{1}{2}}} \cdot \frac{\partial\varphi}{\partial x_i}$$

and x_j by

$$\frac{\delta x}{[(\partial\varphi/\partial x_i)^2 + (\partial\varphi/\partial x_j)^2]^{\frac{1}{2}}} \cdot \frac{\partial\varphi}{\partial x_j}$$

Hence as before we obtain our new estimate x by

$$x \to x + \Delta x \quad \text{where} \quad \Delta x = \frac{-\varphi(x)}{\varphi'(x)}$$

and the magnitude of $\varphi'(x)$ is

$$\left[\left(\frac{\partial\varphi}{\partial x_i}\right)^2 + \left(\frac{\partial\varphi}{\partial x_j}\right)^2\right]^{\frac{1}{2}}$$

so that the increment of our original variable x_i is

$$\Delta x_i = \frac{\varphi(\partial\varphi/\partial x_i)}{(\partial\varphi/\partial x_i)^2 + (\partial\varphi/\partial x_j)^2}$$

the equation for Δx_j being similar.

We can of course extend this argument to any number of variables so that

(6.78)
$$\Delta x_r = \frac{\varphi(\partial\varphi/\partial x_r)}{\sum_{r=i}^{n} (\partial\varphi/\partial x_r)^2}$$

or to write the result in vector form

(6.79)
$$\Delta \mathbf{x} = \mathbf{x} - \frac{\varphi\nabla\varphi}{|\nabla\varphi|^2}$$

where x is a vector $[x_i, x_j \ldots x_r \ldots x_n]$

and $\nabla\varphi$ is a vector $\left[\dfrac{\partial\varphi}{\partial x_i}, \dfrac{\partial\varphi}{\partial x_j} \ldots \dfrac{\partial\varphi}{\partial x_r} \ldots \dfrac{\partial\varphi}{\partial x_n}\right]$

Equation 6.79 above represents the generalized Newton Raphson iteration method for n variables. Note that although it guarantees a step in the right direction it does not guarantee a step of the right length, as Figure 6.20 illustrates. However, without repeating the whole calculation, it is easy to test for $\varphi(x) < \varphi(x + \Delta x)$ and in the event of failure try a scaled-down increment $k\ \Delta x$, where $k < 1$. Thus the least we have achieved is a step length in the right direction of the order and dimensionality of x, and we would otherwise be reduced to trying arbitrary numerical increments which would be in error by orders for each component of the vector. It is, of course, necessary to recalculate the magnitude and direction of the gradient at each step, as the one-dimensional approximation is only a short range one.

The success of a gradient method depends entirely on how well the gradient can be evaluated; even then it is restricted to finding a local minimum. When the gradient can be obtained analytically it is often possible to achieve rapid convergence to the minimum.

There is no quick foolproof method of finding a global minimum, and, as Figure 6.18 illustrates, noise corruption can convert even a local minimum search into a global one. One must assume that the range of each variable is restricted to a finite region, otherwise the global search time is bound to be infinite. The strategy adopted depends largely on the exact nature of the problem, and/or prior knowledge of φ. In some applications, for example, it is possible to proceed in the main calculation with a temporary optimization while continuing the search for a better one as a background program. In others we can prescribe a level of the criterion function φ which is low enough to be acceptable so that the search can be terminated. Otherwise we are obliged to search the whole space, though if it is known that the magnitude of grad φ has an upper bound it may be possible to use a fairly coarse-meshed search grid and use a gradient search for the final home run.

In problems such as the unimodal (one minimum) function which has been converted to a multimodal one by noise corruption, as in Figure 6.18, we have the prior knowledge that the path to the global minimum is through a succession of better and better minima.

In this case a possible procedure is to alternate a gradient search method with a random search one so that we find each minimum exactly before probing around in the near space for a better one. Figure 6.18 also reminds us that the stabilizing factor k, referred to above, may have to be very small in such a case.

The random search method here would consist of calculating the present value of $\varphi(x)$ then generating a pseudorandom vector ξ, calculating $\varphi(x + \xi)$ and testing for $\varphi(x + \xi) < \varphi(x)$. If the test fails we repeat the process with another ξ; if it succeeds we initiate a gradient search for the new minimum. Sometimes a Gaussian distribution is used for the components of ξ, but the Laplace distribution is easier to generate (equation 6.71) and it has the properties required—a zero mean value, a single dispersion parameter and an unbounded domain. It is possible to increase the dispersion parameter slightly on each failure so that on average the search is progressively widened, though it is wise to put a limit on this process.

The ideal method of establishing φ is of course very dependent upon the nature of the process being controlled or measured. Often we have prior knowledge of the values, say $\hat{y}_i$, of the output variables required in which case φ can be made equal to the square of the euclidian distance from this ideal point

$$\varphi = \sum_{i=1}^{n} (\hat{y}_i - y_i)^2$$

or we may require to establish some functional relationship

$$f(y) = 0$$

where f itself would be a suitable form for φ.

We might have some model, defined by parameters μ so that the model for the given x provides outputs Y through some functional relationship

$$Y = f(\mu, x)$$

and the squared euclidian distance is again suitable

$$\varphi = \sum_{i=1}^{n} (y_i - Y_i)^2$$

Some variables might be considered more important than others, so the first form, for example, would be modified to

$$\varphi = \sum_{i=1}^{n} W_i(\hat{y}_i - y_i)^2$$

where the W_i are weighting coefficients.

The most complicated case is where the fundamental relationship which produces y from x is stochastic and time varying. In that case the criterion function would need to be some sort of average over time, weighted in such a way that values in the distant past are given less import than more recent values, for example.

$$\varphi(t) = \int_t^\infty \sum_{i=1}^n [\hat{y}_i - y_i(t)]^2 \exp [-a(t - \tau)] \, d\tau$$

or in discrete form

$$\varphi(h) = \sum_{k=0}^\infty \left(\sum_{i=1}^n [\hat{y}_i - y_i(h)]^2 \exp [-a(k - K)] \right)$$

This form is not as difficult to realize as it looks since it represents a smoothing process on φ of the leaky-integrator type which as we have seen (equation 6.31) can be realized by means of a simple iteration.

6.13   Conclusion

In this chapter we have merely dipped into the vast store of mathematical knowledge that is available to enhance our use of the on-line computer, and have completely ignored many techniques such as curve fitting, interpolation, etc., which are part of the standard repertoire of off-line computing [CoMeLaFa] in order to find space for aspects of a more on-line, real-time nature. There are other aspects of mathematical technique which are normally considered to lie in the realm of pure mathematics which can also greatly increase our understanding. Examples of these are linear algebra [LinAlgMir], the theory of functions [FuncTitch], and especially functional analysis [FuncAnVul]. The last named gives a beautifully complete picture of the meaning of techniques such as Fourier transformation and optimization, and it provides a framework on which to build an overall view of on-line measurement techniques.

In particular functional analysis provides a number of powerful theorems in a highly condensed form. One of these is the contraction mapping theorem which can be used in appropriate circumstances to generate algorithms of guaranteed convergence. There are various other methods which we have been unable to mention, such as conjugate gradient, and their description as a group is best presented in the language of functional analysis. Incidentally, we have not encumbered this chapter with descriptions of some of the well known methods (such as binary search, Regula Falsi, Secant, etc. for root solving) as these will be found in any text-book of off-line computing [e.g. CoMeLaFa]. Also in the literature of control can be found a discussion of gradient-free methods of hill climbing.

Part 2: Using the Tools

Chapter VII

The Scientific Instrument as a Computer Peripheral

7.1 INTRODUCTION

We are at present going through a transitional period during which a wide range of special devices is being produced to perform various measurements on physical systems; for example, system response in the frequency or time domain. These are often very elegant in concept, and carry out their restricted range of tasks efficiently. They represent the consummation of the hardware approach to the measurement problem. In most fields they are bound eventually to give way to the general purpose on-line digital computer. For, though they possess the advantages that go with a dedicated design; namely, efficient use of components and ease of application; they also carry heavy penalties. Principally, they are extravagant in their demands on that most expensive commodity—the time of skilled designers and producers; they are immutable and so cannot fulfil the need for slight changes in the measurement procedure which inevitably occur; at times when the particular dedicated task is not required the hardware is idle.

What is tending to occur at the moment is that a computer is being drafted into the laboratory to cope with tasks for which there is no special instrumentation. It is then found to have spare capacity which makes economic nonsense of the purchase of further elaborate instruments whose functions can be carried out by program.

It is important not to confuse this trend with one which is perhaps apparently contradictory—the appearance of special hardware processor units. The principal difference is that these are conceived as computer peripherals, though they may eventually become inherent parts of the computer. Common examples are the processes of Fourier transformation or correlation, which if frequently required can monopolize central processor time. In such cases it makes economic sense to provide a separate dedicated box to which the computer can delegate the task to be performed quickly and efficiently in parallel with other calculations.

Briefly, we are saying that a suitably programmed computer is sufficiently versatile to personate any advanced laboratory instrument. There are two major restrictions to this statement. Firstly, the computer's performance is constrained by the transducers available to it. Secondly, measurements to be made at speeds which strain the resources of current technology demand dedicated instrumentation. Thus in the computer-based laboratory, instruments tend to be retained to perform the functions of transduction and condensation. Consider some instruments culled at random from the scientific literature:

> gas chromatograph
> automatic ellipsometer
> Langmuir probe
> laser doppler flowmeter
> Hall effect probe
> ion vacuum gauge
> strain gauge with auto-balance bridge
> sampling oscilloscope

Each is related to a specific physical quantity which needs to be measured; each is capable of producing an electrical signal which contains a measure of this quantity; each has its own characteristic response time, dynamic range and noise amplitude; each is capable of playing the part of a sense organ to give a computer access to the physical quantity with which it is associated.

Equally one can name any number of devices which are *active* in relation to a physical quantity and are therefore capable of allowing a computer to exercise control over that quantity.

For example:

> electromagnetic flow valve
> light modulating crystal
> stepping motor
> electromagnet
> flash tube
> heater element

Obviously, the discussion of a wide field such as that covered by the instruments and devices mentioned can only be at a very general level, and in this chapter we will attempt to establish some general principles. They will probably be best appreciated if the reader has in mind some specific application. The best stimulus to learning computing is the desire to solve a particular problem, and this is more effective than any number of text-books and courses.

7.2   ELIMINATION OF THE HUMAN ELEMENT

The influence of human intervention on the result of a measurement can be most subtle and unexpected; so much so that the only safe strategy is to try to eliminate it altogether. The experience of one of the authors with a particular measurement problem might be a suitable illustration of this point.

Measurements of the breakdown strength of insulating oils have been made for many years by the simple procedure of raising the applied voltage manually, and when breakdown takes place, recording the level of voltage that had been obtained immediately before the discharge. The literature contained quotations of many results obtained by such a technique, and since they showed remarkably low scatter, the situation appeared to be most satisfactory. When one of us tried to make such measurements for the first time, however, the results were highly scattered; but *with experience* this scatter began to reduce. Now in the art of measurement there is a mystical school which would nod approvingly at such evidence of skill increasing with practice, but it should sound a warning bell in the mind of one interested in objective determination of physical values.

An experiment was carried out in which a number of unskilled operators were asked to make several determinations of the breakdown strength of a particular sample, and the voltage/time waveforms were recorded separately. It was found that the raw recruit would apply the voltage slowly and almost linearly with time, while watching the kilovoltmeter intently so as not to miss the vital moment. However, once he became a 'skilled' operator, he would raise the voltage rapidly at first and then more and more slowly as the expected value was approached, and his results became more consistent.

Further study with completely automatic apparatus controlled by an accurate ramp generator showed that in fact the breakdown strength was a highly scattered phenomenon which tended to increase slightly with the rate of rise of voltage, since this tended to control the time spent in any stress range, while breakdown itself tended to occur randomly at an average rate which increased rapidly with stress. Indeed, the statistical distribution turned out to be of a special shape (characteristic of weak-link processes) which had hitherto been completely hidden by the 'skill' of the operators. Nowadays, all our breakdown measurements are made by a computer.

In general, the influence of the human experimenter, if any, is an unknown and indeterminate factor, and owing to the incredibly devious power of the subconscious, it can be subtle yet far reaching. Computer control of an experiment forces the experimenter to lay his cards on the table by declaring at the programming stage precisely what rights of intervention he wishes to reserve, and ideally this arrangement preserves the rôle of the human brain as the presiding control element while constraining its capacity for underhand mischief.

7.3   Practical Aspects of the Controlling and Monitoring of Processes

Like the human brain, the on-line computer is required to interact with the outside world through its transducers, and to do so on the basis of a distorted view of the external conditions. It does not possess, however, those vast resources of what amount to inspired guesswork in the brain which make it so effective under adverse conditions of information distortion. For the same reason it is not, in general, prey to gross errors of interpretation such as those characteristically produced by optical illusions. The experimenter must therefore base his programming on a sound understanding of both the physical process and the limitations of his access to it. This understanding will be partly quantitative and partly intuitive, and the object of preliminary study of the problem should be to maximize both of these, but especially the former. Close study will then be required to assess the demands to be made on the digital processor, and to pare these down as much as possible; for such demands are the factors which circumscribe one's future freedom of action.

When the experiment is under way, the computer will perform a number of tasks. The following are some examples:

> control of the stimulus applied to the test object
> acceptance of data
> recording some of these
> monitoring data without recording
> generating an alarm if these exceed certain limits
> taking cognisance that various events have occurred
> relating these to real time
> operating subsidiary control loops, e.g. for temperature control
> varying the function or procedure.

Depending on the circumstances the operator may also play a substantial rôle (or none at all). This would consist of such activities as

> separate (e.g. visual) monitoring of the test object
> taking note of monitoring information provided by the computer
> intervening, if necessary, to abort or change direction of the experiment.

Needless to say, all such activities must be anticipated at the program development stage, but well before this the ground will have been prepared in the preliminary study of the physical process and of the methods of interacting with it.

One of the most important aspects is the inherent speed of the process, and a principal design quantity will be the highest *essential* frequency present. This will immediately determine the minimum sampling frequency and the cut-off frequency of the low-pass pre-filtering. A further important quantity is the number of calculations necessary between samples. Wherever possible this will be set at zero by relying on sampling through data interrupts with calculations being initiated by program interrupt when the data are assembled. At the other end of the time scale, a very important factor is the longest response time present. This will immediately set a lower limit on the period used for periodic testing (e.g. by repeated pulses or by PRBS).

A further set of design criteria arises from the anticipated range of the experimental variables. Naturally an attempt will be made to make this correspond to the dynamic range of any instruments employed, and correspondingly the full length of the transmitted word should be utilized. On the other hand it is usually necessary to tolerate some redundancy in this respect for the sake of avoiding amplitudes greater than full scale and the corresponding digital overflow.

Concerning the range of variables, we also have to consider various constraints which may occur, and whether these are of the 'hard' or 'soft' variety. This may involve dealing with combined functions of the variables. Some important quantities may not be directly accessible, and they may have to be computed with some loss of definition. To illustrate these let us consider a very simple measurement that would not normally require the capability of an on-line computer—the measurement of the characteristics of a transistor. The test-object might be placed in a temperature control bath with an input and output transducer, e.g. a thermistor and a heating element, which would enable the computer to set the environmental temperature. The constraining factor in this case, however, would be the junction temperature, which is not directly accessible. The quantities measured and controlled would be voltages and currents, which would require D–A and A–D converters, with resistors to act as current-to-voltage transducers. A common procedure is to avoid the direct issue of the constraining factor in such a case by placing the constraint on a quantity closely related to it, namely the electrical power input to the device. Even this quantity would have to be computed indirectly from $W = VI$, and the constraint is familiar to us as a rectangular hyperbola on the plane of collector voltage and collector current, which must not be transgressed.

This simple example illustrates quite well some of the features of the constraint problem in general. The actual physical constraint has been replaced by a more accessible one, i.e. one which can be expressed directly in terms of measured and controlled variables. There is inevitably a loss of definition with such a substitution, and for this reason one is usually forced to set a more pessimistic limit than might otherwise be necessary. The transistor circuit designer is well aware that the static power maximum can actually be greatly exceeded during a brief transient, as it is only a stand-in for a device temperature. The response pattern relating the two quantities is intuitively understood to be of a low-pass nature. A closer, though in a sense more indirect, approach to this particular constraint might be to try to estimate the relevant physical quantity. This would require not only a knowledge of the measurement and control variables, but also a reasonably accurate model of the system. Such a model would need to be based on estimates of the thermal capacity and thermal resistance of the device, and the ambient temperature would enter as an important measured variable. An experimenter who is concerned with the detailed structure and behaviour of the device might go as far as setting up an elaborate three-dimensional discrete model with calculation of the nodal temperatures by a relaxation process.

At such a stage, however, the dangers of sophistication have to be considered. The foundations, which are the degrees of precision to which variables and parameters are known, may not be sufficient to support the structure. Not only the accuracy but also the response of the transducers must be considered. Temperature, for example, can only be sensed through a transducer which has a thermal capacity and resistance of its own, so there is always a characteristic time lag associated with its measurement.

Thus when any elaborate indirect method is contemplated one must always ask the question—How well is it justified by the source material available? The central rôle of transducers in such considerations is clear: they are as important as one's senses are to oneself. There was a Hitchcock thriller in which a disabled photographer foiled the intentions of a would-be assailant by firing flash bulbs in a darkened room. He was using his knowledge of the adaptive characteristics of the human eye as a transducer to incapacitate the central processor which was dependent upon it. Similar occurrences can arise in the experimental situation where there is, for example, a characteristic slow recovery from overload. Several factors affect the definition of the data received by the central processor: the effective 'closeness' of the transducer to the events in space and time, transducer error, sampling and quantization noise, etc.

Further questions must also be asked in relation to the employment of a particular method. Does it rely on some assumption (e.g. of linearity in cross-correlation with a PRBS stimulus) which may not be fully justified? Is the process under consideration stationary? Is the signal transmission problem likely to be important? The answer to this last question will depend upon the physical distances involved, the speed–accuracy demands of the measurement and the hostility of the electromagnetic environment. It may also be partly resolved by the answer to another important question: Is it possible to condense the data before transmission?

7.4 SPEED AND ACCURACY REQUIREMENTS

The establishment of the Heisenberg uncertainty principle as one of the basic tenets of physics has made us very conscious of the essential importance of various 'trade-off' relationships which appear, if in a rather more loosely defined form, in applied science and technology. The most important of these in computer applications is the relationship between speed and accuracy. In general we can say that, for a given technology of construction, either of these can be enhanced at the expense of the other. It is also convenient to think in terms of a speed–accuracy product which is a constant, characteristic of any particular system and a measure of its efficiency (and incidentally its cost).

Consideration of this factor is at its most important at the initial stage of the computer system development, and the control of a slow process such as a chemical plant would obviously be less demanding than that of a fast process such as a ballistic missile system. On the whole, as these ideas are rather vague, we tend to make the system rather more capable than our requirements seem to dictate, but not grossly and expensively so.

The same idea enters into software development, especially in on-line work: so we can, for example, locate the roots of an equation either quickly and crudely or slowly and precisely. Here, however, speed and accuracy will be individually bounded by the hardware capability in the form of basic operation time and word length.

Each peripheral of the computer also has its own speed–accuracy characteristics, and when we are developing a new one we must think in these terms. The aim should be to employ the simplest (and therefore the cheapest and most reliable) methods possible. If the speed–accuracy requirements are high, then problems such as D–A conversion, signal transmission and interface control can be formidable. If they are low, various short-cuts and multiplex arrangements become available.

Indeed, it is convenient to group together peripherals of low requirement, and to this end some manufacturers supply a slow multiplexed channel to obviate the unnecessary duplication of interface equipment. Obviously both the speed and the accuracy are individually fixed at the actual interface by the word length and transfer speed, but prior to this they are interchangeable. Thus a 24 bit parallel interface can handle 8 bit words at three times the rate if they are grouped together in three bytes of 8 bits via a suitable hardware buffering arrangement. We have seen that in some correlation applications a 1 bit accuracy is sufficient, so the same interface could handle these, even if they arrive at 24 times the maximum transfer rate. Conversely, some instruments have a wide dynamic range and accuracy, and to do them justice more than one transfer may be required for each sample of the data. One way of doing this would be to transfer only increments and decrements of the data, with an enhanced sampling rate to ensure that these are in range, but this is of course an error-perpetuating process. In its extreme form this method can be used to convey complicated information such as audio signals along a 1 bit channel (delta modulation).

On the whole, the accuracy requirement will be determined by the inherent accuracy of the peripheral instrument, but it may be relaxed in a particular application (though if it is grossly so one must consider whether one is using a sledge-hammer to crack a nut). The speed will be determined by the application, but the response time of the instrument will place an upper bound on it. In a non-buffered system, the maximum speed is determined by the permissible transfer rate in the slowest part of the channel, though, as we have seen, buffering allows this restriction to be reduced slightly to apply only to the average speed.

We have not in this discussion so far suggested a unit for the speed of the channel, but it is fairly self evident that bits per second is the only satisfactory one as this is the quantity for which a strict continuity equation applies. It is quite common for the effective parallel word length to take on two or three different values at different points in a complete channel, so it is too mutable a quantity on which to base a measure of speed.

Usually, then, it is desirable to convert information rates to bits/second at the outset when planning a channel. Thus if an instrument measures to a precision of one part in a thousand of full scale and the process to be maintained has a highest frequency present of 100 Hz, then effectively one 10 bit word must be generated every 5 ms, and the channel throughout its length must maintain the capacity of 2000 bits/second. If the computer interface were a 24 bit parallel one, the required transfer rate would be 2000/24 words per second in theory, but this would require such complex hardware juggling that undoubtedly a 20 bit unit would be preferred so that the transfer rate would be 100 words/second. Note that the multiplexing necessary in the hardware for this example would be mirrored by a demultiplexing process in the software to unravel the 20 bit stored words into their 10 bit meaningful components, so the designer might well decide to eschew such complications and use only 10 bits of the interface. This could only be allowed if the computer system has spare capacity: by which we mean mainly that the consequent doubling of the interrupt demand on this channel would not seriously impair the overall interrupt handling capacity, though other factors, such as efficient use of the store, may also be significant. Note that if in the above example each sample were to be consecutively stored, the store would be used up at a rate of nearly 1 K every 10 seconds, so an important consideration in speed determination is what is to be done with the samples when they arrive in the computer. At minimum, certain housekeeping orders have to be carried out between data interrupts, e.g. compare the total number of samples so far received against the total number required, add one to the index register containing the destination address of the samples, etc.

We see that there are constraints at either end of the channel on the speed requirement, and the middle part—the transmission system—has to be tailored to fit these. Difficulties only really arise if either high speeds or long distances are involved. For high speeds and short distances, a parallel transmission system is usual. For low speeds and long distances a serial form is preferred. The combination of high speeds and long distances is to be avoided by anyone who does not wish to change his research topic to one of data transmission. In our experience it is wise to try to keep all transmission distances for high-speed channels to less than 20 metres.

Note that we have used the word accuracy rather loosely here, and in the general measurements sense we really mean precision, but one would normally make the effort to balance these. For example it would be nonsensical to state currents to a 10 bit accuracy if the transducer were a 10% tolerance resistor, *unless* the object of the experiment was simply to compare currents through the same transducer, in which case stability would be a far more important factor than tolerance. Within the computer, accuracy and precision can only be equated if care is taken not to discard foolishly the least significant bits of the word, by for example, allowing intermediate values in a fixed point calculation to be too small.

7.5   MODES OF OPERATION (CONTROL AND STATUS WORDS)

Data do not constitute the only information we require to transfer between the peripheral and the computer. The more complex peripherals may be capable of acting in a variety of different ways, and the precise interpretation placed on the transmitted data word is just one of the factors which may vary with changes of function. It is obvious that there must be absolute unison between computer and peripheral as to the function that any intercommunicated data relate to. Such unison can only be achieved by the communication of extra information in the form of one or more words.

The computer may be required to instruct the peripheral to execute some action, for example:

  hesitate, no more data available
  interpret the following data in a specified way
  change the sampling rate
  scan a different combination of input channels.

Words conveying such information in the direction computer-to-peripheral may be termed *control* words.

Similarly the peripheral may be required to apprise the computer of its current condition, for example:

the pen (of a plotter) has crossed the edge of the page

the requested action has been completed

the action cannot be completed because . . .

this is the number of ones sent so far, check it against the number received

the format of those data is not acceptable.

We assign the name *status* word for this type of information transfer in the direction peripheral to computer.

A good on-line computer will have some means of labelling such information by means, for example, of a separate line in the standard interface format. Otherwise it is necessary to sacrifice one bit of the full possible data word to represent such a label.

The designer who is creating a new peripheral from a scientific instrument will usually find that the number of distinctive control or status combinations required is extremely limited, if only by the necessity to provide for their interpretation (by hardware in the case of the control word). Thus even a short computer word will have more than enough information capacity, and normally only a few bits of the word will be used for this purpose. This means that extra gating to direct the received word to the control section of the peripheral logic need only be applied to a few of the input lines. In a more advanced computer-style instrument, such as the one discussed at the end of this chapter, however, the more extensive establishment of digital control means that much fuller use is made of the capacity of control and status words.

The interpretation of the control and status words is one of the prime functions of the software–hardware package associated with the instrument. The main constraints upon this package are that the extra hardware should be kept to a minimum and the software interface to the user's program should be as simple and logical as possible within the context of the way the instrument is to be used. This means that the duty of assembling the control words and analysing the status words is delegated to the dedicated software. In a complicated situation, where there is, for example, a large number of possible control combinations, such words would be assembled in a stored table, and to obviate the repetitious transfer of constant information, one bit may be reserved as a flag to mark the fact that an entry to the table has been changed; so that the output subroutine would scan the flags and only initiate control transfers where a change is required, resetting the flags as it does so. This technique simplifies the user's task and minimizes the number of transfers.

7.6 TRANSFER FAILURES

One of the most important aspects of the integrated design of a hardware–software package for a particular instrument is consideration of possible fault conditions. Only too often lack of foresight allows an irretrievable situation to develop unnecessarily. One example of such a case occurred in a software package supplied to the authors for use with a digital plotter. It was found that if through some miscalculation the plotter pen hit the end-stop, the subsequent condition could only be cleared by reloading the whole program; this is inexcusable. In such a case after resetting the pen the user should be provided with the alternatives of continuing the program from the point at which it was interrupted or going back to the beginning.

This sort of bad design can make the whole system reliability much lower than it need be, since it then becomes critically dependent on each component, whereas in many instances a fault situation could be quite easily redeemed, or at least a major part of an experiment could be completed. On the other hand, of course, there are many cases where a single transfer failure logically invalidates the whole experiment. Thus the designer should feel obliged to give the user the maximum freedom of choice.

A point worth re-emphasis is that, though the designer and user may be the same person at different points of time, it still pays to keep the user in mind as an independent person (indeed, there is more merit in taking the precaution of visualizing him as something of a simpleton). All of us, unless blessed with a photographic memory, have the experience of puzzling over one of our own old designs or programs with the feeling that it was produced by a stranger.

The most fundamental form of transfer failure is one which occurs within the actual basic handshake sequence. It is one of the strengths of the handshake system that such a failure cannot go undetected, as the interface circuits would not normally return to quiescence unless each signal has elicited its appropriate response. Obviously such a condition could not be allowed to persist, and it is expedient to provide simple timing circuits which monitor the duration of the handshake, and, in the event of its exceeding a certain interval, initiate appropriate actions. During the failed handshake, the channel concerned is monopolizing the data highway by preventing any other channel being gated into it, so the actions to be taken, in order of importance to the rest of the system, are

1 Reset the interface logic
2 Set a flag to record failure
3 Initiate a program interrupt.

Thus we see that one of the first duties of the interrupt program is to inspect the transfer failure flag.

Of course, a wide variety of failures can occur, and there are various degrees of subtlety in their effects. For example, the parallel transmission system might lose one of its bits through component failure, and any numerical sequences passed through it would be effectively distorted by added binary random noise. Data containing parity, such as 8 bit alphanumeric characters, are protected against corruption. Numbers can be protected to some extent by the separate transmission of test numbers at intervals. For example, if all-noughts and all-ones can be transmitted successfully, then the channel is free of permanent faults. Such a check will not, however, avoid the effects of intermittent faults, which can only be obviated by some form of redundant coding, of which parity is a simple example.

In most experimental applications, it is not disastrous if some data are lost, as the experiment can usually be repeated. The possibility of basing a scientific deduction on some faulty data is much more serious, so the normal response to a faulty transfer will be to abort the experiment (not necessarily by stopping the computer, which may have other processes on-line, but by suspending the peripheral and conveying a suitable message to the operator). The other obvious precaution is never to base deduction on one run of an experiment, though there is always the slight possibility that a persistent fault will corrupt the results of successive runs in the same way.

Thus we return to the point that the design of an experiment, including any special hardware, can only be properly carried out on the basis of a full understanding of its fundamental nature, and this applies to the anticipated responses to fault conditions. Status words can be used as a means of checking that all has gone well. One could, for example, at the end of the experiment, send the total number of binary ones that have been transmitted in the course of the experiment so that it can be checked against the same quantity as received and recorded by the software, or indeed any other global measure which is conveniently obtained, though such a procedure would incur extra hardware and computation overheads.

7.7 RESPONSE

All instruments possess a basic response pattern which determines their range of application. This pattern may be considered in either the time or the frequency domain, whichever is the most immediately applicable. There is always an upper frequency (lower time) bound, and this tends to be a dominating factor. There may also be a lower frequency (upper time) bound; when, for example, direct coupling or its equivalent is absent. Furthermore, the response between these bounds may deviate from the undistorting ideal, which is flat frequency and linear phase (or an impulse in the time domain). The bandwidth of the instrument may be determined by the devices used in its construction, or it may be deliberately restricted to obviate noise problems. In the light of the noise elimination methods discussed in Chapter 6 such a restriction may become unnecessarily excessive when the instrument is employed as a computer peripheral, and it is important to remember that one is often free to remove or modify any filtering circuits included for this purpose.

We are obliged to neglect problems of non-linearity in this general discussion, as such problems can normally only be treated in terms of particular cases. We have, however, noted that the computer is particularly adept at dealing with transducer non-linearities, though if they appear in combination with other forms of distortion the difficulties can be immense. While no active system is actually linear, it can usually be regarded as such over its working range.

Most of the substantive problems of measurement involve pushing the techniques to some limit, e.g. measuring very low currents or very fast transients. In such cases one does not have as much freedom to control the response pattern of the instrument as would otherwise be available. The trade-off between sensitivity and speed is a constant pre-occupation, and the further requirement of undistorting response can be very inhibiting. Fortunately, as we shall see, the computer can often correct for the instrument response, either by direct deconvolution with the known response, or by an adaptive method.

Let us at this stage consider a simple example, the measurement of extremely low current transients. The transducer in this case would be an electrometer amplifier, which is chosen for its very high input impedance. The sensitivity is determined by the value of the feedback resistor which might be, say, 10^{12} Ω giving a sensitivity of 1 volt/pA. At these high impedance levels the response tends to be determined by stray capacitance, which is in turn determined by the need to screen the device. Most users take account of the feedback stray capacitance which reduces the ideal response to the single RC integrating type. Thus a feedback capacitance of 1 pF produces a response time constant of 1 second. Note that a computer process to correct for this would be one which greatly emphasizes high frequencies, and this would tend to be noise amplifying.

An aspect of stray capacitance that is often ignored is the distributed capacitance between the feedback resistor and earth. Its importance came to light in the authors' laboratory after much puzzling over some strange transients observed in a particular experiment. When a physical explanation failed to emerge, the whole measuring system was tested by applying a current pulse to the electrometer. The digital plotter at the end of the chain dutifully recorded, instead of the expected exponential decay, a damped oscillatory response. It was then remembered that the screening of the electrometer amplifier had recently been 'improved'.

An explanation of this phenomenon can be made if one examines an approximate lumped equivalent circuit including the feedback and earth stray capacitance as in Figure 7.1. The reader is recommended to derive as an exercise an expression for the transfer impedance of the circuit assuming a virtual earth at the amplifier input. He will find that it has two poles which are complex if C_2 exceeds C_1. The circuit is critically damped if these two capacitors are equal, and under-damped if C_1 is the greater.

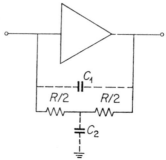

Figure 7.1   Lumped equivalent circuit for an operational amplifier used as an electrometer

We quote this example to underline a moral that we thereby learned the hard way, namely that the response of the measuring system should be checked after any change, however trivial it might seem. Remember particularly that the measuring system includes any test-cell, test-jig or other structure at the input. Having said this we are immediately open to the criticism that the precise input point is not always available to accept a test stimulus, for example in the case of electrodes attached to the human cranium for EEG work. This is particularly unfortunate when we are deprived of access to the variable part of the structure, and one can only recommend applying the test-signal to the first available point in the chain, which leaves us with nothing more than a rather vague phenomenological approach to the preceding part of the system. One can usually, of course, make quite sensible deductions from prior knowledge of the signal source which obviate the need for such checks; for example variations of shunt capacitance are unlikely to be important in dealing with a low-impedance, low-frequency source. In general, however, assumptions are dangerous and there is no substitute for an actual measurement of the response.

We have quoted a case where a short pulse was an adequate test-signal, but there are various other forms of signal which would better suit particular cases, e.g. a swept-frequency sinusoid, or a pseudorandom binary sequence, which has a precisely known harmonic structure, white noise, or indeed any defined signal for which the anticipated response is known. Clearly, however, no information can be obtained about any part of the frequency domain response of a linear system for which the components are absent in the test signal; so, for example, a pseudorandom or any other periodic signal will automatically suppress response information lying between harmonics of the periodic frequency, which should therefore be chosen carefully.

Often our reason for checking the response of an instrument is merely to determine whether we can safely ignore it, and we should not forget that this consideration applies equally to output devices. Minor fault conditions can occur at any time without producing any manifestation other than misleading results. In a D–A converter, for example, one of the output bits might fail, thereby introducing a random element in the response: an electro-mechanical transducer might develop backlash through wear: an electrode might suffer deterioration of chemical origin, such as oxidation. In such cases the computer program would proceed as though the signal applied to the external system were still ideal.

Thus without apology we underline once again the dangers of sophistication, in both its proper and its abused sense (the dictionary definition of sophisticate is: to falsify, to doctor, to artificialize, to give a fashionable air of worldly wisdom to. One can only admire the disarming honesty of the many authors in the scientific literature who describe their new methods as sophisticated). The computer offers enormous possibilities for sophistication, and the only safe attitude is a distinctly suspicious one.

A further important point to bear in mind is that the response we are concerned with here, i.e. the one experienced by the computer, is not necessarily in the same time or frequency range as the signals of the instrument in question. To take an extreme example, the peripheral might be a microwave network analyser, for which the computer would only be concerned with the settling time between adjustments, which might be 10^9 times longer than the periodic time at the measurement end.

Thus we see that response can be measured and represented in various ways, and the precise choice depends on the apparatus and techniques being used. Its measurement is subject to the restrictions that have been discussed with respect to signals in general. For example, response components at frequencies greater than half the sampling frequency used may be aliased into the apparent response in a confusing way. Quite often all we need to know about the response is that the settling time is less than a certain acceptable limit, but in general it must be treated with care as a possible source of distortion by convolution.

7.8　THE DECONVOLUTION PROBLEM

The existence of a characteristic response of an instrument means that the ideal source signal is corrupted by being convolved with that response, so one of the commonest processes applied to acquired data is deconvolution. When linear continuous methods were the only ones available, this constituted an immense problem involving the solution of an integral equation in the time domain or function division in the frequency domain. As for performing it as a simultaneous input/output process, this was in general ruled out by the concomitant realization problem.

Digital signal processing, however, places at our disposal a number of methods of deconvolution, and the precise choice of method depends upon the nature of the measurement problem as presented. Some of the possibilities are mentioned briefly below.

7.8.1　z DOMAIN CORRECTION

Quite often the response of the instrument is a known simple form which is capable of a straightforward representation in the z domain as a transfer function $H(z)$. In this case a suitable correcting filter is immediately available in the form $1/H(z)$. Take for example the commonest form of instrument impulse response $H(\tau) = a \exp(-a\tau)$. This can be represented by a single pole transfer function $H(s) = a/(a + s)$, and the z domain equivalent is found by the method of impulse invariance (i.e. noting that the pole at $s = -a$ is mapped to $z = \exp(-aT)$ and equating gains at zero frequency) as

$$H(z) = \frac{1 - b}{z - b}; \quad \text{where } b = \exp(-aT)$$

The correcting filter is given by $1/H(z)$, which yields a simple non-recursive relation

$$y_i = \left(\frac{1}{1 - b}\right) x_{i+1} - \left(\frac{b}{1 - b}\right) x_i$$

This is, of course, a filter which emphasizes high frequencies, and we can show that it corresponds to

$$|H(\omega)|^2 = 1 + \frac{2b(1 - \cos \omega T)}{(1 - b)^2}$$

Since we are correcting for a form of response which is often included for the very purpose of noise limitation, we must therefore be prepared to deal with the enhancement of the noise component which is consequent upon our correction.

7.8.2 DISCRETE FOURIER TRANSFORM

Often, of course, the response is not capable of simple z domain representation, and if we are dealing with finite blocks of signal it is possible to use a DFT procedure (which is in effect a z transform calculation on the unit circle). This relies on the fact that deconvolution is a function division process in the ω domain. There are, however, the difficulties associated with the use of snippets of signal, that is if the signal is not conveniently time limited (we assume that the response of the instrument itself is limited, so that it has a unique transform). It is therefore necessary to acquire a block of input samples larger than the required block of output samples so that some can be sacrificed for shaping with a window function. The procedure then is to obtain the DFT of the input signal, divide it ordinate-by-ordinate by the DFT of the response (so they have to be of the same order and sampling frequency), then find the DFT of the result (Figure 7.2). Remember that the form of convolution corresponding to the DFT is effectively circular or periodic.

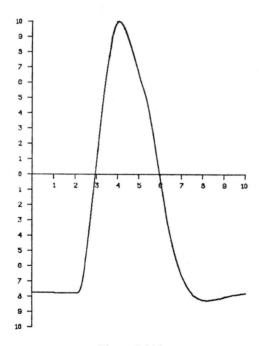

Figure 7.2(a)

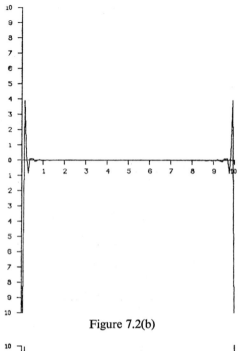

Figure 7.2(b)

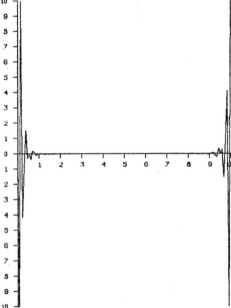

Figure 7.2(c)

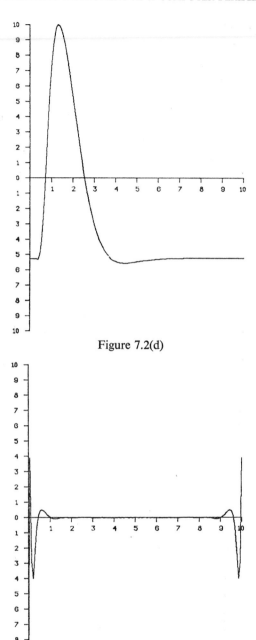

Figure 7.2(d)

Figure 7.2(e)

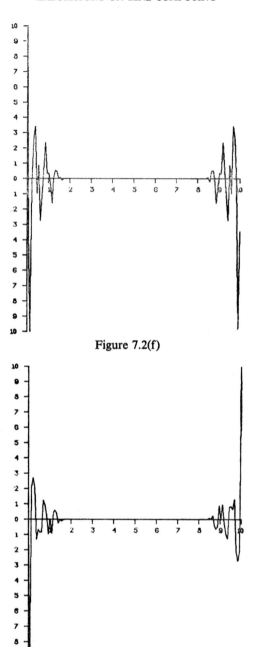

Figure 7.2(f)

Figure 7.2(g)

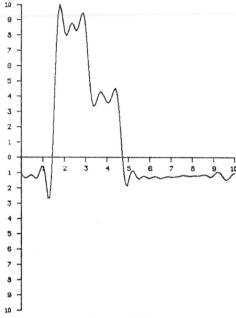

Figure 7.2(h)

Figure 7.2   Deconvolution by DFT. (a) A waveform, which should have been a stepped pulse, corrupted by a measuring instrument, with its real (b) and imaginary (c) Fourier transform components. The impulse response of the instrument (d) yields further real (e) and imaginary Fourier components which by complex division into (b) and (c) enable the Fourier components of the uncorrupted waveform (f and g) to be determined. Finally inverse Fourier Transformation of (f) and (g) yields (h) to the deconvolved waveform. The ringing on the waveform is caused by the inclusion of a low-pass filter to obviate noise introduced by division. It can be eliminated by slightly more complicated procedures. (*Realized by Kieron Pocknell on FM* 1600*B*)

7.8.3   MATRIX INVERSION

The discrete form of the convolution integral is a summation formula (equation 6.2) which can be written as a matrix equation

$$\mathbf{y} = \mathbf{H}\,\mathbf{x}$$

where the elements of the vectors $\mathbf{y}$ and $\mathbf{x}$ are the samples $y(nT)$ and $x(mT)$, and the elements of the triangular matrix $\mathbf{H}$ are

$$\{H\}_{ij} = h(iT - jT), \qquad i - j \geq 0$$

Hence deconvolution is accomplished by multiplication by the inverse matrix

$$\mathbf{x} = \mathbf{H}^{-1}\,\mathbf{y}$$

These methods mentioned above are the basic ones, and, as would be expected from the fact that they are ways of performing the same operation, they are closely related. A full appreciation of this relationship can be attained through a study of the elegant formulations of functional analysis and linear algebra [FuncAnVul, LinAlgMir], where ideas such as orthogonal bases in function space and canonical matrix forms give a clear background to the very practical problems that concern us here. It is important not to fall into the delusion that the errors associated with the idea of window functions are unique to the Fourier transform method. They are caused purely by the process of extracting a block of signal, and arise from the attempt to characterize the whole signal from a part of it, so are common to all methods once this has been done. Other deconvolution methods are variations of the above produced by differences in the amount of knowledge of signal and system. Two of them are discussed below.

7.8.4 CROSS-CORRELATION

This is a way of extending the above method to the case where $h(T)$ is initially unknown. Let us suppose that the input is a signal $s(t)$ to which we can add an injected signal of our own $x(t)$ and that the output is $y(t)$. Then

$$y = s * h + x * h$$

and it can be shown from the fact that averaging and integration are linear and interchangeable operations [ProPap] that this relation is extended to auto- and cross-correlation forms

$$R_{xy} = R_{xs} * h + R_{xx} * h$$

and if x is at our disposal we can choose it to be uncorrelated (random or pseudorandom), in which case $R_{xy}(\tau) = h(\tau)$. In practice we can only obtain an estimate of R_{xy} which will contain errors, some of which are induced by the presence of $s(t)$. When the measurement problem is one of simply obtaining $h(\tau)$ itself, $s(t)$ will only be present in the form of the system noise. If, however, the required information is in subsequent realizations of $s(t)$, $R_{xy}(\tau)$ can be used as the basis of deconvolution by one of the above methods.

7.8.5 ADAPTIVE MODELLING

Quite often the objective of the measurement exercise is to find the response of a system, and this frequently needs to be done in the presence of noise on a system which is not immutable. Then the various forms of adaptive modelling are attractive. The type of model can, of course, vary greatly, and for the present purpose we restrict ourselves to the linear impulse response model. If $h(\tau)$ is the system to be measured we set up a computer model $h_m(\tau)$ which is intended to be the closest possible discrete representation of $h(\tau)$, i.e. a non-recursive digital filter which is adjusted to be an impulse invariant form of $h(\tau)$. There are various ways of altering h_m to produce an improved version h'_m; one is to cascade it with an updating model, say h_u, so that $h'_m = h_m * h_u$. The determination of h_u is an exercise in deconvolution, as can be seen by reference to Figure 7.3(a). In essence we ask: what model would have to be

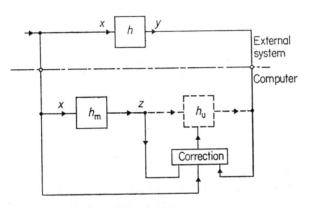

Figure 7.3(a)

cascaded with h_m so that its output is transformed to the same output y as the system to be measured? A cross-correlation method (due to M.S. Beck, *Electronics Letters*, 1968, **4**, 64) allows this to be done in a noise eliminating way. For, assuming that x is uncorrelated, we have

$$R_{xy} = h, \qquad R_{xz} = h_m, \qquad R_{yz} = R_{zz} * h_u$$

and h_u can be found by evaluating R_{zz} and R_{yz}, forming a matrix as above from R_{zz}, inverting it and multiplying the vector form of R_{yz} by that inverse matrix. h'_m is then found by convolving h_m with h_u by a further matrix multiplication.

This method can be extended to a powerful two stage adaptive method by which an accurate model of a system can be formed despite the existence of an undesirable response in the instrument through which the system response is acquired. In this method two cascaded models are held in the computer store, one for the test-object and one for the measuring system, and these are learned separately in two stages as shown in Figure 7.3(b).

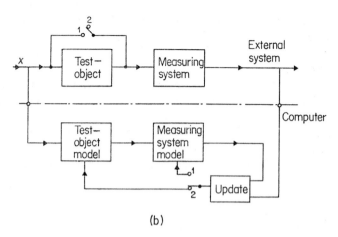

(b)

Figure 7.3   (a) A form of adaptive modelling (b) two-stage adaptive modelling to deconvolve an undesired instrument response from the response of a test object

7.9   The intermediate logging and reduction of data

Quite often the raw data supplied by an experiment are highly redundant in terms of the information required, and though the redundant part can be discarded in the course of computation, this will be at the expense of unnecessarily increased computer loading. Furthermore practical problems, such as signal transmission, may be aggravated needlessly. Many scientific instruments have a built in logging and reduction capability, which is one of the main justifications for using them rather than simply supplying the computer itself with the relevant transducers. The introduction of microprocessors, ROMS and RAMS has also greatly reduced the labour required for the provision of pre-processing for the purposes of data condensation.

Pulse height analysis is a good example of a measurement procedure which is amenable to this sort of treatment, and it was indeed one of the earliest applications of small on-line computers. In this case the source signal is a continuous function of time, usually of low level and wide bandwidth, so the noise content is an important consideration. With no pretreatment it would be necessary for the computer to sample the signal at an appropriate high rate and by means of a suitable algorithm select features of the waveform which appear to be pulses and record their heights. Such a procedure would impose an absurdly heavy load on the computer and it is useful to examine by stages the ways in which this load can be reduced.

The first point to examine is the signal acquisition stage, and here it is found that for many applications the physical quantity to be monitored corresponds to charge rather than current, so a charge-sensitive amplifier can be substituted for a current-sensitive one. This device effectively causes an integration of the current which gives an advantageous ω^{-2} shaping of the noise power spectrum. The perfect integrator, however, is represented by an operator in the s plane with a pole at the origin, and this causes difficulties not only with the amplification of low frequency noise drift but also with the build up of charge from successive pulses so that the device will eventually saturate. For this reason the common practice is to use an imperfect current integrator, an amplifier with both R and C in parallel as the feedback element, but, provided that the duration of the pulse is short compared with RC, this still produces a rise in output amplitude proportional to the charge in the pulse; also there is a clearly defined peak whose height represents the charge.

The charge-sensitive amplifier is a linear continuous processor which reduces the effective bandwidth while preserving the pulse height information, and it proves possible to make further gains in this direction in the subsequent amplification by including further relatively long time constants of the integrating and differentiating type.

The basic principle of the design of this subsequent network is that, provided the source signal can be regarded as an impulse, the peak response of any network will be proportional to the intensity of the impulse; so the system is designed to provide the minimum bandwidth consistent with the absence of spurious positive response peaks (which would occur if the circuits exhibited resonance, i.e. complex roots). The resulting response pattern in the time domain is a positive lobe followed by a negative one with a smooth approach to zero. Standard amplifiers available for pulse height analysis contain switched RC networks which allow the response to be adjusted to suit the speed of the phenomenon being monitored.

At this stage the possibilities of linear continuous processing have been exhausted and the next stage is analogue–digital conversion, but of a special type. The A–D converter for pulse height analysis is not subjected to a synchronous sampling signal, but produces a sample for every pulse which represents the height of that pulse. Hence two types of compression have occurred: the signal has been condensed into numbers which represent certain of its features and the scale of time has been abandoned.

The data are now suitable for feeding directly into the computer. This is done in a special way (which was mentioned in Section 6.10 with reference to ensemble averages) by interpreting the numbers as incremental addresses, so that unity can be added to the contents of the location thereby specified. Note that such a procedure is only justified if the source signal is stationary, or if it can be divided up into blocks of time over which it is effectively stationary. Evolutive processes are much less amenable to such a form of data compression.

We have so far described one of the first uses of laboratory on-line computers, but subsequent developments have tended to change the approach further: for there is still an element of redundancy at the computer interface as far as most applications are concerned. Although the scale of time has been abandoned, the order in time of the pulses is preserved, and as we are usually interested only in estimating the distribution of heights this information can also be discarded in the pre-processing. To this end modern pulse height analysers incorporate their own digital storage and the distribution is assembled in the instrument to be transmitted to the computer as a complete entity. This is an example of external buffering easing the load on the interface by making the transfer requests independent of external events, besides the more obvious reduction in the number of requests involved in a particular experiment.

Thus by a combination of linear-continuous and digital pre-processing it is possible to minimize the noise corruption in the signal and pare down the data input to the computer to the point of being no more and no less than required. In the more general case of data logging as such, the rôle of the external process is to gather data from a diversity of points in space and time so that they can be funnelled through a single channel, thereby obviating, for example, the duplication of A–D converters. There is obviously scope for wide variation in the degree of sharing of tasks between the computer itself and the external hardware, and this can only be properly decided by reference to the problem in hand, but the important point to remember is that the computer is the versatile component of the system. One must give full rein to this versatility by striking a correct balance between giving it enough information to work on and loading it with the chores of acquiring the information.

7.10   CONVERTING SCIENTIFIC INSTRUMENTS INTO PERIPHERALS

The nature and difficulty of the problems associated with the task of adapting a scientific instrument for computer connection are widely variable. There are two chief classes of problem which require to be solved. First, there is a need to convert the signals of the instrument to and from electronic digital form, which, if they do not occur in a convenient continuous electrical form, also involves a process of transduction. Second, the concept of the instrument as an operating system must be adapted to suit its rôle as an adjunct to the computer. This will involve channelling as much as possible of the control information through the interface, thereby reducing manual intervention at the instrument panel to a minimum, in such a way that the instrument presents a convenient image to the software.

A–D and D–A conversion have been reduced to minor problems by the introduction of packaged electronics (except where the speed–accuracy demands are high, and this introduces other complications). The great majority of modern instruments are electronic in nature, and therefore tend not to present extra transducer problems, but when these do occur the calculating power of the computer can be of great assistance, so that, for example, a non-linear transducer with subsequent numerical correction is permissible, whereas it would not be with linear continuous electronic processing.

The most frequent non-electrical variable to occur in instrumentation problems is mechanical displacement, since there is often a need to perform a spatial scan of a test object, and there is a variety of transducers available for this purpose, from shaft encoders to Moiré fringe devices, and the one chosen will depend upon the range and accuracy required. It is advisable in this case to measure the actual displacement of the test-object rather than rely on the setting of a driving transducer, since mechanical systems are subject to such defects as backlash, and as a general principle it is always preferable to use a direct measurement of a quantity rather than assume that the output channel has produced its expected effect.

The whole question of *accuracy* is more difficult than the usual casual treatments of it would imply, particularly in the light of the precision with which computer variables can be stated. Ideally the digital precision of an input/output channel is selected to be slightly greater than the accuracy of the incoming data, but this ideal may often be ignored, especially in the case of an instrument connected to a general purpose channel, and it is easy to fall into the trap of confusing precision with accuracy in such a case. Those aspects of accuracy which fall within the realm of the *art* of measurement, will largely be abandoned when the instrument is operating under the rigours of program control, but this is not a great loss as their subjective nature will always make them suspect. Furthermore there are balancing gains in that techniques such as cumulative averaging to eliminate random errors become available, while systematic errors can be reduced by the use of stored calibration tables.

Most instruments preserve their accuracy over a wide dynamic range by the provision of switched ranges. In a modern instrument such switching is accessible by direct digital instructions, but in traditional instruments range changing is performed by mechanical switches. For this reason it is very useful for one of the slow output channels of the laboratory computer to take the form of reed relays driven from the staticized digital word, one per bit, so that the manual controls may be usurped by means of a simple piece of rewiring. The response of a computer to the event of a signal going out of range can be much more rapid and reliable than that of a human being, and it can be coupled with an automatic change of the range multiplier in the dedicated software package for the instrument, so that the received data preserve their correspondence to the signal over the entire dynamic range. Action may need to be taken, however, to interpolate data which are lost around the switching time. Variable controls of the potential divider type can often be replaced by D–A converters, perhaps deriving their reference supply from within the instrument. The degree of complication to which one is prepared to go is, of course, dictated by the potential usefulness of the instrument as a computer peripheral, and there are various stages of compromise between full manual control and full automation which are acceptable. The justification for using an available instrument in this way is the obviation of the necessity to repeat the engineering that has gone into it, but one must always bear in mind the alternative of designing a new peripheral from scratch, which may be more desirable if extensive re-engineering is necessary.

An important advantage of the conversion of an instrument into a computer peripheral is the enormous increase in potential work rate that is obtained, a prime consideration in the use of very expensive instruments. There is always a residual activity, such as preparing the test-object and presenting it to the instrument, that is irreducible, but the business of taking the measurement, processing and presenting it can be handled by the computer with a speed and reliability greatly in excess of that of the human operator. This does, however, place an onus on the programmer for the correctness of the consequent results, and the computer unless otherwise instructed will quite happily carry on processing absurd results which would be immediately rejected by its human counterpart. This is one of the basic reasons why we urge the measurement specialist to learn the relatively simple art of programming rather than attempt to communicate the problem to a specialist programmer.

Most newly designed instruments will henceforth be of a digital nature, as much for the cheapness of integrated digital circuit techniques as for the advantages of computer connection, so many of the more annoying problems of adaptation will tend to be transitory, though none the less urgent. It is important, therefore, to ensure that the ramifications of any crudities or complexities associated with the use of an existing instrument do not find their way into the more general software which should retain its validity in the event of a later change of instrument. For this reason the software directly associated with the instrument must be designed to provide a simple and sensible interface to the general software, and is as important a part of the connecting package as the hardware. We pursue this point further in the following chapter. At this stage it is more important to examine the problem of transduction.

7.11   THE THEORY OF TRANSDUCERS

It is quite obvious that the transducer forms a vital link in the chain between the physical entity to be studied and the processor. It is very much that part of the system whose quality is limited by the state of current technology, and it is the factor which most fundamentally prescribes the definition of the image formed in the computer of the exterior physical world. Some transducers are essentially of a discrete nature, and therefore lend themselves to a particularly direct form of coupling with a digital system, e.g. the Moiré fringe transducer for spatial displacement. The majority, however, are essentially continuous in their operation, and tend to be based upon some device whose electrical behaviour is modified by its physical environment.

In our study of the physical world we observe that many of the variables are linked in pairs, which by analogy with the behaviour of fluids we might describe as *potential* and *flux* variables (some authors use the descriptions *across* and *through* variables). The transducer acts as a bridge between two such sets of variables by exhibiting behaviour with respect to one set which is conditioned by the magnitudes experienced in the other set.

Table 7.1 shows some of the system types with the variables separated under the across and through headings. In this formulation (due to L. Finkelstein), there is also a further distinction between quantity and rate variables under the respective headings 'extensive' and 'intensive'. In each physical system we can identify a dissipative component with a characteristic equation of the form $x = Ry$. There are also two types of energy storage

Table 7.1 *Table of system types and their associated variables*

	Across variables		Through variables	
	Extensive	Intensive	Intensive	Extensive
General system	$x(t)$	$\dot{x}(t)$	$\dot{y}(t)$	$y(t)$
Mechanical translation system	$x(t)$ displacement	$\dot{x}(t)$ velocity	$f(t)$ force	$h(t)$ momentum
Mechanical rotation system	$\phi(t)$ angular displacement	$\dot{\phi}(t)$ angular velocity	$T(t)$ torque	$H(t)$ angular momentum
Electrical system	$\lambda(t)$ flux linkages	$v(t)$ voltage	$i(t)$ current	$q(t)$ charge
Fluid flow system	—	$p(t)$ pressure	$\dot{g}(t)$ volume flow rate	$g(t)$ volume
Thermal system	—	$\theta(t)$ temperature	$\dot{Q}(t)$ heat flow rate	$Q(t)$ heat

components. The one associated with the through variable has the form $\dot{x} = (1/C)y$ and the one associated with the across variable has the form $L\dot{y} = x$. By using R, L and C as the constants we identify these components with their electrical analogues.

The through or flux variables are each subject to a law of continuity at a point, whereas the across or potential variables are subject to a law of balance round a closed path, i.e.

$$\sum_{\text{node}} \dot{y}_i = 0 \quad \text{and} \quad \sum_{\text{circuit}} \dot{x}_i = 0$$

The electrical equivalents are Kirchhoff's current and voltage laws respectively. It is these laws which determine the classification into potential and flux, and not any others, such as spurious ideas of causality.

Conceptually, the transducer can be divided into three cascaded blocks. These are (1) a system of elements of the type associated with the input variables, (2) an ideal lossless transducer, and (3) a system of elements of the type associated with the output variables.

The mathematical description of linear bilateral transducers is familiar to us through our knowledge of electrical–electrical transducers such as the transistor, which is an element performing transduction between different impedance levels. The convenient representation is in terms of a 2×2 matrix relating two vectors, but complications arise from the fact that the elements of the vectors $\dot{x}_1$, $\dot{y}_1$, $\dot{x}_2$, $\dot{y}_2$, can be arranged into 12 different pairings, some of which are particularly applicable in certain circumstances. Thus we find such variations as Z, Y and h parameters, where the letters refer to the dimensionality of the matrix elements as impedances, admittances and hybrids. Let us take as an example the cascade or A parameters.

$$\begin{bmatrix} \dot{x}_2 \\ \dot{y}_2 \end{bmatrix} = \begin{bmatrix} A_{11} & A_{12} \\ A_{21} & A_{22} \end{bmatrix} \begin{bmatrix} \dot{x}_1 \\ \dot{y}_1 \end{bmatrix}$$

where

$$A_{11} = \left. \frac{\partial \dot{x}_2}{\partial \dot{x}_1} \right|_{\dot{y}_2, \dot{y}_1}, \qquad \text{etc.}$$

This is a particularly useful formulation, as we often create a required transducer by cascading two available ones. For example, to measure pressure electrically we might combine a pressure-translation transducer (pneumatic bellows) with a translation-electrical transducer (potential divider or capacitor), and the two matrices could be combined by multiplication to give the matrix for the whole device. Note that in general the elements of the matrix will be differential operators which are conveniently presented in s domain form, though as with circuit design we try to obviate complications of response by selecting a device whose behaviour is simple in the relevant frequency range, which means that one term in its characteristic differential equation is dominant. This would normally be the constant term, as with the transistor, but it could be a differential term as with the capacitance transducer.

For measurement purposes, as opposed to energy conversion, one usually only requires to relate one input variable with one output variable, in which case other relationships implied by three of the four matrix elements have only nuisance value and again tend to be minimized within the appropriate range of frequencies.

Thus, while in the great majority of cases we are able to ignore the complications of transducer behaviour, it is most important to do this in the full knowledge of the nature of such complications, and not simply by default. The variety of transducers is very great and it is not possible to dwell on detailed descriptions here, the best source of information being the manufacturers' literature which is extensively surveyed in the technical press. Non-linear transducers can be used where they offer advantages such as enhanced sensitivity in the relevant range, since it is a relatively simple matter to use a non-linear calibration table in the computer, and this is one of the extra features which is not available in linear-continuous processing. It should be noted, however, that non-linearities are often associated with significant storage elements, and the combination of non-linearity and time dependence can be difficult to unravel. A simple example is the thermistor, which might be chosen in preference to a thermocouple as a temperature sensor on the grounds of sensitivity, but it exhibits a very slow response time. As a matter of passing interest it is possible to construct a very low frequency electrical oscillator from a lamp and a thermistor in which the essential elements of inductance, capacitance, and negative resistance are realized thermally—a good illustration of the familiar electrical elements being 'imaged' in another physical form.

A transducer coupled with an A–D or D–A converter represents the minimum hardware constituting a computer input/output channel, and as such imposes the maximum processing load on the computer. Where there is little essential redundancy of information in the received signal (or in the specification of the output signal) such a combination would represent the definitive form. Otherwise a processor in the form of a scientific instrument would be included to lighten the load from a channel which is to be extensively used.

Note that there is some measure of artifice in the sort of classification performed above, and it can do more harm than good if allowed to detract from the essentially practical art of transduction, for which the best source of information is the manufacturers' literature.

7.12 PROTECTION

It goes without saying that the computer represents a major financial investment, and the laboratory computer, unlike its mathematical counterpart,
may find itself working in a hostile electrical environment. The great danger
is the intrusion of relatively high voltages into the circuits of the machine. A
single accidental short pulse can wipe out thousands of integrated circuits at a
stroke.

The only safe approach in these circumstances is the belt and braces one.
Besides adopting rigorous worst case design for the input circuitry, it is
necessary to assume that anything that can fail will fail. For example, one may
wish to measure the current in a high-voltage circuit by placing a small
resistor in the ground return path, but what happens if that resistor fails by
going open-circuit? In the event of a discharge elsewhere in the circuit what
voltage will be induced in the residual inductance by the surge current,
particularly in the earth connection loops? In most cases it is possible to take
some *ad hoc* precautions, such as using two double value resistors in parallel
for the current measuring resistor, but it is often particularly difficult to control
self and mutual inductance or to predict the possible site of a discharge. So
after taking all the design precautions possible, it is still advisable to insert
circuits specifically designed to provide surge protection. Gas discharge tubes
and zener diodes will both provide breakdown at a specified voltage and
therefore may be used to divert a surge. Figure 7.4 shows a useful circuit. Two
zener diodes are connected back to back so that if the breakdown voltage is
exceeded in either direction one diode breaks down and the other is forward
biased. Most of the applied voltage will then be dropped across the series
resistors.

In high-speed and low-current applications it is important to remember
that in Figure 7.4 we have added a resistance in series with a small non-linear
capacitance, and these will introduce a distorting response. For such reasons
safety and speed tend to be conflicting requirements giving us another trade-
off situation.

Although we are discussing instruments it is important not to lose sight of

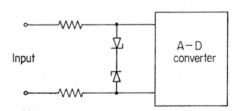

Figure 7.4   A simple zener-diode protection circuit

the necessity to protect the computer's data highway, and this is a subsidiary though important rôle of the peripheral controller. The highway is the route into the heart of the computer and a surge on it could wreak great destruction. Also to be avoided is the situation where the highway is paralysed by a faulty device, and avoidance of this situation is part of the overall philosophy in which the input/output facility is cushioned (on both hardware and software sides) by carefully designed packages.

One of the recurring problems in connecting together expensive and delicate pieces of equipment is the possibility of the propagation of electrical faults among them. Such faults could range from simple earth-loop defects to large-scale destructive surges. This is one of the reasons for the increasing popularity of optical links, the other major reason is the wide bandwidth they offer. In the simplest system the signal is converted to optical form by means of a light-emitting diode, transmitted along an optical fibre and reconverted to electrical form by a light-sensitive diode. The wide bandwidth allows high data rates to be achieved with serial transmission through a single channel, and as the transmission medium is a good insulator complete electrical isolation is provided, yet the mechanical flexibility of coupling is preserved.

7.13 SIMULTANEOUS OPERATION OF PERIPHERALS

In a computer well designed for on-line work, the simultaneous operation of peripherals should not overburden the programmer, and this applies to any special additions to the system of the nature discussed in this chapter. There has certainly been a design failure if the programmer is involved in detailed timing calculations, although this has apparently occurred with some machines sold for this type of work. There are only two questions of timing with which the programmer should concern himself: (1) Is he asking for the data before they are available (or conversely overwriting before they are used)? (2) Is he asking for too much calculation to be done between interrupts? These questions obviously have much in common, and can usually both be avoided by using a proper programming technique.

Questions of overall interrupt loading should have been decided by the choice of computer and hardware allocation of priority to the various interface channels. Calculation between interrupts should be avoided where possible by transferring data into store through data interrupts, and then using it when it is assembled via a program interrupt. This is, of course, not possible when a continuous input/output process is being realized. Buffering, both in software and hardware, is the key to efficient simultaneous operation. Each standard peripheral offered by the manufacturer should come with its own standard software package which will include one or two buffer areas of store which as far as the user is concerned are self-emptying or self-filling. So, for a new peripheral, the obvious thing to do is to imitate this arrangement. It is difficult to offer detailed advice on how to go about this, as it is the area of programming most dependent on the mode of operation of the individual machine, and study of the manufacturer's software is an invaluable aid. However, even without such an aid it should not be too difficult a task to develop the software half of the combined package. The overriding aim should be to make the use of the peripheral easy for the programming user (even if it is only oneself).

Undoubtedly, as the price of storage falls, we shall eventually see a trend towards hardware buffering in the sense that each peripheral will have its own temporary store to iron out the relative fluctuations in the demand for and availability of data. Furthermore, main stores will tend to be multiported so that fast peripherals are able to access them directly without monopolizing central processor time. Meanwhile, we must rely on efficient software techniques.

The normal state of affairs when several peripherals are operating in interrupt mode is that each peripheral will be communicating with its prescribed buffer areas of the store taking data from the output buffer and/or putting it into the input buffer. The computer program will be performing the reverse process. Obviously this procedure will break down under two conditions (1) when data are required from a buffer which is in fact empty and (2) when data are destined for a buffer which is full. In most cases such a breakdown is of little consequence, as the peripheral is able to hesitate or the computer to loop until the condition is rectified (note that it should still be able to deal with separate interrupts while obeying a loop order). Difficulties arise when the peripheral is supposed to be working synchronously, in which case he who hesitates is lost. Then the failure is much more fundamental. At best it represents a slight miscalculation of the buffer size required to iron out the fluctuations. At worst it represents a gross miscalculation of the magnitude of the computing task.

For it is fundamental to the whole concept of simultaneous on-line operation that the demand on the computer, averaged over time, is well within its capability. Hence an output buffer should be thought of in terms of a natural state of being full, and an input buffer should be naturally empty. Deviations from these natural states only arise through the exigencies of coincidence of interrupts or other demands. Let us emphasize that such problems are rare and only concerned with the fastest peripherals; the conventional electromechanical input–output peripherals impose a negligible demand on a modern fast computer. If the average demand on the computer is, however, excessive, no amount of increased buffering can cure this.

There are some circumstances in which the completion of the overall task is bedevilled by the slowness of one peripheral, a common example being the requirement to plot a graphical result on the digital plotter but also to proceed with the next stage of the experiment. The solution to this problem also involves a buffering technique but one taken to an extreme; for the buffer area is set up in a backing store such as disc, drum or tape. This technique is sometimes known as dumping or spooling. In the example mentioned, the computer generates plotter orders, but is programmed to dump them into the backing store, so that the backing store behaves as though it were the plotter. Simultaneously it is possible to provide a separate autonomous piece of program to ensure that the plotter will in its own plodding manner take orders from the backing store and execute them. As a slow device it will have been allocated a lowly position in the priority hierarchy, and will not therefore interfere with the activities of the faster peripherals.

The reader will, we hope, understand at this stage why we regard peripheral autonomy as one of the prime requirements of a computer system for on-line work. Without it, programming a complex experiment becomes a veritable Gordian knot, and it would certainly be beyond the scope of a brief text to suggest ways of unravelling it. It is impossible to predict the coincidences of events which may take place in the course of an experiment, and soundly designed hardware can entirely remove the need to do this. Equally self-evident at this stage is the importance of priority and its allocation. In particular a peripheral which is allocated a priority higher than is merited by its inherent speed can damn the whole system.

Synchronous operation is something to be avoided where possible, though in activities such as signal processing, where the sampling frequencies play such a dominating rôle, this is clearly not feasible. Simultaneous operation for its own sake should also be avoided. If it is possible to put incoming data into store for later processing when they are all assembled, do so, but this is not likely to occur in the applications where an on-line computer can make its greatest contribution. As in most computer work successful simultaneous operation depends on foresight and common sense.

7.14   REVERSING THE RÔLES

In our discussions of scientific instruments as computer peripherals, we must not lose sight of the freedom that modern technology gives us to reverse the position—i.e. to make the computer a dedicated adjunct to the instrument. At the time of writing, a processor is available in a one inch long d.i.l. package at a price considerably less than, for example, an oscilloscope. There will no doubt be many applications where it is sensible to incorporate such a device (in conjunction with other packages for storage, control, clock generation, etc.) directly within an instrument. In these cases the computing procedure would tend to be simple, repetitive and immutable, with no call for a variety of input/output peripherals, i.e. a task which would waste the capacities of a more powerful, versatile computing system.

There will also be a further range of circumstances in which an extra dedicated microcircuit processor would be included to relieve the central processor of some of its more mundane tasks, and by allowing them to be performed simultaneously with the main program enhance the speed of the overall system. There is no reason why a peripheral controller should not contain an integral processor if it is required to execute logical sequences of some complication. This will soon, indeed, be the rule rather than the exception—under the pressures of standardization, the rise in the cost of manpower and the fall in the cost of microcircuit packages; for such techniques reduce the logic design of controllers to a software problem.

The principles of programming subsidiary microcomputers are similar to those discussed earlier in this book except that they are much more firmly rooted in the hardware constraints. It is not yet, for example, economic to include comprehensive priority-assessing interrupt facilities at this level, and the permanently stored program needs to be constructed with full reference to the basic timing limitations of the hardware environment. This is one of those areas of computing which can only be described in such terms of airy generalization, whereas in an actual practical problem the design constraints are self-evident, once the critical decision has been made as to which level of technology one proposes to pitch the design solution.

A possible mode of use of microprocessors which may have great potential in laboratory situations is one in which they are allowed to operate independently but rely on a larger computer for compilation, assembly, etc. This introduces the possibility of a series of small versatile instruments which merely need to be plugged into the computer, like a battery to a charger, to be converted from one mode of behaviour to another.

7.15　LABORATORY HIGH-VOLTAGE SOURCE

We end this chapter with two examples of laboratory instruments which benefit from computer connection—one traditional and one modern. For the traditional example we have chosen the controlled laboratory high-voltage source, which, though not perhaps typical of laboratory instruments, provides a nice simple example of a special hazard which can be dealt with at the design stage.

There are two main types of laboratory high-voltage supply. One is based on a high-frequency oscillator driving a step-up transformer and voltage-multiplying rectifier stack. The other is based on the continuous transport and concentration of electrostatic charge. They are both, in effect, high-gain amplifiers, which gives them the advantage that they can be highly stabilized by means of a feedback loop containing a voltage reference source. This is the only operational aspect which need concern us, since it implies that either device can be controlled by the injection of an appropriate low-level signal. Thus the principal agent of control is an ordinary low voltage D–A converter. Since, however, the device itself is potentially dangerous to man and equipment it is also desirable to have a rapid reset facility which can be initiated by external pushbuttons, by external fault currents or by program. In measurements where breakdown damage is to be avoided, owing to the relatively slow decay of the high voltage once the control voltage has been removed, it is also necessary to provide a fast external reset loop in which a thyratron or other discharge device is fired (by the amplified fault current) to short circuit the supply within a microsecond.

Let us assume that the bottom 10 bits of the output word are used to drive the D–A converter of the high-voltage supply and that we have prepared a subroutine S to derive this word from V1. Under these conditions we can write a small piece of program which would be acceptable in off-line work but in this application would be extremely hazardous. An inexperienced user wishing to program for the end of an experiment might write the following loop to reduce the voltage smoothly to zero. The reader is recommended to examine it for an error before reading further

$$[100] \; V1 = V1 - 1$$
$$\rightarrow SR \; S$$
$$\rightarrow 100, \; V1 \geq 0$$

Now, as we have said, it is necessary to provide a reset facility, and we can kill two birds with one stone by using the sign bit for this purpose. This would not only provide a means of sending out the reset signal, but would also block the type of error occurring in the above example in which the programmer, by calling for one too many loops, has caused -1 to be output. In binary notation -1 is represented by all-ones, so the word output instead of having the value zero will have the full scale value 1023. In the case of the high-voltage supply full-scale output may well be sufficient to destroy the test-object. The reset should act in such a way that positive action is required to activate the unit. It could for example take out a relay connection in the internal power supply of the high-voltage unit. A simplified diagram is given in Figure 7.5 where for clarity only the data-out facility is shown. In practice it is valuable to provide for the return of a status word via program interrupt to inform the program of the cause of reset and confirm that it has occurred.

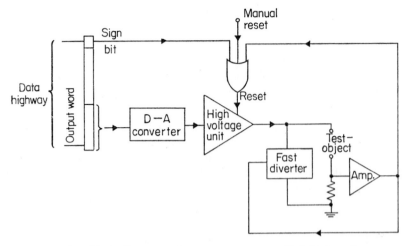

Figure 7.5   Simplified diagram of a computer-controlled high voltage power supply

7.16   THE TRANSIENT RECORDER

Having concentrated on the difficulties of connecting scientific instruments to the computer, it will be salutary to examine a case where this can be accomplished with some ease and to great effect. The transient recorder is an instrument born in the computer era and conceived in terms of digital techniques. The following remarks apply to the model used by the authors (Biomation 8100) but are qualitatively applicable to other models.

The transient recorder was produced in response to a need which existed in a number of areas of measurement for a device which would produce a record of an event including features which occur before the identifying (or triggering) feature. The simplest example, which is within the experience of most scientific workers, is the situation where one needs to examine the front edge of a pulse. An ordinary oscilloscope would at best show only part of that front edge, and even if it were equipped with a signal delay line its application would be rather restricted. The unique feature of the transient recorder is the existence of a pretrigger mode in which the time window can be set in any desired relationship to the trigger event. This is accomplished by using the delayed trigger signal to *stop* recording rather than starting it as in the oscilloscope.

Such an instrument is made feasible by the existence of continuous digital stores of either the *shift register* or *cyclic buffer* variety. The principles of its organization are shown in Figure 7.6. The feature to be particularly noted is the central timing and control block with provision for external digital control. This is what makes the instrument such a natural component of the modern computer-based laboratory; for, although it is very valuable as a stand alone instrument, as a computer peripheral it is many times more powerful. The interface provided is of the simple parallel handshake variety, and as there is also provision for varying the logic polarities by means of separate hard-wired inputs, the task of connecting the instrument to the computer is not

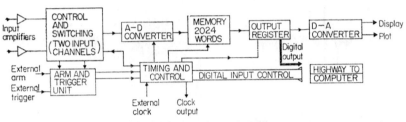

Figure 7.6   Block diagram of the transient recorder

demanding. Furthermore, the device has been designed to be fully program-mable, so that every front panel function except power on/off can be usurped by the computer. The input instructions are 16 bit words containing address, function and operand fields. The output words are of 8 bits, normally representing the signal samples, though there is also provision for a status word which indicates the state of readiness and the occurrence of off-scale signals.

The specification of the 8100 recorder includes 25 MHz bandwidth from d.c.; 10 ns to 10 s sample interval, which means a 20 μs to 20 000 s total sweep time; dual channel operation so that the 2024 word store can be divided into two separate 1012 word stores with their own input circuits; dual time base operation so that the rate of sampling can be changed at some preset part of the signal; every control, including arm and trigger level and delay, input attenuation etc., settable by computer input.

The software–hardware package for the device should be designed to enclose all the complexities of its order structure, so that the user's view from his program is simple, yet preserve all the facilities provided (not a difficult task in an instrument designed with such a mode of use in mind). The rôle of the software part of the package is the assembly of control words with function and operand fields appropriately set up. The operands, which are the values of the control settings, are derived from the user's program, perhaps in the form of a table set up by the user before calling the device subroutine. The functions define the particular controls, and it is not necessary for the user to deal with them in the precise form required by the device. The rôle of the hardware part of the package is simply to match the interfaces of the computer and the device so that the control words and data words can be exchanged under handshake control, and it is again a relatively undemanding task to design this, owing to the versatility built into the device interface.

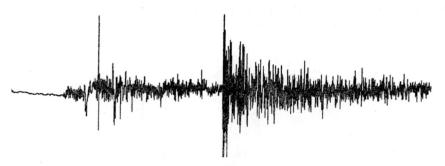

Figure 7.7   Example of a signal captured by the transient recorder—an air gun shot followed by the sound of the slug hitting the target. Note the period of silence before the triggering event and the apparent continuity of waveform provided by 2048 samples at 0·2 ms intervals (*captured and plotted through* 8100 *and FM* 1600*B by Colin Buffam*)

The potentialities of the instrument under program control are enormous; for, not only are the facilities of digital signal processing available to it, but automatic response to changes in the signal time and amplitude scale can be built in, and the range settings can be used in conjunction with the incoming data to provide composite data of very wide range, though of course with restricted precision. Ultimately the majority of laboratory instruments will be designed with this sort of on-line versatility as a natural provision. A computer plot of data acquired by the transient recorder is shown in Figure 7.7.

Chapter VIII

Applying Techniques—Some General Principles

8.1 Introduction

If there is one word which sums up the most important tenet of the philosophy of laboratory on-line computing it is *foresight*. In applying techniques, it is the foresight of the good experimentalist combined with that of the good programmer. Any intelligent person with application can become a competent programmer, but being a good experimentalist only comes from depth of experience in a particular field; for example, having an instant appreciation of which among the physical constraints are the important ones, and having an intuitive feel for the likely nature of the move after next in the experimental game of chess. What must be avoided is the situation where it becomes necessary to abandon everything done previously and start all over again. In computer work it is very easy to drift into a blind alley and the contrast between success and failure in this respect is much greater than in other fields, mainly owing to the bootstrap effect in software development. One must therefore at every stage be aware of the various trade-offs being juggled with, especially the one between flexibility and exigency.

8.2 Aiming for Flexibility

The economics of technical effort are similar in many ways to domestic or commercial economics. There is a certain amount available and a decision must be made as to what proportions are to be expended on immediate ends and on investment for the future. Remember Mr. Micawber's dictum:

'Annual income twenty pounds, annual expenditure nineteen pounds, nineteen and six, result happiness. Annual income twenty pounds, annual expenditure twenty pounds ought and six, result misery'.

The prime investment of technical effort is in *flexibility*. Its need gives rise to certain rules of procedure, and though they are the rules which will inevitably be broken from time to time in the interest of scientific advance, this should always be done with reluctance. These rules constrain the manufacturers as well as the users of computer systems, and the degree to which they have been adhered to will largely determine the usefulness of the particular system. Two aspects need to be considered—flexibility of construction and flexibility of operation, which correspond roughly to hardware and software.

In the laboratory such considerations must always be set against the background of an overall scientific policy (we are definitely not concerned here with computing for its own sake, as is often practised) and specific scientific aims always come first. As in all experimental work the first action is a careful analysis of the objectives and constraints associated with the proposed program of measurements. Skill in anticipation is an important factor in determining the rapidity with which objectives are achieved, but in original work total anticipation is not possible even for the most skilled experimenter; so at each stage we have consciously to keep all our avenues of retreat intact.

As far as software is concerned the main agents of flexibility are modularity and generality. This applies in all branches of computing and not only in the on-line variety. As we have observed in Chapter 4, the modules are the cells from which the programs are constructed, i.e. the smallest units capable of independent testing and utilization in various programs. Generalization is achieved in two ways; firstly by adhering to a common pattern of entry and exit to subroutines, and secondly by adding just a little bit extra to extend the usefulness of the subroutine beyond the bounds of the program being written. Let us illustrate this with a rather trivial example.

Suppose that the need arose to find the roots of a quadratic equation and that a standard subroutine for the purpose does not exist. We have three input quantities, the coefficients a, b and c, and two output quantities, the roots (possibly complex) given by $x = [-b \pm (b^2 - 4ac)^{\frac{1}{2}}]/2a$. In the program being written a, b and c will be contained in specific storage locations and it is easy to insert a section of code to calculate the roots and put them in other specific locations. However, it may be required to make the same calculation in a later section of the program with coefficients taken from somewhere else, or in another program by the same author, and it will certainly be needed by later authors. Therefore, with a little greater effort the author would be well-advised to write the procedure as a subroutine with simply organized entry and exit conditions. The entry condition, for example, could simply be that the address of a is specified, with b, and c following at consecutive addresses, and on exit the destination of the most positive root would be specified with the other root being placed in the following address. Thus only two numbers, which happen to be addresses, need to be specified for the subroutine to be used.

Of course, this process introduces overheads of storage and execution time, since the data have to be organized appropriately and the entry and exit of the subroutine with their attendant procedures have to be executed. Once the subroutine is available, programs would tend to be organized in such a way as to use it efficiently, especially if its entry conditions conform to an agreed standard, so the overheads would tend to be partly recovered, especially where the subroutine is used repetitively.

This is only a very simple illustrative example, and one would normally be dealing with more complicated procedures on larger blocks of data, but the ideas are the same, and the extra overheads are proportionately smaller. These rules for software organization should only be broken where the exigencies of time or storage exert great pressure, and then with reluctance. This often happens in programming for specific systems, and it is a sad fact that some of the most ingenious and potentially useful programming that has been done is not consigned to the pool of human knowledge in the form of specified subroutines, but merely enjoys a brief existence as an anonymous block performing a single task. Manufacturers who specialize in the provision of complete digital systems are particularly prone to this offence, but in the scientific laboratory where labour is at a premium and a small group of people tend to be pursuing common aims not shared by external organizations one cannot afford to consume one's seed corn in this way.

There are other flexible features of modular software. Subroutines with the same entry and exit conditions can be substituted for one another where a variation of procedure is required. For example a root-finding routine based on Newton's method might be replaced by one based on a random search method if the function being dealt with turns out to be ill behaved, but there is no need for their external appearance to differ, so that the main program requires no change. Another form of subroutine which is very useful for 'quick and dirty' solutions to some on-line problems is the conversion subroutine which is an outer shell round the software of one peripheral to make it look like another. Say for example you are offered an attractive utility program which you cannot use because it was written for a drum backing store whereas your system has only a disc. If the program is provided in modular form you merely need to write a simple conversion routine which has the same entry condition as the drum subroutine but instead calls the disc subroutine for reading and writing of data. This would not use the disc very efficiently but it would make the program available without the need for extensive revision. Enormous savings of labour are possible in this way, at the expense of a loss of efficiency, and one can make a VDU look like a plotter, an external computer look like a tape reader/punch, etc. This is suggested only as a useful dodge and not as a standard procedure.

Flexibility in hardware is obtained by much the same philosophy. If a piece of hardware is built rather than bought, it is likely to be conceived for a particular specific task, but often a little more thought and a little more effort can make it more generally useful. Thus, for example, an instrument put on-line to perform a specific task may not need its full dynamic range, and computer controlled range changing might not be required in its dedicated mode, but if this facility were provided perhaps it would be more widely useful and its very existence might generate unforeseen applications. Modularity is of course the order of the day in modern electronics, and components such as D–A converters will be bought as complete packages, so it is helpful to standardize on one range of such products. Conversion units can be constructed so that one piece of hardware connects to the computer via another, thus avoiding duplication on both sides of the interface. A fast A–D converter, for example, will branch out into various other more complex peripheral instruments each of which has its special software, but the hardware and software grouped round the interface will be common to all.

Multiplexing is often possible to avoid duplication without loss of flexibility. The authors, for example, developed two VDU peripherals for their system—one storage and one stereoscopic. The former did not require continual refreshment of data from the computer and therefore imposed a very small load on the interface channel, so it was able to share most of its electronics (and software) with the latter, and a control word was used to select one or the other. It is often easy to make the speed of a channel higher than is immediately required in anticipation of future developments (but this does not mean neglecting the prefiltering requirements of the sampling theorem) so that awkward modifications do not become necessary later. Various other hardware additions are easily incorporated at the development stage, but would be difficult later, so it is worth while giving thought to such possibilities.

In the conception of the overall experiment, monitoring and control are key features in the quest for flexibility. Extensive keyboard control using a carefully thought out scheme of messages combined with comprehensive monitoring, of both graphical and alphanumeric information, are invaluable aids in the actual performance of the experiment. The format of the input and output information is worthy of some forethought. For example, the popular method of decoding messages by selecting say the first three letters inevitably leads to the use of abbreviations which are not immediately comprehensible and complicates the business of finding new words to add to the list, as many of the words we use share common beginnings, which is why we propose the admittedly more complicated procedure of removing redundant elements described in Section 4.15. Compare the following lists of abbreviations:

STA   STO   RUN   BEG   SEA   REP   PLO
STRT   STP   RN   BGN   SRCH   RPT   PLT

In some instances typing the wrong message can destroy a long and expensive preparation, a consideration unique to on-line computing.

Before leaving the subject of flexibility we shall examine a hardware example, one which is often tackled in an *ad hoc* way each time the requirement arises, yet could be solved in one design which is applicable to the majority of cases.

One of the characteristic features of laboratory on-line computing is that a wide variety of signal sources is experienced, and in particular the format of timing information tends to vary widely. This information may be inherent in one of the input signals, or it may appear on a separate line as a pulse or signal burst of defined characteristics. The most common function of such timing events is to mark the point in time at which a sequence of regularly spaced samples should be initiated. As the hardware controlling the sampling also imposes constraints on the acceptable type of triggering signal, we are faced with a minor problem of interfacing. It is good practice to save repetitious work by providing one adjustable unit which can cope with the majority of triggering problems.

Such a unit is shown in block diagram form in Figure 8.1(a). It is basically similar in operation to a pulse height analyser module in that it produces a standard output pulse if and only if the input signal exhibits a maximum whose amplitude lies within a window between two adjustable levels. To do this the device must remember the event of the signal amplitude passing upwards through the lower window level by arming itself to be ready to produce an output pulse when the signal amplitude passes downwards through that level, but it must also disarm itself should the amplitude pass upwards through the upper window level. The response of the device to an input signal exhibiting several maxima is shown in Figure 8.1(b). Note that the part of a peak occurring within the window can only logically be established as the amplitude falls below the lower level, so that there is an inherent delay, which may be a disadvantage in some applications. The device can be made to respond to negative peaks by means of a preceding inverter, or to edges by means of a preceding differentiator. Other forms of filtering can be used to ensure that noise peaks do not fall within the amplitude range used to define the trigger signal.

8.3   THE CHOICE BETWEEN SOFTWARE AND HARDWARE SOLUTIONS

One of the recurrent themes of this book is the fact that software and hardware often present alternative approaches to a specific measurement problem.

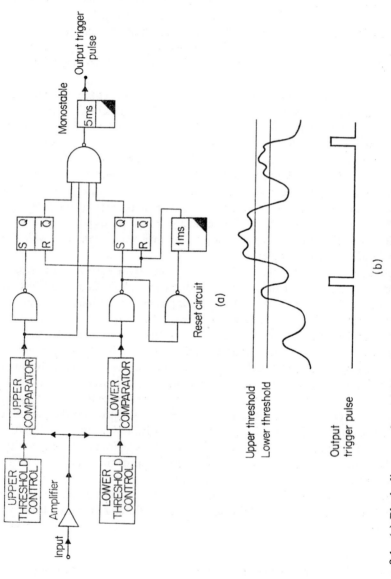

Figure 8.1 (a) Block diagram of a pulse amplitude discriminator suitable to act as a Sampling Sequence Trigger Unit (b) triggering action with a complex waveform

In general, software solutions offer versatility and rapidity of implementation, while hardware solutions have the prime advantage that they tend to liberate the central processor from a burden of routine operations, thereby increasing the capacity of the system. Let us consider three examples of practical problems which illustrate this point.

Firstly, suppose that we have a requirement to generate a sinusoidal signal whose frequency and amplitude are disposable by means of programmed instructions. An example of the occurrence of the problem is in the realization of vocal output from a computer, where three basic formants of speech have to be generated simultaneously to constitute the voiced sounds. Let us enumerate some of the many ways of achieving such a signal.

8.3.1   SOFTWARE SUBROUTINE

This is the most obvious method, and the one which requires least effort. The programmer has merely to generate the appropriate incrementing angle ωt, utilizing some form of timing information, such as interrupts generated by a digital clock, and call a standard subroutine which yields the sine of the angle. The value has then to be multiplied by the amplitude coefficient. He may not know the method by which the function is generated, but if he is a good on-line programmer he will make it his business to find out. The usual approach adopted by authors of such subroutines is to utilize a polynomial, probably of the Chebyshev form, and the accuracy will be determined by the level of truncation of the series. However, the alternative method of using a stored table is favoured in real-time work, as it reduces the computational load at the sacrifice of some storage. This underlines one of the great differences between real-time and off-line computing; for, in the latter it is a matter of complete unconcern to the programmer how the function is generated, provided the accuracy is sufficient. With the table look-up method, a given accuracy can be achieved at various levels of trade-off between storage and interpolation computation, but in the application quoted, where the signal is generated for aural reception, the accuracy demands would not be high.

8.3.2   SOFTWARE RECURSION

The previous method requires a certain amount of storage whichever form is chosen, and it is redundant in the sense that the techniques used are designed for random accessing of sine values. Our discussion of digital filters in Chapter 6 gives a clue to an alternative approach. For, just as an active filter can become an oscillator by bringing it beyond the verge of instability, so a digital filter can become a numerical oscillator by adjusting its coefficients so that the poles appear on the boundary of stability (the unit circle on the z

plane). Hence all we need is a transfer function in z domain form with the poles in the appropriate place to give instability at frequency ω. The reader will readily confirm that an appropriate form is

$$H(z) = \left\{ z^2 - 2\cos\left(2\pi\frac{\omega}{\omega_s}\right) z + 1 \right\}^{-1}$$

The transform in the time domain yields a recursion, which, given a pulse stimulus by setting the first sample at a finite value {sin $(2\pi\omega/\omega_s)$ for unit amplitude}, produces a sinusoidal variation in the subsequent values (this can be easily checked by a manual calculation for, say, $\omega = \omega_s/8$). This method is much more economical in storage than the first method because it relies upon the sequential nature of the required output, rather than wasting what is effectively a random access facility. However, characteristically of software realizations of quasi-continuous signals, it is again very wasteful of computer time since calculations have to be performed every $2\pi/\omega_s$ seconds. The higher the frequency required, the more the computer activity will be dominated by the signal generation process, up to a limit at which there is no time to do anything else. Furthermore, an unstable recursion such as this is subject to cumulative errors.

8.3.3 HARDWARE CONTROLLED OSCILLATOR

A completely different approach would be to utilize the classical linear electronic method of generating sinusoids, the oscillator. This is effectively an unstable active filter, e.g. an amplifier with an RC feedback network. Our purpose would be achieved simply by making the parameters adjustable. This would be done crudely by means of a servo-controlled motorized dial, or more subtly by incorporating voltage-controlled resistor circuits within the oscillator, or more directly by using electronic switching to change the components in discrete digital steps. Computer intervention would only be necessary when a change of output amplitude or frequency is required. On the whole this would not be a very elegant solution to the problem, but a quite plausible one.

8.3.4 HARDWARE DIGITAL CIRCUIT

Finally, let us consider the application of a modern digital technique based on a ROM integrated circuit. A standard ROM is available commercially which contains 32 consecutive values of a sine table in the range 0 to $\pi/2$, i.e. a quarter sinewave. For any input 5 bit address a corresponding output 8 bit fraction is obtained. Thus the complete circle of 2π radians can be represented by a 7 bit number. But, how do we make use of the two most significant input bits? The answer is that one of them is used to control an operation on the 5 bit address and the other to control an operation on the output fraction. We leave it as an interesting exercise for the reader to determine what these operations are and which bit controls each.

It might occur to the reader that a disadvantage of this method is that the output frequency for a given sampling rate is confined to the restricted range of values offered by the division of the sampling frequency by powers of two, but this is not so. If the 7 bit number representing the angle is obtained from the most significant end of a longer number contained in an appropriate register, increments of any size can be applied to the long number; and though only the bits which overflow into the top seven places affect the present output, the less significant bits are stored to contribute to the calculation of future sample points. With such a system the computer is only required to output a number representing the size of increment each time a change of frequency is to occur (the value of increment for frequency ω being (ω/ω_s) for a sampling frequency ω_s); so the output device in addition to the logic associated with the ROM needs two registers and an adder to be capable of autonomous operation between changes of frequency.

Thus we have suggested four possible answers to our sinusoidal signal problem—two software and two hardware. Of these the last is by far the most elegant. It is based on modern technique: it is capable of being multiplexed to provide a number of channels, and it relieves the central processor of the burden of trivial calculations. Like the first two methods it is basically a sampling method and does therefore require a continuous filter at the output. The software methods are only suitable in situations where there is plenty of computer capacity available. The main disadvantage of hardware methods is that they involve a certain amount of design and construction effort, so they would be avoided for experiments which are only to be performed once or twice.

Of course, a composite solution has now become economically feasible, the use of an independently programmed microprocessor, and one could readily see how variations of the above solutions could be achieved in this way. Let us, however, pursue this question of the hardware/software choice a little further.

A second simple example of a case where both software and hardware solutions to an on-line measurement problem are available is in the evaluation of system response by means of a pseudorandom stimulus. As we have seen, such a response may be generated by means of a shift-register with a modulo-two feedback network. Obviously with less physical effort one may reproduce the same process in the computer by means of a suitable sub-program. A third possibility, which would be advantageous for relatively short sequences, is to store the entire sequence, packed into whole words, and write a simple subroutine to output it bit by bit.

The question of which is the best solution can only be answered by careful consideration of the circumstances. For example, what speed (sampling frequency) and accuracy (number of ordinates, 2^{N-1}) are required? Do these need to be changed frequently? Are other measurement or control operations to be carried out simultaneously?

There is little doubt that the hardware solution has considerable advantages in terms of maximum speed of operation, as it frees the computer from the performance of a number of instructions, which are in fact carried out in parallel by a simple external electronic circuit. Figure 8.2 shows the way such an operation can be realized most simply and effectively.

There is a one-to-one correspondence between the binary stimulus bit and A–D output sample, so it makes sense to treat this bit temporarily as part of the sample so that the input and output signals can be transferred to the computer in a single data transfer. Provided the converter output does not occupy the whole interface word this is easily arranged, particularly as great precision is not required with this type of averaging process which tends to reduce quantization noise. It is also convenient from a software point of view to have the input and output values attached to each other in this way. In forming the cross-correlation at a particular delay we require to consider the input and output signals separated by the number of samples say V1 corresponding to this delay. The output value is masked out from the least significant end of the word, say VN1, while the single bit is extracted by means of a strobe order for V(N1 + V1), if this bit is positive the output word is added to the total, and if the bit is zero the output word is subtracted. A further gain of speed could be made by taking no action when the input bit is zero; this would produce a positive bias in cross-correlation function, but since this is produced by the positive bias of the input autocorrelation (see Section 6.11) it can be allowed for.

A software solution of this problem would demand the use of an additional output channel, which while requiring only one bit also demands an extra data transfer for each sample. Furthermore, the sampling rate must be dictated by a real-time clock, though when this is available as a software-programmable device an extremely versatile scheme can be realized, since the experimental parameters, sequence length, sampling frequency, etc., can all be chosen by program or a teletype message. Also it is easy to switch from the cross-correlation method to another, say cumulative averaging under a pulse stimulus, by a simple change of program.

As a final example of a frequently occurring problem which is amenable to either method of solution consider the generation of characters for a visual display. Let us assume that we have chosen the dot matrix rather than the

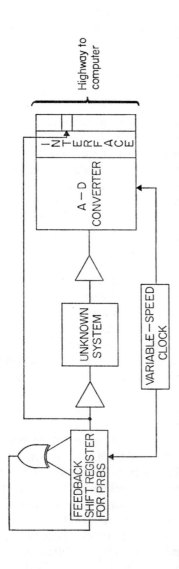

Figure 8.2   On-line identification of unknown system response using a hardware PRBS generator to save computation

vector generation method. The problem we are faced with is that the *representation* of a character requires a much larger number of bits than its *specification*, so it is not feasible to use the former as a vehicle for storage and transmission of characters. Yet there is a one-to-one correspondence between the highly redundant representation number and the more economical specification number, which has to be realized as a conversion process for the display of information. In either form of solution the agent through which this conversion is performed is a stored table.

Obviously the software approach permits a number of different arrangements of the stored table. We shall consider one which is of illustrative value. It would be absurd to waste storage in such a commonly used data block, so some form of data packing is desirable. Let us suppose that 8 bit bytes (or fields) are convenient subdivisions of the basic word length. A more than adequate size for the dot matrix is 7 × 6, so six bytes could be used to represent the columns of the character and each one could contain seven possible dots, each represented by a one, or blanks, each represented by a zero. Furthermore there is one bit left in each byte which can be put to good use in the following way. If this bit is zero let it mean that the character is completed: if it is one there is at least another column to follow. This device simultaneously provides variable width characters and saves display time.

The interpretive subroutine to go with this table is required to take an 8 bit number specifying the character, use it as an incremental address in the table to point to the words which contain the representation of the character, and then issue x and y incremental instructions so that the character is scanned dot by dot. A variety of output peripherals can be used to display the character, for example chart recorders or storage tubes. As with all software methods the great advantage is versatility. Extra symbols can be incorporated into the scheme by utilizing some of the numbers not allocated in the standard character code, e.g. mathematical symbols such as Σ, and extra control characters can be created.

Control characters require certain action other than the straightforward generation of a symbol from the table, and in both hardware and software solutions they have to be trapped. The mechanism for doing this is quite simple, since the need has been foreseen in the construction of the code, and control characters occupy the earlier positions in the table. Thus in software one could subtract 31 from the code number after the parity has been removed; if the result is negative it represents a control character, while if it is positive it represents a symbol and its value is the address in the table.

The hardware solution is again greatly simplified by the availability of a standard ROM which contains the dot-pattern representation numbers at addresses in the same order as the code specification numbers. The incoming number is held while the columns are strobed in turn by pulses to produce the row patterns serially at the output lines. The ROM can be used in exactly the same way as the look up table in the software solution to produce x and y increments for output via D–A converters, but there is an even more elegant solution which dispenses with converters altogether and forms the characters by means of timing alone. In this method, the information defining the characters is set up, in a system of circulating stores based on long shift registers, and is continuously presented row by row as a binary signal modulating the brightness of the display tube subjected to a synchronized raster deflection. Again, the great virtue of the hardware solution is that it imposes no software burden on the central processor, and this is paid for by loss of versatility in that only those characters foreseen in the construction of the ROM may be generated (although even this disadvantage is mitigated by the emergence of programmable ROMs).

The three examples quoted in this section have been chosen to present fairly clear-cut cases of the software/hardware choice. In practice this question of choice exists at every stage of the design of an experiment, and it can only be answered in the light of the responses to further questions about the particular application, such as:

How often will the experiment be repeated?
What tasks have to be handled simultaneously?
Will the processor loading approach a critical level?
Might there be a need to modify the technique at a later stage?
Are relevant microcircuits or subroutines already available?

8.4   SOFTWARE AND HARDWARE AS A COMBINED PACKAGE

The peripheral equipment, be it a standard item or a special design, exists to provide the connection between the user's program and that aspect of the physical world he wishes to measure or manipulate thereby. The chain of command making this connection may be complex, but it is only the two endmost links which concern the user. The central link is the standard interface whose nature is common to all input/output channels. On either side of this, however, are the software and hardware links which are peculiar to the operation of the peripheral. They are designed to simplify and optimize the operation of the particular channel without concern for the convenience of the user. In the interest of progress it is vital that the user should be shielded from the domestic chores that go with the maintenance of the particular channel, and the device for achieving this is a special subroutine whose design is linked with the design of the peripheral controller under the constraint that it is to afford maximum simplicity to the caller. The caller might be required to call a special entry at the beginning of the program to set up the channel, but apart from this he would normally only be expected to nominate the source or destination address for the relevant data and call the subroutine for each transfer or block of transfers.

The sort of activity covered by this special subroutine would be the setting up of pointers for the data and the interrupt program entry, initiation of the transfer by setting the appropriate staticizers, checking that the transfer has been successfully completed, restoring the channel to its appropriate quiescent state, etc. It would be wasteful for such specialized pieces of program to be written more than once. A great advantage of this approach is that the only pieces of program which have access to the basic critical instruction such as staticizer settings are these fully tried and tested subroutines, so that even inexperienced users should be incapable of inducing fundamental clags.

The best way of defining this software interface to the user program is to conform to the practice of the manufacturer with his standard peripherals. This should ensure that user programs do not need to be greatly modified in the event of changes such as the institution of a more advanced operating system, though there will almost certainly be discrepant features between programs written for operation on a very small basic system and ones written for operation under very advanced operating systems with backing store files, unsolicited teletype messages, etc.

Once again, we are prevented from giving the reader the information he really needs in this context, as its nature will be completely bound up in the design of the machine he is concerned with, but at least we are saved from obscuring this important point of system development philosophy by the inclusion of details which should be readily available in the appropriate handbooks. To summarize this point—the development of every new input/output channel consists of a software as well as a hardware problem, both of which must be carried out in conjunction, so that the user is presented with a simple combined package. A major advantage of the approach is that the computer is protected from the ravages that the unskilled or careless user can wreak from either the software or the hardware side of the interface.

A particular instrument or experiment may use more than one special channel. It could, for example, be allocated a fast analogue input channel for the actual readings and a slow relay output channel for range changing. The concept of the combined package can be usefully extended to cover this eventuality by the provision of two further outer layers in the sandwich, as illustrated in Figure 8.3. These layers would be the software and hardware interfaces which connect the channels respectively to the user program and the instrument. The user then knows that he has merely to plug in the instrument on one side and call a certain subroutine in a specified way on the other. A different instrument would use different outer layers but these would again link with the common inner layers relevant to any channels used. As we

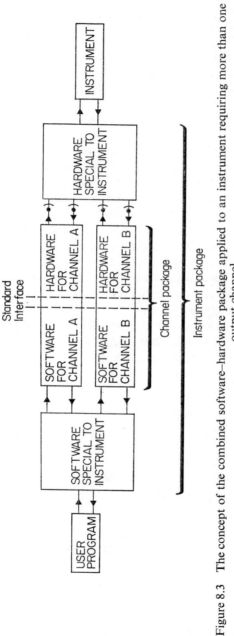

Figure 8.3 The concept of the combined software–hardware package applied to an instrument requiring more than one input/output channel

have implied in the previous chapter this technique allows general software to retain its validity even if the peripheral instrument is changed.

8.5 DOCUMENTATION

We return without apology to the subject of documentation, which in our experience is the one aspect of on-line computing which laboratory workers are likely to fall down on. Virtually everything mentioned so far in this chapter loses its point entirely unless it is supported by full and correct documentation. A subroutine without an accurate specification is worse than useless, it is a positive impediment, and in addition a full listing in source language should be available in case any queries arise concerning its precise nature. A piece of hardware without a circuit diagram is equally troublesome, and a functional block diagram is also of great value in case of a fault developing or modifications being required.

Like many of the aspects of laboratory on-line computing, documentation is also an important feature of ordinary experimental technique (every good experimentalist keeps a detailed log book) but its importance is greatly intensified by the mutual interdependence of the hardware and software elements. These function in such complex co-operation that it is very difficult to unravel a malfunctioning system.

As an example of the need for a comprehensive set of documents consider the pulse height analyser, which is discussed elsewhere as a computer peripheral. The list of documents maintained by the authors for their analyser and its peripheral control unit is as follows:

    logic/circuit diagrams
    wiring diagrams and lists
    connector data
    user's guide
    subroutine specifications
    subroutine master tapes and listings
    test program and description
    list of modifications.

In addition to the local documentation, a large amount of paper will be provided by the computer manufacturer for both hardware and software, and this also needs to be efficiently maintained. The most critical aspect of all documentation is the proper recording of modifications, and, if this is not attended to, the irretrievable situation will be reached where all faith in the documents is lost, and the only possible result is unmitigated chaos in which true scientific progress is impossible.

8.6 STRATEGY AND TACTICS

Definitions from the Concise Oxford Dictionary:

Strategy: ₁Generalship, the art or war (lit. and fig.); management of an army or armies in a campaign, art of so moving or disposing troops or ships or aircraft as to impose upon the enemy the place and time and conditions for fighting preferred by oneself.

Tactics: The art of disposing military or naval or air forces esp. in actual contact with the enemy; procedure calculated to gain some end, skilful device.

A measure of the excellence of an army would be the degree to which its efficiency in carrying out routine tasks frees the general to concentrate on planning and broader policy. Similarly, a good on-line computer system (hardware or software) is one which gives the user maximum freedom to concentrate on strategic decisions in the knowledge that routine and tactical decisions are already catered for. Thus the decision, of which position in the priority scale a particular peripheral is to occupy, is a strategic one which requires the serious thought of the user, while the urgent tactical decision of how to deal with a particular chain of interrupts will, in a well designed machine, be delegated to the computer hardware.

This principle also underlies the practice of building up software on a hierarchical basis, so that once subroutines at a lower level have been proved to carry out their tactical tasks efficiently, one need not concern oneself with the details of their operation. Thus the chain of command will usually proceed from the user at a keyboard down through a sequence of subroutines to the actuators connected to the experiment. Apart from his own input/output (e.g. teletype) subroutines, which correspond to the general's low ranking personal messengers, those closest to the user are the most specialized in the strategic sense (of narrow application) while furthest from him are the most specialized in a tactical sense (but of wide application).

Words like strategy and tactics tend to be relative, and once the program is in motion the user will make what are to him tactical decisions, but in relation to the sequence of complex procedures thereby initiated they appear as strategic. Tactical decisions are ones made in face of the enemy—*time*. With a poorly designed machine the programmer will have to worry continually about timing problems and other such trivia. With a well designed machine there is only one timing question, i.e. 'Am I asking it to do too much in the time available?'

From his own point of view, however, the intelligent user will plan his strategy to give the maximum amount of tactical freedom achievable without degrading the capabilities of the system. Thus his program may permit him, through the keyboard, to vary the parameters for data acquisition beforehand, to vary the treatment of data after acquisition, to halt acquisition prematurely and perhaps abort the experiment. The method of achieving this is to determine at the outset the vocabulary of messages required and build the program round the actions corresponding to these messages. Note that a facility such as premature halting of data aquisition may imply that the time wasting process of examining an unsolicited message flag is included repetitively, though if the data are being acquired through data interrupts this will not necessarily cause any deterioration of performance. At any instant during the running of the active part of the program the state of the computer is completely unpredictable, as varying quantities of data are absorbed in the elasticity of the buffers, so tactical intervention by the user is only possible at the crudest level, or during a natural hiatus.

An important point about tactical intervention for the programmer is that its need must be foreseen at the outset, so in the preliminary analysis of an experiment to be set up for on-line performance it is necessary to include an appreciation of what can go wrong and what might need to be done about it. Of equal importance is the determination of points in the program where humanly inspired variation might be beneficial, but one must always bear in mind the risk of surrendering that often underestimated advantage of the computer—its objectivity, which takes us back to our remarks on the human element in Chapter 7.

8.7   OVERALL CONTROL AND MONITORING BY TELETYPE

The preceding discussion has underlined the importance of the teletype (or VDU with keyboard) in successful on-line computing. It is, of course, quite possible to do without it, either by abdicating the right to intervene at appropriate stages, or by doing so via awkwardly coded handswitch operations, but the consequent penalties in loss of versatility are considerable. Intervention is only possible on the basis of proper information, and the teletype is also the most appropriate channel to provide a monitoring facility. It is not, however, a bulk data channel, as it is a relatively slow device, and there is no point in its exceeding the speed of human interpretation. It is essential therefore that the information passing through it is severely edited to a sequence of succinct and apposite messages.

The output messages from the teletype consist of fixed and variable parts. The fixed parts are pieces of text which either announce a prescribed occurrence or label a variable part, which is a number calculated by the computer. Thus in the following two messages only the figures are variable.

ANALYSIS COMPLETE
AVGE PULSE HEIGHT 0.128 VOLTS

The fixed texts represent a considerable overhead of storage (8 bits per character) and typing them takes time, so there are good reasons for making them terse, though not to the point of obscurity. Input messages similarly contain fixed texts which either cause appropriate action or condition the interpretation of a following variable part, normally a number. It is, of course, quite possible to introduce a grammatical structure so that messages comprise severally significant text elements, but this elaboration would not be justifiable in most laboratory applications. It is usually appreciated by operators when compressed forms of frequently used messages can be substituted, and a decoding system like that suggested in Section 4.15 has the advantage that the low information vowel and space elements can be included or omitted at will (e.g. RPT quoted in Section 8.2 would have the same effect as REPEAT) and one has a choice between speed and comprehensibility.

The teletype will generally be allocated the lowest priority of all the peripherals, and the usual procedure is for the message to be assembled character by character in the buffer area allocated to it. When the prescribed terminator (end of text or new line, etc.) is received, a *message present* flag is set, and the speed with which the message is dealt will depend upon how the flag inspection is organized in the program. Most messages will be solicited or expected, in which case the computer will probably be looping on that particular flag, and response will be instantaneous, but the response to unsolicited messages will depend upon the frequency with which the flag is inspected. It is comparatively rarely that unexpected intervention is required outside the base loop or quiescent state of the program, but if such a requirement is anticipated flag inspection must be built in to the active parts of the program.

The teletype is the principal agent of man–computer interaction in the laboratory and careful attention to the strategy of its employment can greatly enhance the convenience with which a program can be used. It is therefore a good technique to build the program round a repertoire of teletype messages selected at the outset (but with, of course, provision for later expansion). This repertoire should be designed to simplify as much as possible the action and thought required of the operator, for in the laboratory there is usually a sufficient multitude of observations and actions to preoccupy him. A great advantage of the teletype in the laboratory is that it can be moved close to the particular experimental rig being used, and it is important, therefore, that the entire control of the program should be invested in it, so that the operator is not required to go to the computer console to set handswitches, etc.

As the system expands, a stage is reached at which a clash occurs between the teletype's rôles as a conveyor of messages to and from the supervisory program, and the control of individual experiments. The installation of a second teletype then becomes a high priority requirement. Such slow devices are easily multiplexed, so it is not difficult to expand much further in this direction, but it is doubtful whether this would be of great benefit in laboratory work other than allowing the program preparation activities such as text editing to be carried out in parallel.

Quite often it is desirable for bulk information, either graphical or alphanumeric, to be available for the perusal of the user, and the teletype is not the suitable medium for this. A VDU is more suitable and the storage type is preferable for its low interface and processor loading. In this instance the rôle of the teletype would be to convey the requirement for data and to specify their source, it would also be used to indicate that hard copy is required via a digital plotter, tape punch, or line printer. Again anticipation is the key to successful programming in this respect, and when the experiment is running it is generally too late to start thinking about the nature and format of the data that might be required.

Another important function of the keyboard is as an adjunct to utility programs. Examples of these are the *text editor*, which is most important, as it obviates the old fashioned manipulation of paper tapes; and the *core post mortem* program, which is useful when one is trying to determine what went wrong.

In short, the teletype is one's personal link with the computer and the experiment, so it pays to treat it with care and respect at the programming stage. Its value is best appreciated by those who have had to operate a system without an on-line teletype.

8.8   COPING WITH CLAGS

Clag is a useful piece of jargon from a Scandinavian word meaning mud, and it is used to describe the state of a computer system when it becomes 'stuck' in a loop or at an illegal instruction, resisting attempts to free it. Some common causes of clags (apart from actual hardware failures) are:

> The corruption of program words by a previous writing of data with an incorrect address;
> Attempts to obey data words as instructions, usually as a result of jumping to an incorrectly calculated address;
> Careless use of flags, and neglect of the need to provide for resetting in the event of a breakdown;
> Improper or incomplete setting up procedures;

Waiting for an event whose occurrence has been precluded by prior action or which has already occurred during overlong intermediate calculations.

In addition there is the whole range of common programming errors such as:

Forgetting the return link statement on exit from a subroutine;
Failing to zero a count or cumulative data area before using it;
Doing one loop too few or too many owing to faulty indexing.

Clags can be very difficult to deal with for two main reasons. Firstly, because they are often the result of an illegal jump, the site of the clag is often remote from the site of the error. Secondly, the error may have remained undetected in a frequently used subroutine and may suddenly be activated by a chance circumstance, so that its actual location is not readily suspected. They are particularly unpleasant in real-time systems since it is usually impossible to locate them by stepping through the program as this interferes with the timing and prohibits the occurrence of interrupts. Ours is a field of study in which prevention is immeasurably better than cure, and the approach we have tried to engender in this book—one of anticipation, self-discipline and progressive development—is designed to obviate the need for a cure.

Nevertheless, when a clag does occur despite all precautions, one is left with the difficult problem of locating its cause. A first procedure is to try clearing the store before loading the program—to test whether the error lies in the use of an unassigned entity. Failing this it is necessary to prepare special test versions of the program. Firstly, one can eliminate any subroutines which are apparently irrelevant to the quest and are not essential to operation. This may be done by removing the calls to them, or perhaps more conveniently by assembling with dummies which contain only return link instructions. Check whether the clag still occurs, and think again if it does not. Next lace the program with flag instructions at critical points.

Flag instructions are a convenient means of ascertaining that a particular piece of program has been executed. For the present purpose we often only wish to identify the last flag passed and the first flag not yet reached, so that when the clag occurs we know that its source lies between these two. A suitable flag instruction is therefore one that sets the contents of an unused location to a value unique to that flag, so that the contents of that location may be examined after the clag has occurred. The particular computer system may in fact provide a simpler means of inserting flagging instructions. It is sometimes possible to insert the flags manually by overwriting certain non-essential instructions. Note that the presence of the flags will change the timing of the program, which is a further reason for avoiding critical timing. Once the general area of the fault has been established it should be possible to identify it by useful examination of the program; if not, the area can be further subdivided by more flags. As we point out below, even this procedure can fail totally to locate the error.

One can, of course, be lucky and find that the clag occurs at the point of error, or that its source is obvious by inspection, but a little experience of these happenings usually convinces one that the best time to deal with them is at the program writing stage. Careful flow charting and modular writing and testing provide a good basis, but at each stage of the program one must train oneself to be continually asking certain questions, such as:

> What information do I require at this stage, and have I ensured that it is available?
>
> What prior events am I assuming, and is it possible for them not to have occurred yet?
>
> Have I initialized this flag, count, sum or data area, and is it reset on re-running the program?
>
> Does the sequence I am writing here require the existence of a corresponding sequence in some other part of the program?
>
> Could I, without too much loss of efficiency, make this module more self-contained so that it can be fully and independently tested?
>
> What should I include in the test program to cover this sequence?

The answers to some of these questions may require additions or modifications to another part of the program, and an invaluable aid to programming is a sheet of notes for action which are written down as soon as the point arises and crossed out as soon as it is dealt with. Debugging is inherently more difficult in real-time, and one cannot afford the laxity which sometimes develops in off-line programming because of the efficiency of debugging aids in high-level compilers. We cannot over-emphasize the depredations that can arise from a simple obscure error. Let us quote a final example. In a program the data pointer for a block of data from a particular peripheral was set up indirectly, and owing to a subsequent error the setting did not occur, so that it was pointing to the address zero. As soon as the peripheral was activated it began to write in data from zero upwards. It overwrote registers used by the program, then the loader and other core-resident material until it came to the data pointer itself, which it gave another value, so that it began overwriting the program. Eventually it collided with the piece of program being executed, an illegal jump occurred, and the computer came to a halt at a remote address. Imagine the situation! The program, the loader, the interface data were all destroyed and all had to be reloaded for a re-run. The same thing happened to flags when they were included. All the executable parts of the program were free of error when they were examined, and the fault did not occur when parts of the program were stepped through. The error was only found by dint of hours of hard thinking, but the programmer never made that mistake again. This type of fault is peculiar to on-line programming, and the possibility of such occurrences is the reason behind our emphasis of the importance of setting up procedures in Chapter 4. A little foresight is better than a lot of hindsight!

8.9 PROBLEMS OF STATIONARITY

Stationarity is one of the most fundamental aspects of measurement, but it does involve conceptual difficulties, and often tends to be glibly assumed or glossed over. In the formal development of probability theory [ProPap] it can be given a precise meaning, and for most purposes the wide sense definition is sufficient, i.e. *a process is stationary in the wide sense if its expected value is constant and its autocorrelation can be expressed as a function of one variable* (this variable being the time difference τ). Such definitions, however, are based on the concept of the *ensemble average* which is not always accessible in a physical situation, and we are often forced to make the *ergodic assumption* which allows us to substitute a *time average*. Even time averages have the inherent difficulty that they are expressed as limits, and can therefore only be *estimated* by calculation over a truncated time range. Thus in practice we tend to regard such definitions in the light of our knowledge or assumptions regarding the range of time or frequency covered by the phenomena being observed. In these circumstances one man's stationary signal can be another man's non-stationarity, e.g. a 1 Hz component would be part of the signal in EEG measurement, but to one intent on measuring 1 ms carrier transit times in a semiconductor it would be a non-stationarity.

In the measurement of ripples on the sea the waves would be a non-stationarity. In the measurement of the waves, the tides would be a non-stationarity. These, however, are the simplest type of non-stationarity, the additive ones. They are a form of low-frequency noise which can be removed by filtering. High-pass digital filtering is fairly easily accomplished, but there is sometimes a good reason for preferring conventional linear-continuous filtering prior to A–D conversion. This arises from the need to utilize the full information capacity of the digital word—to steer an optimum course between overflow and under-flow. The low-frequency drift form of non-stationarity can be the wind that blows us off that course, and in order to accommodate it we may be forced to reduce gain at the input, thereby relegating the signal component of interest to just a few bits rather than the whole word. With high-pass pre-filtering this situation can be avoided. Note that we already have low-pass pre-filtering for sampling reasons, so the net result is that we are applying band-pass pre-filtering to select the band covered by the desired signal.

A more difficult form of non-stationarity to deal with is one in which the low-frequency component is in effect combined multiplicatively, so that the measured process itself is evolutive. In such instances the practical problems of range setting can be immense. One solution is to use non-linear (i.e. logarithmic) pre-amplification. This problem often arises in electrical conduction measurements, where currents can drift over several decades of magnitude. Logarithmic electrometers are available to assist the monitoring of such processes, and as they are equipped with auxiliary output, they make useful laboratory peripherals. An alternative approach is to provide for automated range switching by means of control words.

A common form of non-stationarity is the transient response of a process to the sudden establishment of experimental conditions, so that the process tends towards a stationary form in time. The degree of difficulty this engenders depends on where the sought information lies, it may be inherent in the terminal stationary process, or in the first rapidly changing regime, or in the effective 'time constant' with which the change occurs, or as a randomly occurring feature of the signal. The approach to such problems depends entirely on the understanding gained from preliminary study of the processes involved. The worst situation is one in which the initial transient condition needs to be studied and the experiment is difficult and expensive to set up, yet it cannot be repeated on the particular test-object because it has become 'conditioned' by the experiment. There is then inevitably a risk of losing the result, and it is important to try to calculate and minimize that risk. The authors have found themselves faced with such a problem, and while the main ingredients of its solution were faith, hope and dogged determination, it was only the availability of an on-line computer that made one possible at all.

Another aspect of non-stationarity is the requirement for the acquisition of large amounts of data, which is why an on-line computer often provides the only means of tackling such problems. This is because the idea of non-stationarity implies the existence of essential low (complex) frequency components. Much of the powerful probabilistic approach to signals [ProPap] is largely restricted to stationary forms, so one is often reduced to an *ad hoc* or intuitive approach, which is fraught with dangers, but better than nothing.

Nevertheless, non-stationary problems are common to today's research, and are often the motivation for calling on the assistance of an on-line computer. The techniques applied to such problems range from the assumption of piecewise stationarity to the application of advanced mathematical developments by Wiener and his followers [SigProBeau]. The non-stationary autocorrelation is a two-dimensional form, so it follows that the corresponding power spectrum is also two-dimensional, and unfortunately physically rather meaningless, though sometimes useful analytically. The concept of an instantaneous spectrum is proscribed by the uncertainty principle, but the idea of a changing short-term spectrum is often used, so that a process can be represented as a three-dimensional plot on an (ω, t) plane, though the representation, except in the case of very slowly varying processes, is likely to be a rather crude one. EEG is a good example of a field in which a crude time varying estimate of the spectrum can be a useful diagnostic tool (and another is speech recognition). A quantitative study, however, can only be based on a sound understanding of the principles [ProPap] and practice [SigProBeau] of current mathematical techniques.

8.10 TRIAL AND ERROR VERSUS ANALYSIS

For reasons which are partly historical and partly aesthetic, most scientific workers have a prejudice in favour of mathematical analysis in the general approach to a problem. The historical reason is that the scientific method was evolved before the present era of great computing power, and many of our courses of instruction are deeply rooted in the established tradition. The aesthetic factor is also of some importance—it is one of the main reasons that most of us are in the business of science, and a great deal of pleasure can be obtained from an aspect of beauty which is sadly hidden from the innumerate majority.

Mathematical analysis of a problem can lead to a deep understanding of the influence of the various physical parameters within it. Indeed, it is an important tenet of this book that on-line computing can only properly be carried out with the support of a sound analytical understanding of its principles, as outlined in Chapter 6. Nevertheless, having said that, one must also remark that this understanding is often limited by the physical–mathematical interface; i.e. by the degree of correspondence it is possible to establish between a tractable mathematical model and the physical reality. Once obtained by analysis, however, a solution is global in the sense that any values of variables and parameters can be inserted in the knowledge that no better solution exists. Also one must not underestimate the value of the intuitive appreciation of the properties of mathematical functions that it is possible to acquire and put to good use.

On the other hand, for most of us, mathematical analysis is difficult and time consuming, and with previously undreamed of computing power to hand it is possible to husband our own mental resources by confining analytical effort to those areas where it is most productive of enhanced understanding (or in some on-line applications, most productive of a desired physical outcome). The alternative procedure of trial and error often has considerable advantages of speed, but has its own pitfalls.

Whereas an analytical method will often produce what is demonstrably the *best* solution, in general, there is no way in which a trial and error method can tell us just how good the present solution is. Thus a computer working to a trial and error scheme can only say 'this is *better*' or 'this is *worse*' (and that only in a certain prescribed sense). It cannot without the support of at least some analytical work say 'that is *best*'.

Many problems of on-line computing are complicated by the presence of such features as non-linearity, randomness, non-stationarity and a profusion of parameters. In such circumstances one cannot assert at the outset that an analytical solution exists in terms of current mathematical tools, whereas trial and error will always produce some form of solution. Many of our methods are, of course, combinations of analysis and trial and error. Analysis can, for example, put bounds on the parameter spaces that need to be probed, or it can produce a scheme for proceeding from one trial solution to the next, but here we must take great care that our assumptions are valid (see for example the discussion of local and global minima in Section 6.12). In the complete absence of analytical support, the trial and error method can be far too cumbersome to use, since random probings in a space whose dimensionality is determined by the number of disposable variables are likely to offer a miniscule probability of success in a reasonable time, but some form of analysis, however approximate, will greatly simplify the problem by placing bounds on the space to be probed and producing a first guess, however crude. In the laboratory situation a feel for the physics of the problem can often be equally helpful in circumscribing the search area. Between the ideal of a completely analytical solution and the anathema of an unconstrained random search lies a spectrum of hybrid methods one of which suits any particular case. As in many other fields of activity one can often get away with 'quick and dirty' methods, but being able to do so successfully is always a manifestation of skill and knowledge. Try this one with a scientific calculator before reading further—find numerically the solution of $x = e^{-x}$.

There is certainly no need for the sense of shame that some scientific workers seem to feel when they admit to using a trial and error method. The exploitation of such possibilities is one of the very reasons for bringing the computer into the laboratory. They do, however, suffer from the great disadvantage of the computer—if you ask it to do something damned silly it will! This is fertile ground for some of the great howlers of student programming. The classic mistake is to forget that the method is trial *and error*, i.e. using a technique such as Newton's iteration repetitively without checking that the error is in fact decreasing.

Newton's method is what most people would choose for solving the example given above, i.e. $x_{n+1} = (x_n + 1)/(1 + e^{x_n})$. Starting from a guess of 1·0 this produces a five figure accuracy in three iterations ($x_4 = 0.56714$). The quickest way to obtain the result, however, is to start with a random number and punch the exponential and reciprocal buttons alternately. This is a quick and dirty method for the particular case, which happens to be in suitable form and convergent for the *direct iteration method* [CoMeLaFa], i.e. $x_{n+1} = e^{-x_n}$.

Now these methods of solving equations are adequately dealt with in more mathematical texts [e.g. CoMeLaFa] as are others such as *regula falsi* and *binary search*, but in general, our knowledge of on-line problems does not extend to the certainty of good behaviour (in terms of smoothness, continuity, time independence, etc.). Indeed, we can more often be assured of ill behaviour. Frequently a modification of an existing method is usable—for example Newton's method may not work with raw data yet be satisfactory with smoothed data—but remember that this only produces a way of proceeding from trial to trial, and the assessment is the critical stage.

Sometimes a wholly random search is feasible, especially if it can be conducted as a background program. In such cases the parameters would be altered by small random quantities, using a simple scheme such as sampling from a Laplace distribution (Section 6.11), and the goodness of the resulting solution compared with the current best to see whether the new values of the parameters should take over.

The analytical support for trial and error methods is increasing all the time. An example of a technique which has recently found increasing use is the application of the contraction mapping theorem of functional analysis, which, while not always giving the most rapid convergence, is at least able to guarantee convergence under appropriate conditions. Often what we are trying to do in on-line computing is find the inverse of a system operator, for example in measurements unavoidably made through a corrupting system, which in the linear case is a deconvolution problem. Simply stated, this problem is: 'given the output find the input', and in the last resort it is solved by trying various inputs according to some scheme and finding the ones that minimize the error between the given output and the trial output. Here again the methods of functional analysis are widening the analytical support, but they are often powerless in the face of some of the more difficult experimental circumstances such as non-stationarity, in which the very concept of 'best' may change with time.

Finally, it is important to note that any methods used are subject to the peculiar errors which appertain to the on-line computing method, such as quantization and sampling noise, the buffering delay and other factors discussed in earlier chapters. This implies that the error itself is to some extent a corrupted quantity, but let us not overestimate this defect—it is often far less serious than the defects introduced by the assumptions which are made to obtain a convenient mathematical model.

Chapter IX

The Computer Oriented Laboratory

9.1 INTRODUCTION

A computer is not installed in a laboratory for the purpose of performing a single measurement; it is more likely to be brought in to support a lengthy experimental programme. Also, once available it can earn its keep by providing facilities for associated programmes and activities. Such programmes tend to be open-ended, if only because it is usually impossible to forecast accurately the directions an original study will take. This is why, throughout this text, we have emphasized methods of approach which tend to keep the options open without sacrificing the benefits of cumulative growth, for the growth of a laboratory computer system, hardware and software, can be almost organic in nature; and like organic growth it may be healthy, organized and fertile, or it can be cancerous, chaotic and sterile.

These characteristics are particularly beneficial in the education of young engineers and scientists, who are thereby subjected at an early stage to the disciplines of group work in the knowledge that their individual efforts can help make or mar the overall project. So, unless engaged in the highly unsatisfactory business of artificial projects in computing for its own sake, every worker at whatever level is bound to be involved in a variety of computing whose nature is very much determined by the scientific or technical purpose in hand. We have tried so far to concentrate on general principles of laboratory computing, in so far as they can be extracted, but at this stage it is necessary to consider specific examples of laboratory arrangements to bring out some of the remaining points. The arrangement of a system is not solely the business of its conceiver, and it is important for every user to understand why the system he is using is configured in a particular way, so that he can use it efficiently and contribute to its development, even if only by adding to the capital of software invested in it.

260

We shall restrict ourselves to two very different examples of research facilities which are organized around an on-line computer, and the first of these will be the authors' own laboratory. These are put forward not as models to be imitated but as illustrations of the response to a particular set of measurement problems.

An example of the sort of question which has to be answered at an early stage in the development of a computer system is how the peripherals are to be distributed, both in space and in interrupt priority order. In general the fastest peripherals need to be closest and of highest priority (note, that by fastest we refer to the maximum speed requirement at interface level, not the speed at the input or output of an instrument, which may be totally unrelated). Such rules may have to be broken in response to specific constraints, and if a fast peripheral *must* be distant, then more time and money must be spent on the transmission hardware of lines, drivers and receivers; but if, as is ideal, the laboratory layout can be centred on the computer, it is usually possible to avoid such complications. The degree of freedom available to the laboratory designer in this respect is determined largely by the relationship between the anticipated computing load and the capacity of the machine.

Evidently, the overall scientific strategy needs to be planned well ahead, as far as this is possible, which at best is usually only in terms of the broader aspects of policy. The first job is always to try to assess the peak computing load, which in this field is likely to concern interface activity rather than the amount of mathematical processing; but it is not always possible to define a limiting load, and the requirement may well emerge as a demand for the maximum speed possible. This is the case in our first example of a laboratory set up, which we shall now proceed to examine.

9.2 A DIELECTRICS RESEARCH LABORATORY

The field of study which has been the chief preoccupation of the authors is examination of the behaviour of insulating materials, and more specifically dielectric liquids. At first sight, one would hardly imagine a simpler test-object than a test-cell containing a pair of electrodes and a sample of insulating oil. Yet this is a system manifesting virtually every possible complication, i.e. low signal levels with high noise, non-stationarity, fast transient phenomena, non-linearity and instability. Furthermore, it turns out to be virtually impossible to prepare two identical samples of liquid despite a most rigorous treatment which constitutes a considerable investment of time and money. Let us devote a few more words to the examination of these complications, as they are characteristic of many physical systems, though fortunately few are so severely tainted.

In materials, electric charge carriers tend to drift under the action of an electric field **E** with a velocity **v** proportional to the field strength, so that $\mathbf{v} = \mu\mathbf{E}$, where μ is the charge mobility. In dielectrics μ is low, and the local conditions are governed by the Poisson and continuity equations:

$$\nabla \cdot \mathbf{E} = \frac{\rho}{\varepsilon}$$

$$\mathbf{J} = \rho\mu\,\mathbf{E}$$

where **J** is the current density produced by the charge, of density ρ in a medium of permittivity ε. The solution of these equations under practical boundary conditions reveals two important consequences: firstly, the amount of current obtainable, even if the charges are injected artificially, is severely limited, and secondly, once ρ is significant the system becomes non-linear. In fact the theoretical situation is even more complicated in liquids because there are terms and equations to be added to account for the mechanical coupling with the liquid; and the overall system proves to be one capable of revealing an electro-hydrodynamic instability, so that under appropriate conditions of charge and stress the liquid begins to move and carry the charges with it.

Practice is even more complicated than theory because of inevitable imperfections in the sample. Impurities dissolved in the liquid are possibly less important than the fact that a critical part of the system, the liquid–metal interface at the electrodes, is largely unknown, unconstant and uncontrollable; in addition to which there are inevitably solid particles present which, though sub-microscopic, are capable of being charged and conveying that charge from one electrode to the other. Any moving charge q between plane electrodes d centimetres apart produces a current in the external circuit of magnitude qv/d. As a result of all this the system is noisy and non-stationary.

Despite all this, liquid dielectrics are technologically important, and since the liquid state is the least understood state of matter, they need to be investigated. One of the most important characteristics of an insulant is its electric breakdown strength, and this itself is a very tricky concept. The value of breakdown strength obtained is very dependent upon how it is measured, and since it is determined by the weakest link in a chain of physical phenomena it is inherently random in character, so the control offered by the computer is invaluable in this context, particularly in view of the demonstrable possibilities for human self-deception.

Breakdown offers a good example of a physical process which does not easily offer bounds on the quantities to be measured for its understanding. Consider for example breakdown time lags. These are usually measured by observing the time between the application of a sudden overstress and the subsequent sudden catastrophic increase in conduction current which represents the formation of the spark. These time lags are statistically highly scattered, but a study of their average behaviour is helpful in understanding the basis of breakdown probability under particular circumstances and the possible underlying physical processes. The experimental difficulty associated with them arises from their enormous exponential dependence upon electric stress (increasing the stress from, say, 1 MV/cm to 4 MV/cm causes a reduction of the time lag by a factor of 10^9!). This means that the only answer to the question 'How small a time interval do you need to measure?' is 'As small as possible'. Other phenomena associated with dielectrics reveal exponential stress dependence, and the result of a preliminary study to determine the on-line computing power required to support such investigations tends to produce the answers 'As much as possible'. The choice therefore tended to fall on a computer which was notable for its speed and efficiency at the level of interface and basic program activity.

As often happens, once such facilities became available they proved attractive to users outside the group directly concerned in the research which inspired their introduction. It is important that a resource as valuable as a computer installation should be used as fully as possible, so potential users are encouraged provided they do not interfere with the mainstream programme of research.

In sum then, we find the need for a general purpose on-line computer system, but one with the capacity for dealing with a particularly high peak demand of interface activity. This means that, apart from the choice of machine itself, the configuration and physical layout of the system are of critical importance.

The detailed considerations and calculations behind such a choice are, of course, far more extensive than we have even hinted at above, and we have only tried to give a general idea of the problem.

Once the choice of machine has been made, the development of the on-line computing system can be a continuous process in response to a need which varies with the progress of the work; and this normally means a steadily increasing requirement for facilities. In our case, we are committed to efficient use of the input/output features, which means that interrupt priority is the main consideration, and a way to approach the problem of choice and distribution of peripherals is to place them first in a league table of priorities. So we shall examine the system from this point of view.

The distribution of the peripherals in order of priority is shown in Figure 9.1 where they are enumerated in accordance with their positions in the hierarchy of 22 channels provided by the interrupt equipment of the computer. For both data and program interrupts, each channel exercises precedence over all those lower down the priority scale (i.e. with higher numbers). The

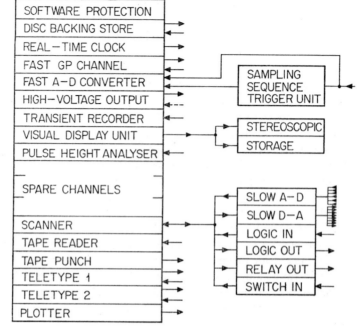

Figure 9.1   Distribution of peripherals *in order of priority* in the Dielectrics Laboratory System

channel allocations therefore require careful prior consideration with due regard to the interface demands of each peripheral and its functional importance (together with some minor technical constraints).

Most of the peripherals have been discussed in various contexts earlier in this text, but it might be useful to add a few words about each channel, particularly in respect of its position in priority. A point to note is that the league table is divided into two quite separate divisions.

9.2.1 THE COMPUTER PERIPHERALS

Disc store The backing store is not an essential part of a laboratory computer installation, but it is certainly a very desirable feature. Perhaps the most noticeable result of its introduction is a great reduction of paper tape handling, and this can represent a considerable saving of time and effort. Nevertheless, the more interesting aspect is the change in the nature of experimental procedures which can be brought about by the file-handling capability. It becomes possible to acquire large blocks of data (say 500 transients via the transient recorder) and compare them, sift them, average them, etc., without having to produce hard copies of each. Although the backing store is slow in comparison with the main store, it is very fast in comparison with any process involving output and input of hard copy, and so greatly widens the scope for manipulation of the results of laboratory measurements.

The backing store, once installed, also tends to become the basis of the computer operating system, which gives it a central importance. Both drum and disc are essentially sequential devices which tend to function via block transfers of data, and any interference by interruption from other peripherals can slow them down by several orders of magnitude of operation speed. For this reason the backing store needs to be well up the priority scale.

Real time clock Many of the operations required of a laboratory computer involve strict time working, and it can be of great value to have the timer installed as an integral part of the system under software control. Indeed, this facility was considered so important in the authors' laboratory that a real-time clock was specially designed and built to provide exactly the features required.

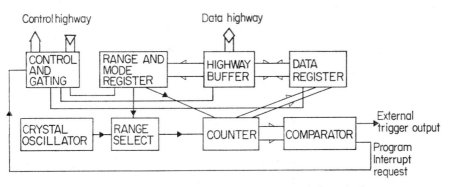

Figure 9.2 Block diagram of the elapsed real-time clock

This clock is based on a crystal oscillator, dividers and comparators as shown in the block diagram of Figure 9.2. At interface level it offers three separate modes of operation:

1 On request, a number is passed to the computer which represents the time interval since the last request and the clock register is reset to zero to restart the count.
2 A number representing a time interval is passed into the clock which thereafter initiates program interrupts repetitively at a frequency determined by the prescribed interval.
3 Instead of a program interrupt an external pulse is generated.

Each of these modes has its own value. In particular it is important not to underestimate mode 3, which combines software control with low processor loading and is particularly useful in high-speed measurements. The external pulse can be used in a variety of ways; e.g. clocking an external feedback shift register used to generate a PRBS, initiating A–D converter samples or directly stimulating a system. Mode 2 is similar but has the additional advantage of introducing software flexibility for applications with a lower speed requirement, while mode 1 provides a general capability for the timing of events within the computer.

A feature of laboratory computing is the wide variation of ranges of time between different experiments—one may be concerned with microsecond measurements and the next with fluctuations over periods of hours. It is therefore imperative to provide for range switching in the clock so that the full word length can be used in the range of interest. Such switching is done by changing the length of the divider chain under software command in the form of control words through the interface. A brief specification of this particular clock is:

Word length: 24 bits.

Oscillator frequency: 2^{21} Hz (giving maximum count time of 8 seconds).

Range adjustments extend the longest time interval to 2^{15} seconds (or 9 hrs 6 min 8 s) at a frequency of 2^9 Hz.

Accuracy: error of 2 or 3 μs on elapsed real time request depending upon the asynchronous nature of interrupts.

Since any input/output peripherals may be required to be under clock control, and the accuracy of the timing may be upset if the clock interrupts are held up by others, the clock requires to have priority over all (except the disc which is outside its jurisdiction).

Fast general purpose channel One of the aspects of laboratory computing which we have so far avoided is the question of 'jury rigging' in response to either a partial system breakdown or an unforeseen but urgent need for a particular computer facility. Once several channels of different types have been established, it is usually found that each of these can be abused in various ways so that a wide range of *ad hoc* arrangements becomes possible. The danger in all this is the possibility of such methods becoming the rule rather than the exception.

It is not only urgent problems which merit the *ad hoc* approach, but also those which are of temporary importance yet do not justify the establishment of a permanent dedicated channel. Most will impose only a low speed requirement on the interface and can be dealt with quite effectively by a general purpose channel of the scanning type, which we shall describe below. Nevertheless, there are always a few of these transient applications which involve very heavy interface demands, and for this reason it is good sense to make advance provision by providing a fast general purpose channel.

The chief characteristics of such a channel should be that it is allocated high priority; it offers a simplified but efficient handshake type of interface to the user; the computer interface is protected by hardware and software packages on either side; it contains all possible options provided by the manufacturer to enhance the speed of a channel (such as extra registers to obviate store cycles for the recovery of pointers) and it allows for program interrupts to be generated externally. Another possible feature, which can be very valuable, but needs to be treated with a great deal of circumspection, is provision of 'locking out' all other peripherals during a block transfer of data to or from the fast channel. This means that, when required, the computer can be made to work flat out at its maximum data transfer rate, which in the laboratory can be very useful indeed. Such a procedure, however, requires special program and operating conditions, since the locking out of important peripherals, such as a disc store, can effectively produce a system breakdown; so this form of ultra fast operation needs to be rationed to the occasions when it is vitally needed.

The fast general purpose channel in the authors' laboratory offers the following facilities; separate 24 bit parallel input and output highways, provision for external initiation of block transfers and program interrupt, an external transfer abort facility, provision for the transfer of short control words and status words between the user's program and his hardware. It is also capable of exclusive occupancy of the interrupt equipment which means that it is possible to transfer words at rates of up to 0.5 MHz when necessary.

Once the fast channel is available it becomes possible to provide a set of standard front ends. A typical example would be a serial–parallel converter, possibly with multiplexing, which allows binary signals in the megahertz range to be handled, and this makes available some very powerful correlation techniques, which may be applied to fields such as laser doppler and sound location, as we observed in Chapter 6. One limitation which must be borne in mind is that of storage; for, at these rates, the whole computer store can be filled in a fraction of a second, and continuous processing is not feasible at these speeds, so the processing is limited to data blocks which, though large, cover a relatively short time interval.

Fast A–D converter The main business of the laboratory computer is measurement, which means that the input process is of great importance. Most laboratory signals are continuous and are translated into electrical form by appropriate transducers. The fast A–D converter therefore occupies a place of high priority, particularly so that its sampling sequences cannot be subjected to interference by lesser peripherals. As we have pointed out in Chapter 8 it is made much more versatile by the addition of a unit to generate sampling sequence trigger signals from a variety of incoming waveforms. The basic A–D converter has no internal buffer store, so though in terms of sampling rate it is slower than the next two peripherals its interface demands are higher and it must exercise a higher priority. The maximum required interface transfer rate is in this case equal to the maximum sampling rate (about 35 kHz, not particularly fast by modern standards, but adequate in view of the presence of the transient recorder).

High-voltage output At first sight it may seem surprising that this channel which we discussed in Chapter 7, is placed so high in the league as it is essentially a slow one, whether the actual high-voltage unit is of the oscillator or the machine type. However, it is important to remember that this channel also has an input, the reset signal, which may require urgent action and should not be held up by the queue of interrupts of a more trivial nature. This is a very good illustration of the great separation between the average and maximum speed requirements at the interface. The high-voltage unit is one of the more important peripherals from the point of view of environmental philosophy as it deals with one of the experimental quantities which has been inadequately controlled in the past.

Transient recorder This is a relatively new laboratory instrument of an impressive versatility which is greatly enhanced by computer connection, for which it has been particularly designed. As we observed in Chapter 7, it has a wide range of controls, all of which can be usurped by the computer, and this implies some degree of complication in the organization of the control words. The actual hardware interfacing problem, however, is a relatively minor one because of the computer oriented construction of the instrument. Perhaps, therefore, a few words on the software problem would be apposite.

With this type of device the input control words tend to be divided into two fields; one specifying the control parameter and the other containing the value to be assigned to that parameter. The software half of the interfacing package therefore has the task of assembling these words in appropriate form to be transferred en bloc. This form, however, is unlikely to be convenient to the user so an appropriate basis for the sub-program is two stored tables; one oriented towards the user and one suitable for block transfer to the device. The user's table is wholly designed to cause him the minimum effort. This means that input is only required when a setting is to be changed, standard default settings are inserted when the user does not define them, and input to the table is by means of easily interpreted character storings (e.g. set control two to 0.5 volts might be represented by the characters 2/0.5, and this is only packed into a single binary word in appropriate format within the standard software). Transfer between the tables is automatic upon receipt of an appropriate brief code from the user.

By its very nature the device is fully buffered, so despite its high speed of operation it does not require a very high position on the priority scale. However, note that the internal storage is of the dynamic MOS variety and because of the need for continual refreshing it is advisable not to reduce the data acceptance rate to below a certain critical value at which the mode of operation changes, because this gives rise to a drastic reduction in the data output rate and considerably degrades the channel. Thus the choice of priority position tends to be fairly critical and it is, for example, important for the transient recorder to be placed above the next mentioned peripheral.

Visual display unit The VDU is one of the most important peripherals for the experimentalist, and its capacity to provide instant peripheral information is one of the principal attractions of the laboratory computer. At its simplest it is coupled to a keyboard for input/output of alphanumeric characters and is merely a teletype equivalent. At its most complex it presents a continuously changing calibrated graphical display with user interaction via a light pen. The light pen is not particularly relevant to laboratory work, save that it does represent the fastest means of indicating a choice, and it would normally only be used where there is subsidiary computer aided design work to be performed. The most versatile form of display is the one that is continually refreshed from the store, offering cinematic possibilities in real time, but this implies a considerable loading of storage and interface operations which would tend to degrade the performance of the laboratory computer.

As we have said elsewhere, visual display offers a wide range of choices of different mixes of hardware and software. The combination chosen by the authors is a display tube of the storage type with character and graph generation by software. This permits some degree of versatility by allowing, for example, extra unorthodox symbols to be included in the character set, yet saves the loading necessary for continually store-refreshed operation. Characters and graphs are output as dot patterns, specified by two 10 bit fields within a single word, giving a 1024×1024 matrix, which is quite adequate for most purposes, while the mode of operation (store, non-store, erase) is determined by separate control words.

The software for such a VDU requires careful forethought if it is to realize its full potential. It is essential that its character output is via a version of the basic character-handling subroutine, so that the whole range of calculating and textual software can be used directly; yet this must be combined with facilities for changing the position, orientation and (possibly size) of blocks of characters. One convenient way of doing this is to utilize the software provided for the incremental plotter (which is usually fairly comprehensive) by writing a linking subroutine which makes the VDU look like a plotter. A further advantage of this method is that an exact hard copy of the displayed information can be obtained by switching to the proper plotter software.

A recurrent problem of some forms of measurement is the production of results which are essentially in the form of a function of two variables. Commonly the extra variable is time, because the system under observation is non-stationary. With well behaved functions it is usually possible to use some form of geometrical projection to obtain an adequate representation, but quite a small degree of scatter, such as is found in experimental results, will completely obscure such a presentation; examples from the pulse height analyser are shown in Figure 9.3.

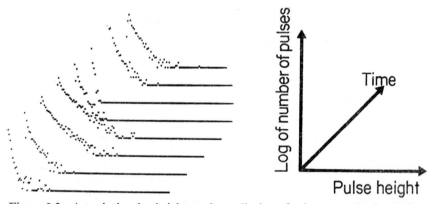

Figure 9.3   A typical pulse height analyser display of minute conduction pulses in a dielectric liquid. Distributions of 128 channels each are displayed in isometric projection to show the evolution of the process in time. Consecutive measurement and waiting intervals are 10 seconds each

These considerations prompted the development of a stereoscopic display unit, which can conveniently be combined with the conventional one to save duplication of interface electronics. The basic difference is that the stereoscopic display requires the presentation of two pictures, one for each eye, and the only difference between them is a small change in the horizontal positions in one picture to represent the degree of parallax associated with each point. Because of the smallness of the difference, it is important not to make the mistake of sending across the information in such a way that resolution is sacrificed by the differing of two nearly equal numbers (i.e. the information fields, transferred must represent y, x, and Δx not y, x_1, x_2, where $\Delta x =$

$x_2 - x_1$). In our case 8 bit fields proved sufficient for each, so only a single 24 bit word transfer was required for each displayed point.

The positioning of the VDU in the interrupt hierarchy is a tricky question. In the continually refreshed mode the number and rate of data transfers is large, and for cinematic continuity they should occur without significant interruption; which all points to a very high position in the priority scale, as is the rule in display oriented systems. However, in our case the display is very much an adjunct to the more characteristic laboratory peripherals, with which it must not be allowed to interfere. For this reason some form of storage operation would tend to be the rule in the laboratory, and the priority position is lowered. Even in storage mode, software character generation is expensive in data transfers, so it is important that these are not allowed to interfere with a more basic laboratory peripheral such as the transient recorder. On the whole software character generation is a bit of a luxury which is difficult to justify in these days of single-ship character generators except on the grounds of uniformity between visual display and plotter hard copy which is a great convenience in the laboratory.

Pulse height analyser This peripheral, which has been briefly discussed in Chapters 7 and 8, is a very useful one in a number of fields of measurement, especially nuclear physics. It has uses beyond the conventional ones—for example, in conjunction with an electronic chopper it can be applied to the estimation of the probability density of signals. It represents one of the most developed forms of peripheral since it arises from one of the earliest laboratory computer applications, and is now a fully buffered device with its own display facilities—an autonomous instrument but one which is even more effective when coupled to a computer.

Because it is so effectively buffered by means of a core store, it can be placed at the bottom of the first division of priorities, but no lower than this, since the speed with which its store can be emptied determines the 'dead-time' between measurements. It is well worth while to provide for two way data transfers, so that, for example, smoothed data can be returned to the analyser for display in its own format.

This, then, is the last of the fast channels in this particular system, and the reader will have noted how the evaluation of the priority positions depends on a number of considerations relating to the interface demands of each device, which are hardly affected at all by the external speed of operation. The following blank channels are for future use and exercise no influence on the process of interruption, so the first channel in the second division is treated as being immediately below the pulse height analyser. The slow channels are of little interest from the point of view of this chapter, so we shall deal with them briefly as a group.

The slow peripherals The only channel in the lower division of priority worth a special mention is the scanning interface (or general input/output unit). This is reserved for the processing of signals which are confined to the range of frequencies below about 1 kHz. Apart from this one restriction, which is imposed by the multiplexing arrangement, the device is extremely versatile, offering input and output of three basic kinds—analogue, logic and switch contact. In the laboratory its great virtue is that it allows *ad hoc* experiments to be set up very quickly. The advantages of such a facility are immense, particularly in respect of the capability of instituting trial runs before a commitment is made to an expensive set up.

The second major field of application of these slow input/output channels is in their rôle as adjuncts to the main laboratory peripherals. There is often a need for the establishment or monitoring of experimental conditions while the main measurement procedure is being carried out, and such activities usually require a very low rate of data transfer. A typical example is temperature control, which requires negligible computing power.

In this particular system there are six basic facilities in the scanning interface —D/A, A/D, LOGIC IN, LOGIC OUT, RELAY OUT, SWITCH IN. The great convenience to the laboratory worker of having all these available is fairly self-evident, and the variety of ways in which they can be used is enormous. The input and output of parallel words at logical voltage levels are particularly significant as they allow logical assemblies to be tested with software aids, besides providing a further means of linking various electronic devices to the computer. The switch and relay facilities (16 of each) are very useful when the need arises to couple some slower (e.g. electromechanical) device to the computer without having to provide a special logic interface. The analogue channels are multiplexed to give six inputs and six outputs, and their usefulness is fairly obvious.

The scanning interface works to a block of the computer store, and every time a scan is initiated each output channel receives a word from a position in that block which corresponds to its position in the scan, whereas each input channel supplies a word to its corresponding location in the block.

The rest of the peripherals are straightforward electromechanical ones. The tape reader and punch are the normal method of preparing and storing hard copy of the programs in the laboratory. The teletype or its equivalent is the commonest way of communicating directly with the machine. In this system there are two on separate channels one to work with the operating system, and one on a roving commission to operate as part of the individual experimental set ups. The plotter is also a peripheral of immense importance in the laboratory, but it is also the slowest and most laborious, having to deal with large amounts of data through an electromechanical linkage. It therefore finds itself at the bottom of the league.

9.2.2 THE LABORATORY LAYOUT

The constraints that influence the distribution of the peripherals in priority also tend to act upon the distribution in space, but there is then a further set of constraints arising from the nature of the laboratory work to be performed. Ideally, to avoid the various problems of signal transmission, it is desirable to have the fast peripherals close to the computer, whereas the slower ones can be treated with a great deal of latitude. A plan view of the system under discussion is shown in Figure 9.4. Some of the peripherals find an obvious place in the partitioned area allocated to the computer. The real-time clock is built into the computer cabinet, and the disc unit is in a special inner chamber

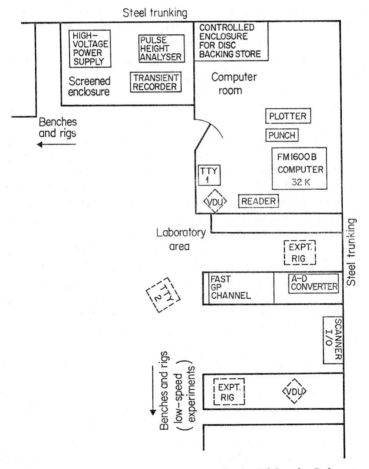

Figure 9.4 Distribution of peripherals *in space* in the Dielectrics Laboratory

with temperature, humidity and dust control. The teletype devoted to the operating system is placed close to the computer and there is also an optional position there for the VDU. As is usual the computer is placed on a false floor with movable panels and all the connecting cables are out of sight. Thus far the layout is conventional and would apply to any small medium computer installation.

It is outside the computer room proper that the peculiarities of a laboratory system become evident. The first point to note is the screened room in juxtaposition with the computer room. This is a great asset in many laboratory measurements, particularly the difficult ones for which an on-line computer tends to be called in. If one has basic problems of low signal levels in high natural noise it is sensible to avoid compounding them by admitting interference from external electromagnetic sources. A peripheral like the transient recorder is often used in such measurements, so it is very convenient to give it a permanent place within the screened volume.

There are two important points which arise from this last observation. The first is that a complicated digital peripheral with external connections to the computer is itself a potential source of electromagnetic contamination of the screened volume, and the greatest care must be taken in the physical distribution of cables and earthing points, etc. The second is that a complicated digital peripheral is likely to have a large number of parallel connections to be made to the computer. Typically this would be of the order of 50, which makes the plug and socket 50 times less reliable than, say, the single analogue plug and socket at the input of the device. The implication of this remark is that, tempting though it may be to make all such peripherals instantly pluggable at various points in the laboratory, this is a temptation worth avoiding. So in our case both the transient recorder and the pulse height analyser are given permanent places in the screened room. Similarly the fast A–D converter is confined to an area which is determined by the arc described by the length of free cable which attaches it via a wall outlet to the computer. These precautions may seem petty to someone who has not had experience of the type of intermittent fault produced by plugs and sockets. Our experience is that permanent fixture, ideally by means of taper pin blocks, saves a lot of wasted effort in subsequent fault finding, and as it is a limited number of rather specialized experiments which require high-speed facilities these can normally be set up in an appropriate position.

Because of the desirability of keeping signal paths short, the computer is usually placed in a central position in the laboratory. In our case 'central' is interpreted rather loosely, as the computer room is set in one corner of the laboratory. This position allows the laboratory walls to be used to support steel trunking which carries the connecting cables, and benches are placed at intervals at right angles to the walls. This allows the accommodation of various types of experimental rig either as bench mounted assemblies or free standing ones between the benches.

The constraints upon the slower and simpler peripherals are much easier, and they can be plugged in at various points along the trunking where there is a box with sockets for teletype and VDU, and multiway connections for the various channels of the slow scanning interface. The setting up of experiments usually needs much more time than their execution, so it is essential to provide as large an area as possible, so that setting up does not interfere with the current use of the computer.

9.2.3 A TYPICAL MEASUREMENT PROBLEM

Rather than try to cover the whole range of measurements carried out in the dielectrics laboratory, let us examine one particular problem and its ramifications to see how relevant the hardware is to its solution. A good example is the time of flight method of determining the mobility of charges within a dielectric liquid. This measurement provides a number of complications, virtually every one in the book; for the dielectric liquid subjected to charge injection can be *non-stationary*, *non-linear*, *unstable* and *noisy*. Furthermore the currents to be dealt with are in the form of transients in the pico-amperes range of magnitude, which implies some noise–gain–bandwidth difficulties.

The non-stationarity of conduction in a dielectric liquid is largely restricted to the standing or background current and may be ascribed to changes in the critical interface between the metal electrodes and the liquid. The non-linearity arises from the mutual interaction of the changes as manifested by the Poisson and continuity equations, and is therefore mainly effective when the amount of charge injection begins to approach the space charge limited value. The possibility of instability emerges because of the momentum coupling between the charge carriers and the molecules of the host liquid and is again restricted to conditions of high injection. The sources of noise are many—thermal agitation, spontaneous changes in the liquid–metal interface, transport of charge by submicroscopic solid particles, etc.

It is fairly self-evident that some knowledge of conditions within the liquid is a necessary prerequisite of the attack on the measurement problem, and this brings out a major advantage of the laboratory on-line computer which is often overlooked—the provision of theoretical support. Generally there are two sorts of program which can be usefully held in the store for immediate reference by keyboard, those based on theoretical calculations and those based on direct modelling of the system. Both are relevant to this case.

Theoretical analysis of the system based on the Poisson and continuity equations allows the internal conditions (space charge density and field distribution) to be evaluated from a knowledge of the externally measured conditions (current and applied voltage). In particular, certain non-dimensional numbers can be calculated which quantify the degree of space charge limiting and the tendency to electro-hydrodynamic instability. The usual way of assessing this information is by typing in the measured values on the keyboard (although there is no reason why they should not be entered by direct measurement other than the fact that one often wishes to explore hypothetical cases before resetting the experimental parameters). The output information is in the form of certain characterizing numbers, with the option of plots of field distribution and charge density.

As often happens, such a purely theoretical analysis is confined to steady state conditions, and we are dealing here with what is essentially a deviation from the steady state, though perhaps a small one. A modelling technique is much more powerful from the point of view of the range of problems it can deal with, but is correspondingly less powerful in its provision of significant information in condensed form. In our case the obvious method of modelling is to divide the volume of dielectric up into a number of cells, each being represented by a storage location (in the computer) which holds a number representing the contained charge. It is then a fairly straightforward matter to calculate the redistribution of charge over small increments of time, taking into account the external conditions of voltage and charge injection. The procedure is based on discrete forms of the Poisson and continuity equations.

Our present problem is typical of one in which modelling is essential to an understanding of the implication of any results. The effects of mutual interaction of the charges and their temporary storage within the system make the relationship between injected charge and resulting current too complicated for unaided interpretation. Perhaps the most significant use of such a model is as the object of some form of iterative correction, so that, given the measured output waveform, the input waveform can be determined, even though this is inaccessible to measurement.

Once we have in store convenient programs for analyzing the situation it becomes possible to make a decision about which method of measurement to use (and more notably which not to use). In order to illustrate this point without labouring it we shall consider just two possible ways of tackling one particular measurement of the current due to the transit of a packet of charge. The first complication to consider is the fact that, under many of the more important conditions of test, the induced transient current will be of the same order as the random fluctuations of the standing current. It is therefore necessary to utilize a method with some form of inherent noise elimination. The most obvious of these is the cumulative averaging method represented by equation 6.68.

The only prerequisite of the cumulative averaging method is the disposability of the stimulus, so that the response can be evoked repetitively in synchronism

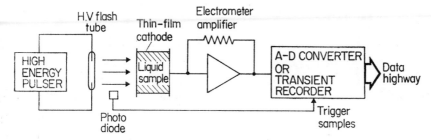

Figure 9.5   The time-of-flight measurement

with the start of each sampling sequence. This is not difficult in our experiment (Figure 9.5) as the easiest way of launching the charge is by means of photo-emission of electrons into the dielectric, and a UV flash tube does this admirably, providing a good approximation to an ideal impulse stimulus. Figure 9.6 shows some results of such a measurement for various numbers of records over which the cumulative averaging takes place. Note that the signal emerges from the noise progressively and that the latter is diminished in proportion to the square of the number of records in accordance with statistical theory. The observed transient, of course, is greatly different from the ideal rectangular form shown in Figure 9.7, being subjected to diffusion and other effects in addition to the ones we have mentioned so far.

There appears to be no practical limit to the number of records which can be absorbed into our cumulative average, other than the time available to run the experiment, and as the averaged result can be monitored on the VDU and only plotted out in hard copy when acceptably distinct, there seems at first sight little reason for turning to any other method. Why then do we need to have an alternative? The answer to this question lies in the concept of stationarity. Experimenters are often concerned with the stationarity of the system on which they are making their measurements, but how often do they consider the stationarity of the test-method? The direct impulse response measurement is in fact fundamentally non-stationary. This is illustrated by the fact that it is not possible to determine meaningful time averages of such quantities as the electrical power applied to the system.

Now we have in Chapter 6 discussed a method of retrieving the impulse response in which the stimulus is in effect stationary. This is the method of cross-correlation under a pseudorandom binary stimulus. It can be particularly advantageous to have this feature when one is dealing with a system which is fundamentally capable of instability, and there are two different ways in which the PRBS method can be superior to the pulse method. The first arises from the fact that it is possible to quote a time average for the PRBS so that the behaviour of the system can be noted as a function of the average

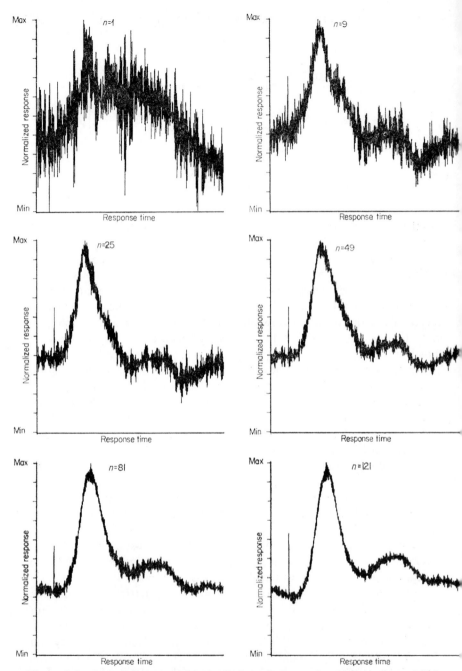

Figure 9.6 Cumulative averaging applied to pico-amp signals from time-of-flight measurements. Note the tendency for the noise content to decrease in proportion to the square root of *n*, the number of records over which averaging takes place. 1000 samples per record at a sampling frequency of 50 Hz. (*Realization on FM 1600B by Terry Hewish*)

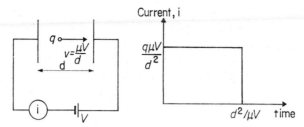

Current, i

Figure 9.7   The idealized time-of-flight current waveform

stimulus and a practical stability bound observed. The second is that the peak stimulus is reduced so that the stability limit is less likely to be transgressed for a given total stimulus. The latter point is illustrated in Figure 9.8 in a simplified way by comparing the distribution of the area under the stimulus time curve as a single pulse or as a short (7 bit) pseudorandom response.

One would not in practice use a PRBS as short as this. Firstly, because it would only give seven points on the retrieved impulse response and secondly because as a stimulus it is only stationary in so far as its fluctuations are faster than the natural responses of the system being dealt with. Both of these

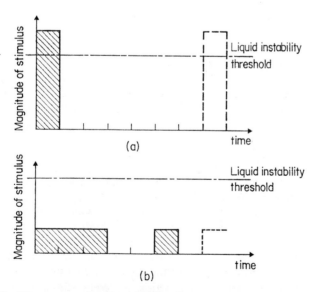

Figure 9.8   The area under the stimulus-time curve can be spread out more uniformly by utilizing a pseudorandom binary sequence, thus avoiding such hazards as instability, yet the impulse response can be retrieved by cross-correlation
(a) single pulse stimulus (b) 6-bit PRBS stimulus

considerations would tend to lead to the choice of a much longer response, and 1023 bits would be fairly typical. A typical transient retrieved by cross-correlation with a PRBS input is shown in Figure 9.9.

The PRBS method obviously has a number of advantages. There is a slight difficulty in that one requires to modulate the stimulus rather than just pulse it, but apart from this we seem to be led again to the question—why do we

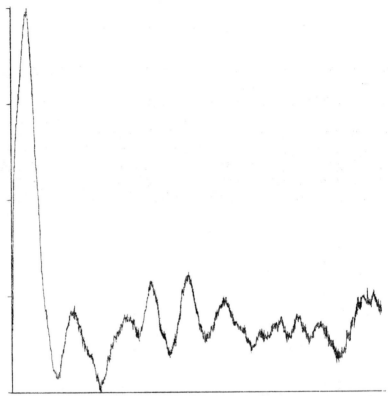

Figure 9.9 An impulse response measurement by cross-correlation. A time-of-flight experiment in which the various complicating features such as diffusion and non-linearity are present. Sequence length 1023 bits. Clock rate 100 Hz. (*Realization on FM 1600B by Terry Hewish*)

need an alternative method? The answer this time lies in the concept of linearity. This concept is implicit in the theory leading up to the important result that the cross-correlation function represents the impulse response (equation 6.66). In our dielectric measurement the system becomes non-linear if the space charge density becomes large, so the PRBS method is ruled out under these conditions. The cumulative averaging method is not necessarily ruled out by non-linearity. The two methods together therefore tend to cover more ground than they would individually, though unfortunately instability and non-linearity tend to go together so the gain is not as great as one might expect, and ultimately even more methods may have to be explored. Note that the areas where such methods are mutually applicable can be used to cross check them.

This section has been headed 'A typical measurement problem'. Perhaps more accurately we should say 'A typical difficult measurement problem', but even then the word 'typical' needs justifying since in the cynic's lexicon it is defined as 'the only one we have'.

This example typifies a class of difficult measurement problems (i.e. the ones that need an on-line computer) because it has the following features.

1 The information required is contained in the response to a given stimulus.
2 There is an adverse signal-to-noise ratio in the received response.
3 There are conditions in the system which determine the efficacy of particular measurement techniques (non-linearity, instability, etc.).
4 These conditions and the constraints they impose do not appear directly in terms of the observable variables.

There is a class of problems which can be even more difficult—those in which it is not possible to stimulate the system so one is forced to accept what it offers in the way of output signals. Our second example of a typical measurement problem in the following section falls into this category.

9.3   AN EEG LABORATORY

If one had to choose the most difficult possible test-object for electrical measurement, it would surely be the human brain. Yet, quite apart from its attractions as the supreme scientific mystery, there are urgent clinical reasons why it needs to be studied and monitored with all the power of on-line computing. The rapid advance of medicine has swept aside a great many diseases which were once regarded as serious, but in doing so medicine has left further exposed its own inadequacies in the residual areas, and one of the most important of these concerns diseases and conditions of the brain.

Some of the early attempts to investigate the behaviour of the brain by electrical measurement must in the light of the complexity of the test-object be regarded as appallingly crude; analogous to trying to investigate the working of a computer by monitoring the potentials induced in its cabinet. So, although technical progress has been remarkable by any standard, it is essential to understand that in terms of the problem in hand only a small beginning has been made. The brain exhibits all of the difficulties so far mentioned (e.g. non-stationarity, non-linearity, low signal levels, etc.), in so far as these have any meaning in the context, and in addition reveals that element of caprice which we were at such pains to point out in our justification of on-line methods in Chapter 2.

Having pointed out the importance of the brain as a test-object and since space does not allow us to include a large number of examples of laboratory installations we shall take one other case, and one which offers a complete contrast to our last example. The laboratory in question is one concerned with EEG signals (in the Department of Clinical Neurophysiology, St. Bartholomew's Hospital, London). It has two characteristics which make it completely different from the previous example. These are:

1 The signals are of low-frequency (<1 kHz) so that the real-time processing demands are small.

2 Human patients are involved so that there are severe aesthetic and ethical constraints upon the techniques employed.

The most obvious effect of the first of these characteristics is the physical extension of the data acquisition network it allows, which in this case becomes a veritable spider's web of cables threading its way through a large hospital site. Signals can be transmitted in analogue form over long distances with comparatively simple op-amp line driver and receiver circuits.

There are, however, other effects which are less obvious, yet are of fundamental importance. In our last example we were concerned with a system which had to deal with a variety of circumstances and a number of sources and destinations of data sometimes at high speed. This inevitably leads to a pre-occupation with the idea of interrupt priority, and it is not without significance that we chose to define the system by means of Figure 9.1 which is basically a priority list. In this example, the primary signal sources are consistent and well behaved (electrically if not conceptually) and the secondary sources are even simpler—slow character streams from keyboards.

The second of our two characteristics, the ethical and aesthetic one, takes most effect at the remote end of the signal line. The EEG signals are always acquired through a standard EEG machine built to the highest ethical standards, so that there is no possibility of danger or discomfort to the patient. This device supplies signals to op-amp live drivers which allow the signals to be transmitted at about a volt along standard twisted pair cables, and at the computer end op-amp line receivers produce a signal of about 10 volts. Typically, a comprehensive monitoring of the electrical activity of the brain will require between eight and sixteen channels. Thus at the computer end we have up to sixteen channels of 1 kHz bandwidth 10 volt signals, and this is ideal for direct application to a multiplexed A–D converter. The whole has therefore resolved to a single digital channel whose demands are by no means immoderate.

In addition to the direct EEG signals it is also necessary to provide for the two way transmission of information between the computer and the clinical staff, but this need only be a teletype grade channel and therefore poses no difficult problems. The only special feature here is the necessity for all equipment at the patient's end to be silent. This implies that one must substitute for the teletypewriter an equivalent combination of VDU and silent keyboard. Graphical information from the computer may be required by the clinical staff, but this can be sent at comparatively slow rates to a storage tube VDU.

The result of these considerations is that a standardized remote equipment module can be assembled on a trolley to be set up at every particular cable termination. This comprises an EEG machine, a silent 'teletype equivalent' VDU, and a storage tube VDU with an attached hard copy unit.

The standard peripherals also require connection to the computer, but they remain in close proximity and save one do not impose high demands. The exception is a magnetic tape unit, whose serial mode of storage is less of a hindrance in this application than it is in many others, since the data to be handled are in the form of consecutive time series. The magnetic tape unit has a measure of direct access to the store, but all the other peripherals are handled on a common input/output bus. A feature of this installation is a comprehensive switching network for analogue signals. A simplified layout is shown in Figure 9.10.

The analytical methods used in the EEG laboratory are many and various, so we shall again select one typical measurement problem to illustrate the use of theory. It is an application of the idea of the matched filter which we introduced briefly in Chapter 6.

One of the clinical areas in which EEG is most relevant is the study of epilepsy. The only point which concerns us about this unpleasant condition

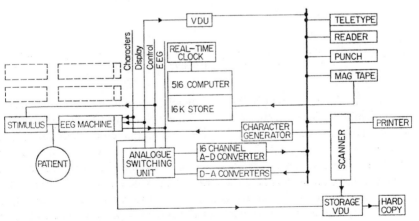

Figure 9.10   The EEG computer and its peripherals

is the observed fact that the epileptic fit has a precursor in the form of a highly characteristic waveform commonly known as the spike and wave. This waveform is quite easily recognized by the trained eye, but automatic recognition of it would be an obvious gain. If we make the simplifying assumption that the rest of the EEG signal constitutes white noise, then the device for recognizing the waveform is the simple matched filter—a non-recursive filter whose pulse response is the sought signal in reverse form.

Figure 9.11 illustrates some results from a program in regular clinical use which performs precisely this function. The first waveform is the EEG signal, while the second is the signal after processing by the matched filter. In this case a rather unusual method of obtaining the binary presence/absence information is used. Instead of clipping the filtered signal directly an approximate second derivative is taken (line 3) which is then clipped (line 4). The model actually used in the filter is shown at the bottom of the figure.

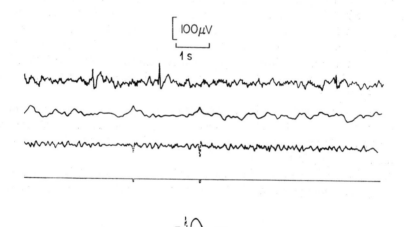

Figure 9.11   The matched filter applied to the detection of epilepsy (*realized on the 516 computer by Colin Binnie and David Lloyd*)

This sort of measurement offers an interesting challenge to on-line computing methods. The precise nature of the spike and wave varies from individual to individual. Not only does each individual require his own model, but the degree of spectral overlap between the sought waveform and the overall EEG varies, and this is what determines the definition of the result; so the method may be highly successful in some cases and useless in others. Nevertheless, without the on-line computer, constant patient monitoring is virtually impossible in this respect, as the human operator does not take readily to a task which requires large periods of sustained concentration.

9.4 DISCUSSION

The two examples chosen for this chapter illustrate one particularly important fact. The choice of computer and system configuration is very dependent upon the nature of the problem in hand. Furthermore, we have noted right at the beginning of this text the fact that the techniques of hardware and programming ultimately used are very dependent upon the choice of machine. It follows that the techniques employed in a particular laboratory will depend very much on the subject matter dealt with by that laboratory. As we confessed at the outset, this fundamentally weakens the value of any text which purports to deal with the computer oriented laboratory, since detailed examples are of limited value. Nevertheless there are certain important general principles which we have tried to bring out in this chapter, and if it is read with a particular problem and machine in mind it should be of some relevance. As in any craft the most important attitude for the craftsman in laboratory computing is to appreciate, enjoy and *know* his tools.

Chapter X

Conclusion

We have seen that on-line computing is an amalgam of three different elements—mathematics, software and hardware. Even more important, however, are the connections between these elements, and it is worth while to recapitulate at this stage to remind ourselves of the nature of the bridges which unite these entities.

The common factors linking the mathematical analysis with the program instructions which make up the associated software are the operations of discrete calculus, and the most characteristic of these is the operation of discrete delay. This operation together with addition and multiplication by a constant gives rise to a structure which, within the bounds of the sampling theorem, aligns neatly with the familiar continuous theory of signals and systems yet also presents a simple task to the programmer. In the language of functional analysis we take advantage of a mapping between continuous signal space and discrete signal space (incidentally, the natural mapping is many-to-one, so it cannot be an isomorphism, which is why the bilinear transform is often used instead [Stieglitz in DiSiRaRa]). The fortunate aspect of this is that the principal tool, the z transform, is particularly easy to use in most circumstances, and we have deliberately avoided complicating the issue by quoting, for example, the contour integration form for its inverse, as our main purpose has been to emphasize those features which are directly relevant to on-line computing.

The great beauty of the z transform is that once the transfer function is given, either in terms of the coefficients of polynominals or the location of poles and zeros, the subsequent realization problem is negligible (though it may be constrained by questions of precision and calculating time). This cannot be said for the equivalent problem in linear continuous processing. There is now a vast literature covering the synthesis of virtually all the filter characteristics that one might require, so there is rarely need to get too deeply

286

involved in the mathematics, though one must certainly be prepared to if the work in hand demands a more specialized approach.

Delay is also an important element in the construction of the second-order functions of correlation which prove to be such great value, and it is only the absence of convenient variable delay elements in linear continuous processing which formerly prevented correlation methods from achieving their present eminence. Both correlation and discrete spectral analysis methods, despite this considerable power, need to be treated with some care. The autocorrelation function, in particular, is notoriously difficult to interpret, and as we have seen there are fundamental difficulties in the idea of Fourier transformation of a stationary signal. Nevertheless, the existence of standard software to perform these rather complex mathematical tricks ensures that the bridge between mathematical analysis and software is a sure one. In this text, of course, we have barely touched the available mathematical tools, and various elegant concepts have had to go unmentioned (for example, the idea of the cepstrum) but we have been at pains to point out the aspects most relevant to the practice of laboratory on-line computing, in the knowledge that the literature of mathematical techniques is vast and accessible.

The other important bridge is the one between software and hardware, and unlike the bridge discussed above, which was common to all computing, it is uniquely vital in on-line computing. Furthermore, and rather awkwardly for the purposes of authorship, it is the most machine-dependent area of computing; so, in contrast to our remark at the end of the last paragraph we have to say that the prime sources of information are not in the general scientific literature but in the specific commercial literature provided by manufacturers. Nevertheless, we have indicated its importance by devoting a chapter to it, and it is worth while restating the remark that began that chapter by observing that this is the most likely factor to dominate in determining the quality of on-line computing work. Computer power in the laboratory is not simply a question of number crunching capability as it is with mathematical machines, but is much more concerned with interface activity and the efficiency with which it is organized. Variety of input/output channels and a high speed capability are the hallmarks of a successful laboratory computer, and other concepts such as peripheral autonomy and interrupt priority are important in the realization of the potential of the computer as a laboratory tool. The writing of the input/output software to give the right balance between data and program interrupts is a task of vital importance, and one cannot over-emphasize the possibilities for disaster in any mistake made in this area. Always remember that the one great disadvantage of on-line computing is that debugging is difficult, and it is most important to discard any laxity which has developed through experience of off-line programming with good diagnostic facilities, and to keep the rigorous habit of separately testing each program module, so that its integrity is beyond doubt when it is absorbed into the system. The best way to optimize the use of a laboratory computer (having chosen the right machine!) is to immerse oneself thoroughly in its philosophy and do things *its* way (certainly not try to transfer alien ideas in a half-baked form from other machines).

The variety of on-line computing methods is very wide: certainly far wider than is implied by the small selection we have been able to refer to here. They range from simple averaging processes to techniques of modelling based on advanced abstract mathematical ideas. Nevertheless, the constraints placed upon the use of such methods by the nature of on-line computing are largely common, and these have been our concern in this text. Thus, the material included in Chapter 6 must not be taken as an exhaustive account of the material covered, but more as a very brief survey with the factors peculiar to on-line computing emphasized. Particularly inadequate, for example, is the treatment of optimization, but here our chief concern was the special problems of the on-line context, and specifically the difficulties which go with the idea of a gradient. For as we showed earlier in Chapter 6, taking a gradient is one of the operations which can never be realized accurately in any discrete system, but can be even more problematical given the additional crudities of on-line data acquisition.

Basically, there are relatively few building blocks from which processing methods are constructed, and a necessary (though not sufficient) condition for a method to work correctly is that all its components should work satisfactorily in isolation before being brought together, and we have made much of the necessity for modular construction and testing. But it is still possible for effective bricks to produce a defective structure. A simple case which often occurs in on-line computing is when at some stage in a cascaded set of processes the numbers become so small that virtually all precision is lost, yet later on they are restored to proper size and the existence of gross corruption is disguised. Obviously, the *gain* of a process, however complicated, is something we need to have some knowledge about, and here again the language of functional analysis can help with its ideas of the *norm* of a function or operator; for in this case it is the working of the processes in combination that goes wrong (and remember we are only discussing the particularly on-line problems, there are other difficulties with processes in combination—stability is an obvious example).

It is relevant at this point to discuss the significance of the relatively new technology of microprocessors in the laboratory. The most immediate application as we observed in Chapter 7 is in the development of peripheral controllers. A prime constraint on the design of a controller is the need to allow the central processor and the interrupter the maximum possible relief from the necessity to carry out mundane and repetitive tasks. This often means that the realization of the required system in terms of logic hardware is quite complex. The microprocessor permits this problem to be converted to a software exercise, which is considerably easier and a lot less expensive in skilled labour.

There is an important further use of the microprocessor in the laboratory which arises from the fact that the rôle of the computer in signal-processing work can be divided into two quite distinct phases. The first phase includes mathematical analysis of the problem with the consequent computation to produce appropriate programmable forms and all the subsequent business of compilation, assembly, etc., to produce a working program. The second phase covers the actual processing of the signal. Now, it is quite characteristic of this second phase that the processing required is comparatively trivial in nature; it might, for example, be digital filtering or correlation or forming some sort of average, or simply determining the existence of an alarm condition. In the first phase the full panoply of computer facilities such as compilers and libraries on backing store is required, while in the second phase these are redundant. Even the most basic peripherals such as tape punch and reader are unnecessary, provided that an electrical connection can be made for the acquisition of program material. Thus we arrive at the concept of the roving dependent processor—a sort of mutable digital instrument capable of carrying out a simple repetitive function which can be changed in nature by plugging into the main processor for a new 'charge'. It would contain its own store including a read-only part dedicated to storing the basic loader for the processor, highway control logic, appropriate input/output devices (e.g. A–D and D–A converters, digital indicators, etc.) and a power supply, in addition to the basic microprocessor with any possible extra function units.

No doubt microprocessors will also be found within self-contained laboratory instruments as fixed program processors, but that is hardly relevant to on-line computing, except for the fact that it implies digital operation and therefore suitability for direct connection to a computer.

It is important to remember that the on-line computer is only a tool. It is a tool for craftsmen, and the craftsman must understand the medium in which he works as well as the tools he uses. In laboratory on-line computing the medium is an area of scientific research, and no amount of fancy on-line processing can substitute for a fundamental appreciation of it. One of the great dangers of on-line computing is that it is so easy to generate complicated activity that this can become an end in itself, without regard to the question of whether it is scientifically the right thing to do. A few simple lines of program can represent a process of some complexity (we have quoted from time to time the example of the running mean which was analysed in Chapter 6), and it is quite easy to impose upon some straightforward data an alien pattern which obscures the truth, or worse generates untruth. This is why it is imperative to develop a familiarity with the techniques of analysis, such as the z transform, which enable us to identify the full signal-processing implications of a given discrete procedure. This is certainly a field of study in which 'a little learning is a dangerous thing'.

A further significant point arises from this discussion. It is the need, in the reporting of experimental work involving on-line computing techniques, for the process employed to be precisely defined. This is not always easy, particularly in public journals where the editorial policy will be resistant to the inclusion of technical detail. Unless it is done, however, the on-line computer may well lose all of its advantage of objectivity, and instead of diminishing the amount of doubtful published experimental work it may end up by augmenting it. All tools, from the knife to nuclear energy, can be used for good or ill and the on-line computer is no exception.

Let us finish this text with a reference to what is perhaps the most significant advantage of the on-line computer in the laboratory, an advantage which is often underestimated and sometimes completely ignored—its objectivity. Any measurement which involves human activity must be fundamentally suspect because of the devious nature of the unconscious mind. The computer controlled experiment starts with its cards laid on the table, it does not change its program half-way through (and even if it did it would not rationalize such a change in the way that a human operator might). Admittedly the prejudices of the experimenter may be built in to the program, but there is a much stronger constraint on him when the entire procedure must be declared in black and white at the outset. It is often difficult to substantiate claims which arise from the art of measurement as practised by skilled operators. The heights reached by the computer (of accuracy for example) may be less, but they are determined and determinable. As a final remark remember that anyone liable to do something silly in the laboratory will find that the on-line computer will give him much more capability of doing it, and will help him to disguise the fact.

Bibliography

The following list is deliberately reduced to less than two dozen in the hope that the reader will make use of them, or their near equivalents if found more suitable, to fill any gaps in his knowledge. Either of the two books on logic [LogGirl, LogLew] gives the background theory and sufficient worked examples, and the two on computer organization and design [CompLew, CoOrgFlo] extend this knowledge appropriately. The compendious [DiSiRaRa] is an essential collection of papers on the subject of signal processing, and [DiSiGoRa] is the first valuable text-book in the subject. [SiProBeau] is also useful, for its comprehensive bibliography as much as anything. Among the texts on fundamental theory [ProPap] is essential reading, [NuMeHam] gives the first glimmerings of signal theory and is very readable, while [FuncTitch] and [LinAlgMir] give a valuable insight into the rigorous background. The transform theory is covered by [FouBra] widely, and by [WidLap] rigorously. The only individual paper cited in this bibliography [ZTraHelm] does not appear to have been absorbed into the text-book literature, unfortunately, but is worth examining for its fundamental derivation of the z transform which many texts simply produce out of the hat in an unsatisfactory way.

Throughout we have assumed familiarity with ordinary mathematical computing, as covered by [CoMeLaFa], but this is not entirely satisfactory in such fields as the discussion of generating random variables of a given distribution, which is dealt with succinctly in [ArtSimToc]. An introduction to functional analysis is given in [FuncAnVul], and the reader will find several fine modern texts, though many of the more practical ones have a bias to control applications. [TaSof71] contains an account of high-level languages appropriate to real-time work, while [AdSemSpec] gives some advanced spectral theory for signal processing. [DetSigWha] treats in depth the problem of signal detection, and [ProLaSe] gives an interesting account of the development and history of computer languages.

[AdSemSpec]   *Advanced Seminar on Spectral Analysis of Time Series*, Bernard Harris (ed.), Wiley, 1966.

[ArtSimToc]   *The Art of Simulation*, K. D. Tocher, E.U.P., 1963.

[CoMeLaFa]   *Computer Methods for Science and Engineering*, Robert L. LaFara, Hayden, 1973.

[CompLew]   *The Theory and Design of Digital Computers*, D. Lewin, Nelson, 1972.

[CoOrgFlo]   *Computer Organisation*, Ivan Flores, Prentice-Hall, 1969.

[DetSigWha]   *Detection of Signals in Noise*, A. D. Whalen, Academic Press, 1971.

[DiSiGoRa]   *Digital Processing of Signals*, B. Gold and C. M. Rader, McGraw-Hill, 1969.

[DiSiRaRa]   *Digital Signal Processing*, R. Rabiner and C. M. Rader, IEEE Press, 1972.

[FouBra]   *The Fourier Transform and its Applications*, R. N. Bracewell, McGraw-Hill, 1965.

[FuncAnVul]   *Introduction to Functional Analysis*, B. Z. Vulikh, Pergamon, 1963.

[FuncTitch]   *The Theory of Functions*, E. C. Titchmarch, Oxford, 1964.

[LinAlgMir]   *An Introduction to Linear Algebra*, L. Mirsky, Oxford, 1963.

[LogGirl]   *Logic and Logic Design*, B. Girling and G. H. Moring, Intertext, 1973.

[LogLew]   *Logical Design of Switching Circuits*, D. Lewin, Nelson, 1968.

[NuMeHam]   *Numerical Methods for Scientists and Engineers*, Richard W. Hamming, McGraw-Hill, 1962.

[ProLaSe]   *Programming Languages: History and Fundamentals*, Jean E. Sammet, Prentice-Hall, 1969.

[ProPap]   *Probability, Random Variables and Stochastic Processes*, Athanasios Papoulis, McGraw-Hill, 1965.

[SigProBeau]   *Signal Processing*, K. G. Beauchamp, George Allen and Unwin, 1973.

[TaSof71]   Towards high-level real-time languages, F. E. Taylor in *Software 71*, Transcripta Books, 1971.

[WidLap]   *The Laplace Transform*, Widder, Princeton, 1946.

[ZTraHelm]   'The Z-transformation', *Bell System Technical Journal*, 1959, Vol. 3, pp. 177–96.

Index